C000198855

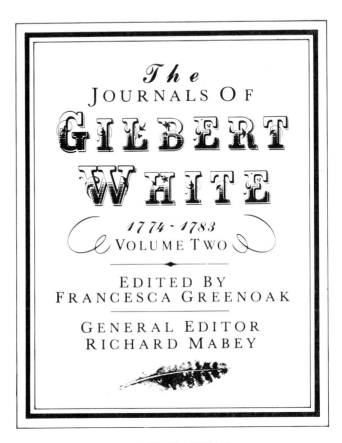

The
JOURNALS OF
GILBERT
WHITE

1774 - 1783
VOLUME TWO

EDITED BY
FRANCESCA GREENOAK

GENERAL EDITOR
RICHARD MABEY

ILLUSTRATIONS
BY CLARE ROBERTS

CENTURY
LONDON · MELBOURNE · AUCKLAND
JOHANNESBURG

Art Direction and Design by
Bob Hook

Introduction and Notes Copyright ©
Francesca Greenoak 1988

First published in 1988 by Century Hutchinson Ltd,
Brookmount House, 62–65 Chandos Place,
Covent Garden, London WC2N 4NW

Century Hutchinson Australia Pty Ltd,
PO Box 496, 16–22 Church Street,
Hawthorn, Victoria 3122,
Australia

Century Hutchinson New Zealand Ltd,
PO Box 40-086 Glenfield, Auckland 10,
New Zealand

Century Hutchinson South Africa Pty Ltd,
PO Box 337, Bergvlei, 2012 South Africa

Set in Caslon Old Face and Caslon Open Face
Printed and bound in Great Britain by
Butler and Tanner Ltd, Frome, Somerset

British Library Cataloguing in Publication Data

White, Gilbert
The Gilbert White Journals, 1774–83.
Vol. 2
1. White, Gilbert 2. Naturalists—
England—Selborne (Hampshire)—
Biography
I. Title II. Greenoak, Francesca
508'.092'4   QH31.W58

ISBN 0 7126 1557 1

CONTENTS

Also from Century
by Richard Mabey
GILBERT WHITE
A biography

THE NATURAL HISTORY OF SELBORNE
A bicentennial edition

Acknowledgements

I should like to thank Robin McIntosh for her painstaking
work in transcribing the hand-written manuscript, and
Moyna Kitchin for copy editing. I should also like to thank
Mr Tony Vincent of the Science Museum for conducting
me around the vaults of the Science Museum and for
giving me an introduction to 18th century barometers, and
the British Museum (Natural History) for identifying
some of the insects noted in the Journals. I am indebted to
Mr Philip Hughes of The Society for the Protection of
Ancient Buildings who illuminated some of the problems
which Gilbert White had in the building of his new
Parlour. Clare Roberts and I would both like to express our
gratitude to Dr June Chatfield and David Standing of the
Gilbert White Museum, Selborne, for their continued
kind assistance. Clare Roberts would also like to give
special thanks to Ludo Beumer, Steve Povey and Ann
Mallinson. Finally, my thanks to the publishing team at
Century Hutchinson for their support and to Bob Hook for
his excellent design.

F.G.

Foreword

Gilbert White is often described as the founding father of natural history and his book *The Natural History of Selborne* is one of the most frequently published titles in the English language. Increasingly White is also being recognised as an important literary figure, who played a key role in the development of descriptive writing about place and nature.

Despite this, his *Journals*, which span more than forty years of observation, have never been published in full. As well as being the source of raw material for *The Natural History*, they are a unique record in their own right, and have a vividness and intimacy of style that was not to be seen again in English journal writing for another fifty years.

These three volumes cover the entire range of White's journals, from the early notes in a *Garden Kalendar* in 1751 to the final *Naturalist's Journal* entries in 1793. They are fully transcribed for the first time, and include all the detailed daily weather data of the original. As editor, Francesca Greenoak's chief aim throughout has been to make these remarkable manuscripts accessible to a wider audience. Annotation has therefore been kept to the minimum necessary for clarity and understanding.

In keeping with a tradition that has grown up around various editions of *The Natural History* of including illustrations of Selborne contemporary with the edition, these three volumes of *Journals* have been augmented by original drawings by Clare Roberts. Her pictures and field notes echo the detail and intimacy of White's writing, and were all drawn in the parish of Selborne and the surrounding countryside during 1985, 1986 and 1987.

Richard Mabey

INTRODUCTION

In 1750, Gilbert White's good friend and faithful correspondent John Mulso wrote to him:

> You are now I suppose to be found . . . ranging your Trees and nursing your Plants . . . I wish you joy of the arrival of the swallows and the swifts and the nightingales. I hope you will send me word how your nurseries go on, and the true state of Selborne Hanger . . .

By this time, at the age of thirty, a year after having been ordained, Gilbert had an evident interest in gardening and in the fauna and flora of his home village, and this was to be steadily extended and amplified throughout the rest of his life. Starting in 1751, he began to keep yearly journals in which he wrote perceptive notes on gardening and natural history, continuing this practice over forty-three years and ceasing to write entries only eleven days before his death. These journals prove his quite remarkable observational skills and, more clearly than any of his other writings, show a man whose scientific curiosity about the natural world incorporated a deep affection for plants and animals, particularly those of his native parish.

The journals fall into two distinct groupings, which differ more in form than content. The *Garden Kalendar*, continued between the years 1751 and 1767, comprise mostly but not exclusively gardening notes, written intermittently on blank quarto sheets. The *Naturalist's Journal* was a printed diary-notebook, each volume holding a year's observations, and Gilbert kept up these journals from the year 1768 and 1793. There was in addition a notebook-journal, the *Flora Selborniensis*, in which he wrote botanical observations during the year 1766.

Keeping regular notes of observations on horticultural, meteorological and natural history matters was a fairly widespread practice among gentlemen of Gilbert White's day. Robert Marsham, who corresponded with Gilbert after the publication of the *Natural History of Selborne*, wrote that he had kept a journal for more than fifty years. Coincidentally, Marsham seems to have been encouraged into the diary habit by Dr Stephen Hales, the notable scientist and botanist, Rector of Faringdon (a parish close to Selborne) and also a friend of the White family. Another friend of Robert Marsham was Benjamin Stillingfleet, in his latter years a gardener and botanist of considerable repute, who in 1759 published the influential *Miscellaneous Tracts relating to Natural History, Husbandry and Physick*. In the printed preface to the *Naturalist's Journal*, its originator Daines Barrington made several references to Stillingfleet's ideas, especially his recommendation of the keeping of daily records and observations. Thomas Barker of Rutland, who resided near Gilbert's uncle and aunt Mr and Mrs Isaacs at Whitwell Rectory, also kept a journal between the years 1736 and 1801. In its initial year, there were two spring-time notes initialled GW, one on wild geese flying northwards, and another on the sound of the cuckoo. It seems, however, that Gilbert did not keep a continuous journal of his own until he returned and settled back into life in his home village of Selborne, following his degree and ordination.

Gilbert White was a keen experimental gardener, and in 1747 bought for himself the most important horticultural work of the time, Philip Miller's great *Gardener's Dictionary*. Later he was to correspond with Miller, to meet him and exchange seeds. The Wakes, the family home of the White family, has its frontage right on the main street, with a considerable garden to the rear, backed by a field and the great beech hanger of Selborne. The garden was augmented and landscaped by Gilbert and his brothers and they adopted the Hanger itself into their schemes as part of the garden vista. Some of their work is still evident today: the lime trees to the front of the house, part of the fruit wall, the ha-ha at the end of the garden, and the two paths up the Hanger – the steep Zig-zag and the gentler Bostal.

The *Garden Kalendar* and the later years of the *Naturalist's Journal* give considerable detail about the plants in the garden of the Wakes. The cottage garden flowers which Gilbert grew in his borders are now once again in fashion – hollyhocks, larkspur, asters, lilies, fritillaries. He also planted trees and shrubs and several experimental crops such as sweet corn, sea kale and certain 'small beans' from Oxfordshire, 'never sowed but once in England'. In tune with the horticultural preoccupations of his time, Gilbert spent a great deal of energy maintaining hot-beds for melons and cucumbers. Yet the innovator, even one of dedication and skill, is, just like any gardener, at risk from the unpredictable English weather. Gilbert White's hot-beds sometimes reached baking point and burned the plants or lost heat completely so that they perished of cold. An entry for 1754 notes bleakly 'uncommon severe winter. Most things in the garden destroyed.'

The beautiful garden upon which his friend Mulso heaped high compliments in later years was won by hard labour and planning. The intractable Selborne soil was improved with cartloads of dung, and good loamy soil was brought over from nearby Dorton. Small parcels of land were bought bit by bit from neighbours, to enlarge the grounds. The 'picturesque' was the prevailing concept of the late eighteenth century, and entering into its spirit, Gilbert made a bastion and a mound. He hung a series of gates, artificially sized and placed to make a vista. He set up oil jars to mimic urns, and made up a two-dimensional board to look from a distance like a statue. He also built alcoves (small summerhouses) at places where the view was especially attractive.

Nearly all the observations in the *Garden Kalendar* are concerned with cultivated plants, but in the 1760s Gilbert was becoming increasingly interested in wild plants. He purchased an important botanical work: William Hudson's *Flora Anglica* in 1765, and amended the title page of the *Kalendar* of that year to include notes on the wild flora also. This was not entirely satisfactory, and in 1766 he kept both a *Garden Kalendar* and a notebook which he called *Flora Selborniensis*, which is a catalogue of his wild plant observations. This was a year of botanical groundwork.

In 1768, he received as a gift a journal devised by the

Honourable Daines Barrington and published by Gilbert's brother Benjamin. *The Naturalist's Journal* was a standardised diary for the kind of observations that gentlemen of a scientific inclination had been making informally on the subject of natural history. At first Gilbert observed the formalities of the columns, which designated set spaces for the first trees in leaf, flowers to bloom, birds appearing and so on, but it took only a few years for most of the information to be written all over the page in sometimes quite lengthy paragraphs. Towards the end of the 1770s, he began inserting blank pages on which to write pieces of more extended observation. The only records he continued to keep in columns were the figures for the barometer and thermometer readings, and notes on wind and rain.

Gilbert White has long been acclaimed for several important discoveries. It was he who first distinguished between the three leaf warblers, who gave us the first and still revealing description of the harvest mouse. He observed the yearly appearance and reappearance of a 'large bat', giving us the earliest notes on the behaviour of the noctule bat in Britain, and he made many pioneering observations on his favourites among the birds: swifts, martins and swallows.

Yet it is not for these achievements alone that Gilbert White is revered and regarded nationally with affection, and his *Natural History of Selborne*, never out of print. Under his serious and affectionate scrutiny, the parish, one of the most ancient units of human community in England, was extended conceptually to include plants and animals – presented not as specimens, but co-existing within an intimate landscape. A follower in White's footsteps will note obvious losses – kites, bustards, the playful ravens over the Hanger – and one has to search for glow-worms or wrynecks. Yet it is significant that walking around Selborne today one may see, as Gilbert White did, a nuthatch in the churchyard, marsh marigolds brightening the church meadow, toothwort on the hazel bank, hellebores in the hollow lanes and along the quiet country roads, and an astonishingly rich mixture of woodland plants: daffodils, golden saxifrage, ferns and even the shy rarity, herb Paris.

As a writer, Gilbert was far from flamboyant. Indeed, so great was his reticence that even in the journals the personal pronoun rarely intrudes itself. None the less, there is a strong sense of the man behind the observations. The arrival of swallows is accompanied in the journal by exclamation marks!! Snow is lying 'shoe-deep' or reaching to a horse's chest; and there are 'cracks in the ground deeper than the length of a walking stick'. These tell a story of the naturalist watching the skies, tentatively trying the snow or barging through drifts on horseback, prodding the dried-out ground enquiringly with his stick. He drew on the resources of English and classical poetry, prose and science as he wrote the apparently simple journal notes which read so vividly:

> May 2nd 1765: No vegetation seems to stir at present.
> May 3rd: This evening the vehement east-west wind seems to be abated; & the air is soft, & cloudy. Ground bound like stone.

As the years passed, Gilbert became more confident and relaxed. He was corresponding with and meeting some of the foremost scientists and naturalists of the period, and it is clear that he recognised the original contribution that he could make to the state of knowledge of the time. He wrote two papers which were read at meetings of the Royal Society, and had, by the mid-1770s, decided to write a book about the natural history of his native parish which was to be a distillation of his enquiries and observations. Gilbert White had a fine critical faculty, and one senses an impatience with headlong and insufficiently substantiated natural history writing. As early as 1770, he was writing to Daines Barrington:

> Though there is endless room for observation in the field of nature which is boundless, yet investigation (where a man endeavours to be sure of his facts) can make but slow progress; and all that one could collect in many years would go into a very narrow compass.

What sets Gilbert White apart from other naturalists is not simply a matter of unusual perception. The clear-sightedness of his observations arises from a continuous endeavour to strike through conventional interpretations or misleading appearances to reach the truth of whatever subject he was considering. He took immense pains with style, not just as a matter of pride, but because he rightly saw a fundamental correlation between precision of thought and exactness of expression. The *Naturalist's Journals* are both field notes and a working manuscript for *The Natural History of Selborne*. They are by no means hasty jottings, but already accomplished and polished notes, many of which were transposed to the published book with only minimal editing, and they provide a close insight into the life-long interests of this remarkable naturalist.

NOTES
ON THE TEXT

This is the first time that Gilbert White's journals have been printed in full. His forty-three years of notes and observations are published here in three volumes:

Volume   I   *The Garden Kalendar; Flora Selborniensis; Naturalist's Journal (1768–73).*
Volume II *Naturalist's Journal (1774–83)*
Volume III *Naturalist's Journal (1784–93)*

Garden Kalendar

The manuscript of Gilbert White's *Garden Kalendar*, kept between the years 1751 and 1767, is at the British Library. It consists of quarto sheets of letter paper which were subsequently stitched together. The work has appeared in print in a facsimile edition with an introduction and notes by John Clegg (Scolar Press, 1975).

Flora Selborniensis

Flora Selborniensis was written by Gilbert White during the year 1766. It consists of a number of quarto sheets of notes principally about the wild flowers in the environs of Selborne. It is now owned by the Selborne Society. A facsimile *Flora Selborniensis* was published by the Society in a limited edition.

Naturalist's Journal

Between the years 1768 and the year of his death in 1793, Gilbert White made an entry almost every day in his *Naturalist's Journal*, taking it with him on his journeys away from home. The format for these annual journals had been devised by Daines Barrington and published by Gilbert's brother Benjamin White, and were in the form of blank diaries split into printed columns headed with items relevant to those with an interest in natural history. A selection of the entries, edited by Walter Johnson, appeared in 1931, but the complete journals have never been published in full. For this purpose, a transcription was made from the microfilm held by the British Library, where the manuscript journals are kept.

Any editor of Gilbert White's works begins with the immediate benefit of the orderliness of the author's method. The writing is clear copperplate, and there are very few indecipherable words. The arrangement of entries is generally easy to follow.

The two main principles behind the presentation and annotation of these manuscripts are maintaining the authenticity of the text, and endeavouring to present it in the way most accessible to the reader. Notes have been kept to a minimum and are intended simply to explain names or terms which would be unfamiliar to a present-day reader, or to indicate instances where the present status of plants and creatures mentioned by Gilbert White has changed dramatically. The variable spelling and the punctuation of the originals have been retained wherever possible, and most of the few crossings-out have been annotated. Gilbert sometimes used archaisms for effect and, as his interest in antiquities grew, drew also on vernacular Hampshire names for topographical details and for plants and animals. Interestingly, the English common names for plants have changed less than the scientific names over the last two hundred years.

Gilbert used the standard English flora of the early eighteenth century, John Ray's great work *Synopsis methodica stirpium Britannicarium* in its third edition of 1724 edited by J.J. Dillenius, and from 1765 he referred also to Hudson's *Flora Anglica*. He was familiar with the work of Linnaeus and, after 1768, many of the scientific names used are Linnaean ones. On the title-page of some of his journals he appends the information that 'the plants are named according to the sexual system [the Linnaean method], the birds according to Ray, the Insects according to Linnaeus'. Every attempt has been made in the glossary/index of this edition to identify the species noted by Gilbert White. Translations of Latin or Greek quotations are to be found under the note for that day.

In the course of putting Gilbert White's written notes into a printed form editorial requirements have dictated a kind of design which differs from the original. While the guiding principle has been to maintain the authenticity of the work, the aim has also been to achieve a result which is more accessible and easier to follow than the original, which was, after all, not intended for publication.

All scientific names have been italicised. Punctuation, including the use of colons where modern usage would dictate semi-colons or full stops, has been reproduced exactly as in the manuscripts. Gilbert White's short forms y^e and Bro^r have also been retained, as has the form *it's* for the possessive.

For the *Garden Kalendar* and the *Flora Selborniensis*, a simple format consisting of date, followed by notes, reproduces that of the originals. In the case of the *Naturalist's Journal* a different procedure has been adopted. The original pages were laid out in nine columns with printed headings. The first six columns of the original journals deal with data: place, date, barometric pressures, temperatures, rainfall, wind and other weather notes. These always relate to Selborne, someone else keeping the records while Gilbert was away.

While these notes are integral to the journals and most interesting when studied in the light of the miscellaneous observations which make up the main text, in themselves numerical and single-word records are by no means light reading. They have therefore been grouped together on the left-hand side of the page where, without interrupting the enjoyment of reading the main text, they may be consulted or ignored at the reader's wish.

Gradually, over the years, everything (except the weather data) comes to be written as 'observations', spreading more or less over the remaining space on the page, irrespective of columns. Sometimes, especially in the later years, notes have been continued over the top or bottom of a page or on to an inserted sheet. Some of these over-runs are dated, and their positioning usually indicates the date within the week to which they relate. Where the positioning is not clear or the comments are of a general nature, or entered retrospectively, the additional material has been placed with the entries for the nearest adjacent day and set in a different typeface.

Some of the barometer readings appear extremely complicated and their meaning is obscure. For instance, on 21st January 1774 the reading is 29½ ½/10.

When one examines barometers of this period, going through the physical process as Gilbert White would have done to make his daily readings, these figures, puzzling on paper, make sense. The mercury in the tube of the barometer, being very heavy, fluctuates only slightly, requiring minute calibration. Measurements are taken in two stages, the first on a large scale, ranged usually on the right side of the tube. In the example above, this would read 29½ inches. Then a more exact fraction is read from a more precise scale on the other side of the instrument, usually in tenths, sometimes hundredths. Gilbert White's small-scale calibration measured tenths but he could discern fractions of tenths: hence ½/10. So the barometer on that day stood at 29½ plus half of a tenth. It could have been expressed as 29 11/20, but he wrote it down in the same way as he read it from the barometer.

The way the columnar information has been inter-preted in print is as follows:

Date and location – the month, year and place head each page and do not appear again unless there is a change. Each individual entry is dated.

Barometric pressures and any movements are next recorded. The end of this column is indicated by a semi-colon.

Temperatures in degrees Fahrenheit are shown next. The end of this column is again indicated by a semi-colon.

Wind direction and any changes are shown, as in the manuscript, by initial letters: SE, SW and so on.

Weather conditions and their changes throughout the day are listed next.

Trees, plants in flower, fungi and mosses follow, preceded by a symbol ⚘. Again the original column divisions are shown by a semi-colon, and the entry ends in a full stop.

Birds and insects encountered on that date appear on a fresh line.

Rainfall and snow measurements in inches and hundredths

of an inch are recorded after 1778 and are entered last.
Gilbert White's comments and notes are reproduced in the
right-hand column just as he wrote them.

Key to symbols

The Editor's notes on the text are indicated thus ¶ and the
notes themselves are grouped at the end of the book under
the relevant dates. They are also identified by date in the
glossary/index.

Gilbert's own notes are marked with asterisks, as in
the manuscripts, and included in the text.

Editorial footnotes relating to the position or author-
ship of certain passages are indicated by a dagger sign†.

Comments or notes added by Gilbert at a date later
than the adjacent entry are set in a different typeface.

Short Lythe
Late April

NATURALIST'S JOURNAL

Saturday 1.
29 1/10½; 31; NW.
Hard frost, bright,
sleet.

SELBORNE
Larks congregate.

Sunday 2.
29 3/10; 32½; NW.
Hard frost, bright,
sharp wind.

Thermom.ʳ abroad 25½.

Monday 3.
29½ 1/10½; NW.
Hard frost, bright,
ground dry & hard.

Thermom.ʳ abroad 22¾.
... at noon ... 30.
... in yᵉ wine vault 43¼.

Tuesday 4.
29½ 2/10; 28; NW,
W.
Hard frost, sun, grey,
dark & still.

Wednesday 5.
29½ 2/10½; 34¾; W.
Frost, grey, mild, dark
& still.

Thursday 6.
29 2/10½; 39; W, S.
Sprinkling, dark, rain,
great rain.

Friday 7.
29½; 39; W, NW.
Grey, sun, grey,
sprinkling.

Saturday 8.
29 2/10; 37; W, S, E.
Frost, grey, great rain.

Sunday 9.
29 4/10½; 41; N, NE.
Steady rain, rain, rain,
sleet, snow.

Rain for 24 hours: vast flood. Could not get along down at the ponds all the day.

Monday 10.
29 4/10; 35;NE.
Frost, grey & sharp,
frost.

Wild ducks about.

Tuesday 11.
29 3/10; 32¾; NE.
Hard frost, sun, still,
frost.

Some snow on the ground.
Aurora.

Wednesday 12.
29 2/10; 31½; E.
Hard frost, sun, flisky
clouds, hard frost.

Thursday 13.
28½ 2/10¾; 32¾, 38;
SE, S.
Dark, warm fog, swift
thaw, rain, rain.

Friday 14.
28½ ½/10, 2/10½;
43; SW, W.
Dark, sun, shower,
showers.

Vast rain in the night with thunder.

A bittern was shot in shrub-wood. A dog hunted it on the foot, & sprung it in the covert. On the same day Mr Yalden shot one in a coppice in the parish of Emshot: & about the same time one was killed in the parish of Greatham. These birds are very seldom seen in this district, & are probably driven from their watery haunts by the great floods, & obliged to betake themselves to the uplands. The wings expanded measured just four feet: the tail-feathers shafts & all were just five inches long, & 10 in number. The neck-feathers were very long, & loose like those on the neck of a roost-cock. These birds weighed undrawn, & feathers & all, each 3 p^{ds} & 2 oun: The serrated claw on each middle toe is very curious! Tho' the colours on the bittern's wings & back are no ways gaudy or radiant, yet are the dark & chestnut streaks so curiously blended & combined, as to give that fowl a surprizing beauty. Both the upper & lower mandible are serrated towards the point, & the upper is emarginated. Two of these birds I dressed, & found the flavour to be like that of wild duck, or teal, but not so delicate. They were in good case, & their intestines covered with fat. In the

Saturday 15.
29 2/10; W.
Bright, soft & sunny.

crop or gizzard I found nothing that could inform me on what they subsisted: both were quite empty. I found nothing like the flavour of an hare. The flesh of these birds was very brown.

It appears since that all these bitterns were killed in Selborne parish, & probably were all of the same family.

Sunday 16.
29; 46½; SW.
Rain, dark, sun,
clouds, clear with wind.

Much rain in the night.
Jupiter, the moon, & Venus being this evening nearly in a line, & almost at equal distances, make a beautiful appearance.

Monday 17.
28½ ½/10; 49; S, SE.
Rain, dark, great rain,
rain & wind.

Bat appears: they are out at times every month in the winter, but not in frost.

Tuesday 18.
29 3/10¼; 39; N.
Rain, snow, snow,
snow, bright.

Considerable snow on the ground. Frost.

Wednesday 19.
29½ ½/10; 34; W,
SW.
Hard frost, sunny &
still, mild, mackrel sky.

Thursday 20.
29 2/10; 34; E, E.
Frost, sun, light clouds.

Snow remains.
Vast halo round the moon.

Friday 21.
29½ ½/10; 32, 34; E.
Frost, bright, frost.

Snow continues.

Saturday 22.
28½ 4/10¾; 31, 35;
SE.
Hard frost, grey, fog,
rain.

Thaw.

Sunday 23.
28½ 2/10; 37½; W,
SW, W.
Bright, clouds, bright,
frost.

Great rain in the night.

Stinking hellebore
Selborne High Wood
25 April

Monday 24.
28½ 4/10½; W.
No frost, bright, sharp
wind, clouds, bright.

Stone-curlews still appear on Temple farm.

Tuesday 25.
29 ½/10; 33½; W,
SW.
Frost, bright, sharp
wind, clouds, shower &
wind.

Yellow wagtail.

Wednesday 26.
29 2/10½; 37; SW.
Bright, frost, sun with
sharp wind, wind.

Thursday 27.
29 1/10; SW, SW.
Rain, rain & wind.

Missel thrush sings.

Friday 28.
29 3/10½; 39; SW,
W.
Dark, sun & wind.

Titmouse begins to open.
Red-breast sings.
Song-thrush sings.

Saturday 29.
29 4/10; 40; SE, S, N.

Snow-drop, wolfs bane,¶ *helleborus foetidus* blow. Gnats appear.

Rain, soft & sunny,   Beetles buz in the evening.
grey, fine.

Sunday 30.
29½ 1/10¾; 39; W,
SW.
Frost, bright day, dark.

Monday 31.
29½ 2/10½; 34; N, N.   Great titmouse chirps.
Hard frost, sun & keen   The water above the lower tap in R: Knight's cellar at Faringdon.
wind, strong wind.   The land-springs begin to break-out on the downs beyond
                              Andover. A certain token that the rich corn-vales must suffer.
                              Considerable snow. Made hot bed.

FEBRUARY 1774

Tuesday 1.   SUTTON
29½ 4/10; SW.
Frost, sun, snow, snow,
frost.

Wednesday 2.
30; N.   The land-springs have not been so high since spring 1764.
Frost, sun, sun, frost.

Thursday 3.
30 1/10; 35½; N.
Sun, dark with snow,
thaw, dark.

Friday 4.
30 ½/10;37½; NE.
Dark, & cold thaw, raw.

Saturday 5.   SELBORNE
30; 37; NE, N.
Frost, sun, yellow
evening.

Sunday 6.
29½ 3/10½; 34; NW,   Bees play much about their hives.
NW.
Hard frost, warm sun,
sun, frost.

Monday 7.
29 4/10; 41; SW.
Sun & wind, swift
thaw, dark & windy.

Continual vicissitudes from frost to rain.
Land-floods advance.

Tuesday 8.
29 1/10½, 29½
¼/10; 36; W, NW.
Rain, sleet, fierce
cutting wind with sun.

Freezes sharply all day.
The cones of last year fall very fast from yᵉ spruce-firs.

Wednesday 9.
29½ 1/10; 33; NW,
NW.
Hard frost, frost &
sun, frost.

Jupiter & Venus approximate very fast.
Venus is very bright, & makes strong shadows on the floors &
walls.

Thursday 10.
29 4/10; 33½, 38½;
S, SW.
Hard frost, thaw,
rain, rain & wind.

Weather shifts continually from frost to rain to the detriment of
the wheat & turneps. Wheat looks sadly, & is almost heaved out
of the ground.

Friday 11.
29; 42; SW, W.
Vast rain, showers,
clouds, sun & wind,
bright.

Saturday 12.
29 4/10; 45; W, SW.
White frost, strong
wind, dark & still,
wind & rain.

Chaffinch begins to sing.
Red-breast, & wren sing.

Sunday 13.
29½ 4/10; 48¼; SW,
S.
Dark & windy, driving
mist, dark & windy.

Hedge-sparrow sings.
Great flock of buntings in the fields towards Faringdon.

Monday 14.
29 4/10; 48; SW, S.
Dark & windy, soft,
rain.

The ivy, *hedera helix*, blows in Sept: Octʳ & Novʳ the berries are
now full grown, & ripen in April: thus fructification goes on in
some Instances the winter thro'. When the berries are full ripe
they are black.

Tuesday 15.
49½; 29; SW, S.
Windy & dark, mild,
wet & stormy.

House sparrows.
The Plestor.
February.

Wednesday 16.
28½ 4/10½; 45½; W.
Heavy shower, strong
wind, hail, bright.

Skylarks mount, & essay to sing.
House-sparrows get in clusters, & chirp, & fight. Thrushes
whistle.

Thursday 17.
29 4/10; W, SW.
Bright with strong
wind, showers & hail,
bright.

Ravens begin to build.
Spring-like weather.

Friday 18.
29½ 2/10; 40; W,
SW. White frost, sun,
soft & spring-like,
bright & wind.

Saturday 19.
29 4/10; 46; SW, S.
Dark & windy, very
great rain.

These great rains retard the preparations for a spring-crop. Grey
crows still on the downs.

Sunday 20.
29½ 2/10; 46; SW, S.
White frost, sunny &
mild, clouds with wind.

The high wind last night blowed down a large old apple tree in
the orchard.

Monday 21.
29 1/10, 29½; 42; S,
SW.
Wind, vast rain, clouds

Ews¶ & lambs look very lank from the drowning rains: the
turneps are very washy food.

& sun with strong
wind, bright with
wind.

Tuesday 22.
29 2/10; 45½; SW.
Frost, vast rain with
stormy wind.

Wednesday 23.
28½ 4/10; 48½; SW.   Several *muscae* appear.
Grey, windy, rain,   Skylarks would sing if the wind would permit.
strong wind.

Thursday 24.
29 2/10; 42½; SW.   Thunder & lightening in some places.
Stormy all night, sun &   Strong winds for several days.
clouds with fierce wind,
hail, bright.

Friday 25.
28½ 3/10, 29; 40; SE,   Much rain.
NW.
Rain, rain, rain & sleet,
wind.

Saturday 26.
29½, 40; NW.   Land-springs rise.
White frost, sun &
clouds, frost.   The titmouse, which at this time of the year begins to make two
quaint, sharp notes, which some people compare to the whetting of
a saw, is the marsh-titmouse.
    It is the great titmouse¶ which sings those three chearful notes
which the country people say sounds like "sit ye down": they call
the bird by that name.

Sunday 27.
29½ 3/10; 41½; NW,   Ewes die in lambing.
SW.
Hard frost, sun &
wind, bright.

Monday 28.
29½; 45; SW, NW.   Much wheat rotted on the ground in the clays.
Rain, rain, showers &
wind, bright & still,
wind.

MARCH 1774

Tuesday 1.
29 4/10½; 42½; W,
W.
White frost, sun &
wind, bright.

Wednesday 2.
29 1/10½; 39½; W.   Venus shadows.
Dark, rain, flights of
hail, & sleet.

Thursday 3.
29 3/10; 37, 40; W.   Crocuss blow out.
Hard frost, sun &
clouds.

Friday 4.
28½ 3/10; 43½; S,   Daws resort to churches.
SW.
Vast rain, sun & clouds,
showers.

Saturday 5.
28½ 4/10; 45; SW, S,   Received as a present from Mr Hinton, (to whom it was sent
SW.   from Exeter with many more) one of Mr William Lucombe's
Dark, vast rain, windy.   new variety of oaks: it is said to be evergreen, tho' raised at first
                                                from an acorn belonging to a deciduous tree. They are all grafted
                                                on stocks of common oaks. My specimen is a fine young plant, &
                                                well-rooted. The growth of this sort is said to be wonderful.
                                                Vid: *Philosoph: transact*. V: 62 for the year 1772.

Sunday 6.
29 2/10: 47½: S, S.   Vast flood.
Great rain, rain &
wind, showers, misty
rain.

Monday 7.
29 2/10½; 50; S.
Great rain.

Tuesday 8.¶   LONDON
Dark, grey, rain.   In the night between the 8th & 9th a vast fragment of an hanger in
                                         the parish of Hawkley slipped down; & at the same time several

fields below were rifted & torn in a wonderful manner: two houses also & a barn were shattered, a road stopped-up, & some trees thrown-down. 50 acres of ground were disordered & damaged by this strange accident. The turf of some pastures was driven into a sort of waves: in some places the ground sunk into hollows.

Wednesday 9.
43; SE.
Vast rain, rain, snow.

This was the last day of the wet weather: but the waters were so encreased by this day's deluge, that most astonishing floods ensued.

Thursday 10.
35; E.
Dark, snow covers the ground.

This rain & snow, coming on the back of such continual deluges, occasioned a flood in the S: of England beyond any thing ever remembered before.

Friday 11.
36; NE.
Frost, dark all day.

Saturday 12.
38; NE.
Frost, bright sun.

Sunday 13.
38½; SE.
Frost, bright sun.

Monday 14.
38; SE.
Frost, warm sun.

Tuesday 15.
44; SE.
be worried
Frost, bright day.

Butterflies appear.

Wednesday 16.
38½; SE.
Sweet soft sunshine.

Thursday 17.
51; S, SE.
Soft & bright.

Friday 18.
50; S, SE.
Soft & pleasant, gentle
rain.

Thomas kept the journal in my absence.

Saturday 19.
50; SE.
Fog, bright.

Sunday 20.
51; E.
Fog, bright.

Monday 21.
49½; SE.
Ditto.

Tuesday 22.
50; E.
Ditto.

Wednesday 23.
46; N, NE.
Dark.

Thursday 24.
49; NE.
Fog, bright.

Friday 25.
50; SE, S.
Frost, fog, soft sun.
Conops calcitrans.

SELBORNE

Saturday 26.
29½ 2/10; 51; SW.
Frost, soft sun.
⚘ *Cucumis sativus.*
Regulus non crist:
minimus, Bombylius
medius, Humble bees.

Peaches, nectarines, & Apricots in fine bloom.
No rain since the 9ᵗʰ stiff ground still very wet.
Thomas began to mow the grass-plot

My new laid turf, where not damaged by the continual standing of
water after the vast rains, looks well.
    Smallest willow-wren chirps: first summer bird of passage.

Sunday 27.
29½ ¾/10; 53; SW.
Fog, sweet day.

Black birds, & thrushes lay.

Monday 28.
29½ 2/10; 54; SW, E.
W, NW.
Bright, blue mist,
thunder clouds,
thunder, no rain,
bright.

Hot sun.
Great thunder-shower at Winton.

Tuesday 29.
29½ 2/10; 55½; NE,
N.
Frost, sweet day.

A fine regular bloom all over the apricot, peach, &
Nectarine-trees.
Sheltered the bloom with some ivy-boughs.

Wednesday 30.
29½ ½/10; 51; NE,
N, SW.
Fog, sweet day.

Thursday 31.
53; 29 3/10½; SE.
Fog, sweet day.

APRIL 1774

Friday 1.
29 1/10½; 55½; SE.
Bright, strong, hollow
wind.

No rain since the 9th of March.

Saturday 2.
28½ 4/10½; 49; E.
Harsh wind, dark
clouds with sprinklings,
hard wind.

The saxon word *Playstow* signifies *ludi locus, gymnasium,
palaestra, theatrum.* ¶ No doubt our little square, called to this day
the plestor, is of the same import: it is moreover the place to this
day where the youths of the village resort for their diversions; &
was moreover no doubt in old days our market-place, when this
village was a town.

Sunday 3.
29; 49; S, SE, SW.
Showers, great rain,
wind.

Monday 4.
29 4/10; 47½; SW.
Bright, hail, sun &
clouds.
Hirundo domestica.

Two swallows appear at Faringdon.

Tuesday 5.
29 4/10; 48; SW, S.   The ground harrows, & rakes well.
Showers, sun & clouds.

Wednesday 6.
29; 48; S.   Stone-curlew whistles.
Rain & wind, great
rain, rain,
bright, rain.
Oedicnemus.

Thursday 7.
29 1/10; 51; S.
Showers with wind.

Friday 8.
29 2/10; 51; SW.
Showers, soft air, large
showers.

Saturday 9.
29 2/10½; 50; SE, S,   The ring-ousel appears on it's spring-migration. It feeds now on
W.   ivy-berries, which just begin to ripen. Ivy blossoms in Octobr In
White frost, fog, soft &   the autumn it feeds on haws, yew berries, &c: also on worms,
sunny, showers, fine,   &c.
Merula torquata.

Sunday 10.
29 4/10; 52; SW.   Cucumbers begin to swell.
Sun, fine day, brisk   Peaches, nectarines, & apricots begin to leaf.
gale.

Monday 11.
29½ 1/10; 53; S.   Grass grows very fast.
Soft rains, wet, wet.   Shell-snails come-out in troops.

Tuesday 12.
29½ 2/10¼; 57; SE.   Three swallows appear.
Sun, soft day, dark.   Several bank-martins about the verge of the forest.
*Luscinia, Hirundo
riparia*.

Wednesday 13.
29½ 3/10; 58½; NE.   Apricots begin to set.
White frost, sweet day.   Planted seven rows of potatoes.
                                   Nightingale in my fields.

Thursday 14.
29½ 2/10¼; 51; NE.
Dark & harsh.
Atricapilla.

The black-cap begins to sing in my fields: a most punctual bird in it's return.

Friday 15.
29½; NE.
Dark & harsh, spitting.

Saturday 16.
29½; 49; N.
Dark & still.

Cut the first cucumber.

In the season of nidification the wildest birds are comparatively tame. Thus the ringdove breeds in my fields tho' they are continually frequented: & the missel-thrush, tho' most shy in the autumn & winter, builds in my garden close to a walk where people are passing all day long.

Sunday 17.
29 4/10½; SW, W,
NW.
White frost, sun, dark
& cold.
*Regulus non-cristatus
medius.*

The middle willow-wren sings with a plaintive, but pleasing note.

Monday 18.
29 3/10; 48; W, NW.
Rain, rain, grey, bright
& cold.

Tuesday 19.
29 3/10½; 44; NW.
Hard frost, dark &
cold, bright.

The titlark begins to sing: a sweet songster!

Wednesday 20.
29½ ½/10; 46; NE,
N.
Cold & dark, sun,
bright & cold.
Turtur.

Turtle cooes.

Thursday 21.
29½ 2/10; 49; NW,
W.

Asparagus begins to sprout.

Hard frost, sun &
clouds.
Musca vomitoria.

Friday 22.
29½ 2/10; 51½; W.   Cuckoo cries.
Grey, brisk air.
Cuculus.

Saturday 23.
29½ 3/10¼; 60; SW.   Some peaches, & nectarines begin to set.
Wh: frost, sweet day.

                          The missel-thrush drives the magpies from the garden with great
                          fury: the welch call this bird Pen y llwyn, the head or master of the
                          coppice. It suffers no jay, or black-bird to enter the garden, & is for
                          the present a good guard to the new-sown legumes.

Sunday 24.
29½ 3/10; 56; SW.   No house-martins appear: they are very backward in coming.
Sun, strong wind.   One swift is seen.
Hirundo apus.

Monday 25.
29 4/10; 53; SW.   Redstart returns.
Sun, strong wind,   Wryneck returns, & pipes.
clouds & sun.
*Ruticilla, Jynx, sive
torquilla.*

Tuesday 26.
29 3/10½; 49; NW.   No house-martins seen yet, save one by chance.
Sun, strong wind with   Apricots, peaches, & nectarines swell: sprinkled the trees with
sun, still & cold.   water, & watered the roots.

Wednesday 27.
29 3/10; 44; W, NE,   Oaks are felled: the bark runs freely.
S, SW.   Many swallows.
Ice, hot sun, flisky   Two swifts round the church.
clouds.

Thursday 28.
29 4/10¼; 48½;   Began to cut a little orchard-grass for the horses.
NE.   Some few beeches are in leaf.
Sprinkling, harsh
severe wind,
sprinklings.

Friday 29.

29½ 1/10; 53; N.
Fog, dark, sun, soft
evening.
*Alauda minima locustae
voce, Gryllus gryllo-
talpa.*

The grass-hopper lark whispers.
Mole-cricket churs.

Saturday 30.

29½ 1/10¼; 58; NE,
E.
Grey, foggy, hot sun,
soft, & still.
Hirundo agrestis.

Vine-shoots have been pinched by the frost.
Two house-martins up at Mʳ Yalden's.

If bees, who are much the best setters of cucumbers, do not
happen to take kindly to the frames, the best way is to tempt them
by a little honey put on the male & female bloom. When they are
once induced to haunt the frames, they set all the fruit, & will
hover with impatience round the lights in a morning, 'til the glasses
are opened.
Probatum est.¶

MAY 1774

Sunday 1.

29 4/10½; 57; NE.
Sun, harsh, strong
wind, calm, & fine.

A pair of Martins of Selborne. Martins very late.
Two pairs of swifts.
Distant lightening.

Monday 2.

29 ½/10; 55; E, S.
Fog, soft rain, rain,
dark.
Scarabaeus melolontha.

There is a good bloom on the pear-trees.
Great bloom of cherries.

Tuesday 3.

29 2/10; W, SE.
Sun, sun & clouds,
sweet even:
*Ficedulae affinis, Musca
meridiana.*

The white-throat returns, & whistles.
Peaches & nectarines swell.

Wednesday 4.

29 2/10½; 55; NE, E.
Vast dew, sun, dark &
windy, rain & wind.

Asparagus in plenty.
Orchard-grass cut for the horses.

Thursday 5.
29 1/10¾; 53; E.
Stormy night, rain,
rain, sun & soft.

Grass grows, & is forward.
Apple-trees blow.
Plums shew little bloom.

Friday 6.
29 3/10; 52; NE, N.
Rain, rain, heavy
showers, rain & wind.

The redstart whistles perching on the tops of tall trees near
houses.
Few swifts yet.

Saturday 7.
29½ 1/10½; W, SW.
Sun, grey, fine day.

† [Whitethroat Warbles: it's common note is harsh and short.]
The ground is well moistened.

In Devon near Exeter Swallows did not arrive 'til April 25; &
house martins not 'til the middle of May. Swifts were seen in plenty
on May 1st. At Blackburn in Lancashire swifts were seen April 28:
Swallows April 29. House-martins May 1st.
    In some former years, I see, house-martins have not appeared
'til the beginning of May: the case was the same this Year; & yet
they afterwards abounded. These long delays are more in favour of
migration than of a torpid state. House-martins afterwards were
very plenty.

Sunday 8.
29½ 2/10; 57; SE S.
Great dew, summer
day, sweet evening.

† [White-throat warbles softly.]
Mistake: it was the black cap: white throats are always harsh &
unmusical.
Chafers begin to abound.

Monday 9.
29½ 1/10¾; 63¼; E.
large dew, sun,
summer's day.
*Regulus non cristatus
major cantat voce
stridula locustae.**

Chafers have not been plenty since the year 1770. Eight swifts
now appear: they arrive in pairs. Martins encrease. Hanger
almost in full leaf. Chafers in vast numbers.

*Shaking its wings it makes at intervals a sibilous stammering
noise¶ on the tops of the tallest beechen-woods: it abounds in the
beechen-woods on the Sussex downs, where the two other species
are never heard. It spends it's time on the tops of the tallest trees.

Tuesday 10.
29½; 64; NE.
Large dew, sun, sultry,
showers about, thunder,
sweet even.
Caprimulgus.

Fern-owl returns, & chatters. Lightening.

The *caprimulgus* is the last bird of passage but one: the *stoparola*
is the last.

---

†Entry crossed out.

House martins collecting mud,
Newton Valence pond.
13 May.

Wednesday 11.
29½ ½/10; 60; NE.
Dark & showery, soft
rains, dark & mild.

Pulled the first lettuces, brown Dutch,¶ which had stood the winter under the fruit-wall: they begin to loave.

Thursday 12.
29½ 2/10; 65½; NE,
N.
Dark, sun, sweet day.
Libellulae.

Swallows & house-martins begin to collect dirt for building. The swallow carries straws to mix with it.
Chafers swarm.

Friday 13.
29½ 2/10½; 61, NE.
Sun, sweet summer's
day.
*Gryllus campestris
stridet.*

Crows bring-out their young in troops.
Field-cricket begins to shrill.
Horses begun to lie abroad.

Saturday 14.
29½ 2/10½; 61; NE.
White dew, sun, hot
sun, summer's day.

Swifts are encreased to their *usual* number of about eight or nine pairs.

The house-martin begins to build as early as when it arrives early. It came very late.

Sunday 15.
29½ 2/10½; 58; NE.
Sun, sharp wind, sun,
still evening.

Mornings cold.

Monday 16.
29½ 2/10¾; 55; NE.
Cold dew, bright sun,
bright, chilly.

A pair of martins began building their nest against my brew-house.

Tuesday 17.
29½ 3/10; 53, 54; NE.
Dark & cold, dark &
chilly.

Rooks bring-out their young: they & the crows, & daws & ravens, frequent the top of the hanger, & prey on chafers.

Wednesday 18.
29½ 3/10; 51; NE,
W.
Sun, cold air, clouds,
hail, bright.

Thinned the apricots & took off a large basket of fruit.

Thursday 19.
29½ 3/10; 55; SW.
Dark, sun & clouds,
fine even.
✿ *Crataegus oxyacantha.*

The first leaves of the peaches & nect: sadly blotched, & rivelled. These leaves seem not to be affected by animals; but are monstrously distorted.

Mem: to observe whether the peaches & nect: whose leaves are so blotched can bear any well-flavoured fruit. They bore fine fruit in plenty, considering the wet shady season.

Friday 20.
29½ 1/10; 55½; E.
Sun, bright, cold air,
fine even.
*Stoparola.**

*Flycatcher appears: the latest summer-bird of passage.

The *stoparola* is most punctual to the 20ᵗʰ of May!!! This bird, which comes so late, begins building immediately.

Saturday 21.
29 ½/10; 58½; E.
Sun, dark, soft rain,
soft rain, dark.

Rain much wanted.
Apple-trees in fine bloom.
Began to tack some shoots of vines. Few white-throats this year.

Sunday 22.
29; 55½; S, SW, W.
Sun, dark, rain, rain.

Fine rain.

Monday 23.
29 ½/10; 55; S, SW.
Rain, rain, showers,
sun, showers.

The ground is finely soaked.

Tuesday 24.
29 3/10; S, SW.

*This curious plant was found in bloom in the long Lythe¶

Showers, showers,
showers, bright.
✠ *Ophrys nidus avis.*✱
Bro. Thomas.

among the dead leaves under the thickest beeches: & also among
some bushes on Dorton.

Wednesday 25.
29½; 51; S, SW,
NW.
Sun, clouds, light
showers, dark.
Apis longicornis.✱

The martins have just finished the shell of a nest left unfinished in
some former year under the eaves of my stable.
Tacked some vine shoots. Some few S^t foin heads blow.
✱bores holes in the grass walks.

Thursday 26.
29½ 1/10¼; 51; N.
Dark & harsh, sun,
mild & still.

Planted one of the *ophrys nidus avis* with a good root to it in my
garden, under a shady hedge.

The shell of the martin's nest begun May 16. is about half finished.

Friday 27.
29½ 2/10; 48; N.
Dark & windy, sun,
mild even:

Saturday 28.
29½ 1/10½; 49; W,
NW.
White frost, ice, sun,
dark & louring.

The crows, rooks, & daws in great numbers continue to devour
the chafers on the hanger. Was it not for those birds chafers
would destroy everything.

Rooks, now their young are flown, do not roost on their nest-trees,
but retire in the evening towards Hartley-woods. Martins roost in
their new nests as soon as ever they are large enough to contain
them.

Sunday 29.
29½; 49; NW.
Sun, dark, rain, heavy
showers.

Monday 30.
29½; NE, S, SW.
Sun, dark, rain, bright.

The shell of the martin's nest begun May 16 is finished.

Tuesday 31.
29½; S, S.
Sun & clouds, mild,
showers about.

Pulled-off many hundreds of Nectarines, which grew in clusters.
The leaves are distempered, & the trees make few shoots.

JUNE 1774

Wednesday 1.
29½ 1/10½; S.
Sun, sweet day.

Vast crop of wall-fruit.
Planted vast rows of China-asters in the Garden.

Thursday 2.
29½ 1/10; 61; S, SW.
Showers, showers, fine
& soft.

Finished tacking the vines for the first time.
Planted-out annuals in the basons down the field.

Friday 3.
29 4/10; 58; S, SW, S.
Sun, showers, showers,
showers.

Martins abound: they came late, but appear to be more in
number than usual.

Saturday 4.
29 3/10½; 58; NW.
Showers, showers,
showers, thunder, vast
clouds.

The leaves of the mulberry-tree hardly begin to peep.
The vines promise well for bloom.

Some pairs of martins repair, & inhabit nests of several years
standing.
   Apis longicornis works at boring it's nest in the ground only in a
morning while the sun shines on the walk. Earth-worms make
their casts most in mild weather about March & April: they do not
lie torpid in winter, but come forth when there is no frost.

Sunday 5.
29 3/10¼; 56; SW,
SW.
Sun, clouds & showers
about, shower &
rainbow, soft even.

The swallows pursue the magpies, & buffet them.
Wall-fruit swells.

Monday 6.
29½; 57; SE, NE.
Dark, showers,
showers, sun. Soft
even, with vast
clouds.

The redstart sits singing on the fane of the may-pole, & on the
weather-cock of the tower.

Tuesday 7.
29½ 3/10½; 61½; N,
NW.
Sun, sun & clouds,
sweet even:

My S^t foin about half blown.
Bees swarm; & sheep are shorn.
My firs did not blow this year.

Bees swarming
Gracious Street.
Early June.

Wednesday 8.

29½ 4/10½; 67; N, S, SW.
Sun, clouds, hot sun, brisk air.

Bees gather much from the bloom of the buck-thorn, *rhamnus catharticus*: & somewhat from the new shoots of the laurel.

Thursday 9.

29½ 3/10; 68; W, NW.
Grey, dark & sultry, still.
Hippobosca equina.

Chafers are pretty well gone; they did not deface the hedges this year.
When swifts mate flying, they raise their wings over their backs.¶

Friday 10.

29½ 2/10; 65; NE, SE.
Dark, close & still.

Young broods of moor hens appear.
Peaches, nect: & apricots swell.
Lettuces that stood the winter are very fine.

Saturday 11.

29½; 68¼; SE.
Mist, dark & sultry, sun, tower-like clouds: flie various.
🌣 *Sambucus nigra.*

Cut my S[t] foin: it is in full bloom, & a good crop: this is the seventh crop.
Swifts have eggs, but do not sit . . . Do they lay more than two??¶

Linnaeus says, that hawks "*paciscuntur inducias cum avibus, quamdiu cuculus cuculat:*"¶ but I find that during that period many little birds are taken & destroyed by birds of prey, as appears by their feathers left under hedges.

Sunday 12.

29 2/10; 63; SE, E.
Sunny, dark, sprinklings, dark & still, rain.

Odd meteorous circle round the sun which the common people call a mock sun.

Monday 13.

29½; 62; NW, SW, W.
Sun, sun & brisk air.

House-martins gather moss, & grasses for their nests from the Roofs of houses.
Swifts stay-out 'til within 10 minutes of 9.

Tuesday 14.

29½ 1/10; 61; S, SE,
Sun, clouds & brisk air.
🌣 *Digitalis purpurea.*
Gryllus: telligonia verrucivorus. *

MIDHURST
Ivy berries are all fallen-off.
*Young grass-hoppers.

Wednesday 15.
29½; 64; S, S.
Sun, whiffling wind,
clouds, heavy shower.

BRAMSHOT, SELBORNE
There seem to be more hirundines, particularly house-martins,
& swifts, about Midhurst than with us.

Thursday 16.
29½ 1/10; 65; W,
SW, S.
Sun & clouds, sun,
dark & still, dark.
🌱 *Triticum hybernum.*

Fern-owl chatters in the hanger.

Friday 17.
29½, 29½ 1/10; 67;
SE, N, W.
Showers, thunder,
dark, sun, shower.

Distant thunder all night.
Turned the S^t foin which is not damaged.

Saturday 18.
29½ 2/10; 66; W, SW,
S, SW.
Shower, sun & vast
clouds, showers about,
variable winds & clouds
flying different ways.

Ricked the S^t foin, four jobbs. Rather under made, but not at all
damaged by the rain. It was made in swarth, & lay 8 days.¶

Most birds drink sipping a little at a time: but pigeons take a long
continued draught like quadrupeds.
    Some swallows build down the mouths of the chalk-draught-
holes on Faringdon-common. House-martins retire to rest pretty
soon: they roost in their nest as soon as ever it is big enough to
contain them. Martins build the shell of a nest frequently, & then
forsake it, & build a new one.

Sunday 19.
29 2/10½; 59;
SW, S.
Great dew, bright,
clouds, rain.

Bees frequent my chimneys: they certainly extract somewhat from
the soot, the pitchy part, I suppose.

Monday 20.
29 1/10 59; S, SW, S.
Showers, showers,
heavy shower.

S^t foin rick sinks very fast, & heats.

Tuesday 21.
W, NW.
Dark & still, rain, rain.

BP'S SUTTON

Wednesday 22.
29½ 1/10; NW.

FYFIELD
Quail calls.

Grey, dark, soft rain.
☙ *Spiraea filipendula,*
Valeriana offic:

Young backward rooks just flown.
Young Nightingales flown.
Mayflies abound on the Whorwel streams, & are taken by
hirundines.

Thursday 23.
NW, SW.
Dark & still, dark,
showers.
☙ *Carduus nutans.*

Nightingales very jealous of y^ir young; & make a jarring harsh
noise if you approach them.

Friday 24.
29½ 1/10; SW, S.
Grey & moist, sun,
dark & chilly.

My Bro: has brewed a barrel of strong-beer with his *hordeum*
nudum. My brother's *hordeum nudum* is very large & forward, &
has a broad blade like wheat: it is now spindling for ear,¶ & the
top of the beards appear. It will be much forwarder than the
common barley.

Saturday 25.
29½ 1/10½; S, S.
Dark & spitting, sun,
soft & warm.

Swifts squeak much.

The swifts that dash round churches, & towers in little parties,
squeaking as they go, seem to me to be the cock-birds: they never
squeak 'til they come close to the walls or eaves, & possibly are
then serenading their females, who are close in their nests attending
the business of incubation. Swifts keep out the latest of any birds,
never going to roost in the longest days 'til about a quarter before
nine. Just before they retire they squeak & dash & shoot about
with wonderful rapidity. They are stirring at least seventeen hours
when the days are longest.

Sunday 26.
29½; S, SW.
Heavy shower, sun &
clouds, dark, sun.
☙ *Vitis vinifera.*

My Brother's vines turn pale on the chalk: the leaves begin to
wither.

Monday 27.
29 4/10; SW.
Sun, dark, sun, dark.
☙ *Orobanche major.*

Tuesday 28.
SW.
Dark & windy, shower.

Young nestling rooks still.
Young partridges, flyers.

Wednesday 29.
29½; 59; SW.

Some swallows this day bring-out their broods, which are

Dark & windy, shower.

perchers: they place them on rails that go across a stream, & so take their food up & down the river, feeding their young in exact rotation.

Thursday 30.
29½ 1/10; 60; W, NW.
Shower, dark, brisk wind, sun, fine even.

Some hay housed.

JULY 1774

Friday 1.
29½ 1/10½; W, SW.
Dark, sun & sultry, showers about, dark & hot.

Swifts, I have just discovered, lay but two eggs. They have now naked squab young, & some near half fledged: so that their broods cannot be out 'til toward the middle or end of July; & therefore they can never breed again before the 20th of August. In laying but two eggs, & breeding but once they differ from all our other hirundines.

Saturday 2.
29½ ½/10; 72; S.
Grey, sun, sweet day.

Scarabaeus solstitialis. The appearance of this insect commences with this month, & ceases about the end of it. These scarabs are the constant food of *caprimulgi* the month thro'.

When Oaks are quite stripped of their leaves by chafers, they are cloathed again soon after midsummer with a beautiful foliage: ¶ but beeches, horse-chestnuts, & maples, once defaced by those insects, never recover their beauty again for the whole season.
June 30: I procured a bricklayer to open the tiles in several places round the eaves of my Bro.rs brewhouse, in order to examine the state of Swift's nests at that season, & the number of their Young. This enquiry confirmed my suspicions that they never lay more than two eggs at a time: for in several nests which we discovered there were only two squab young apiece. As swifts breed but once in a summer, & the other hirundines twice; the latter who lay from four to six eggs, encrease five times as fast as the former: & therefore it is not to be wondered that swifts are never very numerous.

Sunday 3.
29 3/10½; 72, 53; SW.
Grey, sun, sultry, clouds about, brisk wind, sun, cool.

Young swallows come out very fast.
Grasshopper-lark whispers.

Monday 4.
29½ 1/10; SW.
Grey, sun, hard

Fern-owls breed but two young at a time, but breed, I think, twice in a summer.

shower, clouds, shower,
bright.

Tuesday 5.
29 4/10; SW.
Showers, dark, rain,
rain, rain.

Swallows feed their Young in the air.
Martins, & swallows that have numerous famillies are
continually feeding them; while swifts that have but two young to
maintain seem much at their leisure, & do not attend on their
nests for hours together; nor appear at all in blowing wet days. ¶
Swifts retire to their nests in very heavy showers.

Wednesday 6.
29½ 1/10; 50; SW,
W.
Showers, heavy
showers, bright.

Thursday 7.
29½ 2/10; SW.
Sun, clouds, sweet
afternoon.

Farmer Cannings plows with two teams of asses, one in the
morning, & one in the afternoon: at night these asses are folded
on the fallows; & in the winter they are kept in a straw-yard
where they make dung.
Young swallows feed themselves.

Friday 8.
29½; SW.
Showers, sun & clouds,
brisk air.

SUTTON

Saturday 9.
29½ 1/10; SW.
Heavy showers, sun &
clouds.

SELBORNE
Young swifts helpless squabs still.
Young martins not out.

Sunday 10.
29½ ¼/10.
Sun, heavy showers,
vast clouds.

Monday 11.
29½ 1/10; SW.
Sun, showers, showers,
sun & clouds.

Tuesday 12.
29 4/10½; SW, S.
Sun, clouds, wind &
rain.

Martins build nests & forsake them, & now build again.
Much hay spoiled: much not cut.

Church Meadow
4 June

Wednesday 13.
29½; 60; SW, S.
Dark & cold, sun &
clouds.

Martins hover at the mouth of their nests, & feed their young without settling.

Thursday 14.
29 4/10½, 29½ 1/10;
62; W, NW.
Showers & blowing,
sun & clouds.

Swifts, at least 30: at times they seem to come from other villages.

Friday 15.
29 2/10½; 62½; NW.
Sun, sun & clouds,
sweet even.

No young martins out yet.
Creeping white mist.

Saturday 16.
29 8/10¾; 65¼; N,
W, S, SW.
Sun, summer day.

Swallows strike at owls, & magpies.
Cut part of my great mead: grass over-ripe.

Sunday 17.
29 8/10; W, SW.
Sun, dark, spitting,
sun, dark.

Monday 18.
29 8/10½; 61;
NW.
Sun, dark & windy,
dark & still.

Tuesday 19.
29 6/10; W, SW.
Dark & windy, rain.

Put part of my meadow-hay in large cock.

Wednesday 20.
29 6/10¼; 61; W, SW,
NW.
Sun, dark, showers.

Martins not out yet.

Thursday 21.
29 6/10¾.
Sun, dark & misty,
clouds, showers, sun.

Some young martins come-out.

Friday 22.
29 9/10½; 63½; NE,
E, S.
Grey, sweet day.

Hay well made at last.

Swifts pursue & drive away an hawk: but do not dart down &
strike him with that fury that swallows express on the same
occasion. In these attacks they make some noise with their mouths,
squeaking a little.

Saturday 23.
29 9/10; S.
Sun, sweet day.

Cut my little mead.
Ricked the hay of my great mead in fine order: seven jobbs.

Sunday 24.
29 7/10; 71; SW.
Sun, sweet day.
❦ *Tilia Europaea.*

Young swallows, & martins begin to congregate on roofs. These
are the first flight.

Monday 25.
69 6/10½; 73½.
Sun, sweet day, sultry.

Grapes very small & backward for want of sun.
Qu: if they will ripen. They did in Oct.ʳ

Tuesday 26.
29 4/10; 73; E, NW,
N.
Sun, sultry, dark,
distant thunder, small
rain.

Finished my meadow-hay in good order: S.ᵗ foin spoiled. Strong
N: Wind, with clouds rising-up from the south.

Wednesday 27.
29 5/10; W, SE.
Sun, sun & clouds,
dark & spitting.
❦ *Humulus lupulus.*

Turned out the worst of my S.ᵗ foin for thatch for my rick.

Thursday 28.
29 5/10½; S, SW.
Sun, sun & clouds,
dark with brisk gale.

Young swallows & martins continue to come out.

Friday 29.
29 5/10; 64; SW.
Rain, rain, clouds &
wind.
❦ *Sambucus ebulus.*

Sowed turnep, & Wrench's radishes.
Young swallows continue to come out.
Harvest begun on the downs. Wheat not ripe.

Thermom.ʳ 64 on the stair-case; 59 in the wine-vault.
Wrench's radishes come from France, & are said to be a new sort:
are called the Nismes radish.

Sowed a crop of spinage to stand the winter.

Saturday 30.
29 6/10¼; SW.
Sun, sun & clouds, red
even:

Destroyed a wasps-nest full of young *vermiculi* at their several
gradations towards a perfect state.

Sunday 31.
29 6/10¾; 64; SW,
NW.
Sun, soft day, sun &
clouds, rain.

AUGUST 1774

Monday 1.
29 9/10; 64; NE, N,
NW.
Sun, sweet day.

Wheat cutting near Whorwel: much lodged.
Swifts flie up to the tower, & cling against the walls: qu: are not
those young ones that do so?

A colony of swifts builds in the tower of London.
Annuals are stunted, & not likely to blow well.

Tuesday 2.
29 8/10¾; NE, E.
Sun, sweet day.

A chilly autumnal feel in the mornings & evenings.

Wednesday 3.
29 7/10; 71½; E, SE.
Cloudless, sweet day.

First apricots: first french-beans.

Thursday 4.
29 5/10¾; E, NW.
Shower with thunder,
sun, sultry, distant
thunder, dark, small
rain.

Swifts begun to withdraw about this time at Blackburn in
Lancashire.

Friday 5.
29 7/10; 63¾; NE,
NW.
Heavy showers, rain,
sun, soft even:

Saturday 6.
29 7/10¼; W, SW.

Apricots ripen.

Sun, sun & clouds.

Grapes very small & backward.
The trufle-hunter took one pound of trufles at Fyfield.
Swifts disappeard at Fyfield on this day.

Swifts in general seemed to withdraw from us on this day.

Sunday 7.
29 7/10¼; 64, 70; SW,
S.
Sun, sweet day with
brisk air.

Much wheat blighted.
Swifts not have appear'd for these two evenings.

Monday 8.
29 5/10; 67, 70; NE,
E.
Sultry night, fog, grey
dark with thunder &
some drops.

Apricots ripen. Great showers about.
No swifts to be seen.

Tuesday 9.
29 4/10½; 68½, 69;
SW, W.
Fog, dark, sun &
clouds with brisk air.

Young martins abound.
Wheat-harvest begins with us.
Three swifts appear again.

Wednesday 10.
29 5/10¾; 63; W,
SW.
Sun, showers, sun, fine
even:

Showers about.
No swifts: are seen no more with us.

Thursday 11.
29 8/10; 58; W, SW.
Cold dew, sun &
clouds, sweet even:

One of my vines looks pale & sickly.
Ivy budds for bloom: it blows in Oct: & Nov^r & the fruit ripens
in April.

Friday 12.
29 8/10½; 58, 62; W,
W.
Cold white dew, sun,
sun, sweet even:

Fly-catchers brings out young broods.
Mich: daisy blows.
Apricots ripen.

Saturday 13.
29 7/10½; 60, 66; W,
SW.
Sun, sun, dark, sweet
even:

Some martins, dispossessed of their nests by sparrows, return to
them again when their enemies are shot, & breed in them. Several
pairs of martins have not yet brought forth their first brood. They
meet with interruptions, & leave their nests.

Sunday 14.
29 4/10½; 63; SW, S.   Wheat not ripe in general.
Sun, dark, shower.

Monday 15.   MEONSTOKE
SW.   Meonstoke a sweet district.
Showers & sun.

Tuesday 16.
S.
Blowing & wet.

Wednesday 17.
Sun & brisk air.   Wheat-harvest general.
                             Large sea-gulls.

Thursday 18.
29 9/10; NW.   Two swifts were seen again on this day at Fyfield: none
Cold dew, sweet day.   afterwards. Two last swifts seen at Blackburn in Lancashire.

Friday 19.
S.   *Oestrus curvicauda* lays it's eggs plentifully on the legs, & flanks
Grey, sweet afternoon.   of grass-horses; each egg on a single hair. This insect is unknown
                             to Linnaeus.

Saturday 20.   SELBORNE
29 6/10½; 70; SE.
Vast dew, sweet day.
❦ *Aster chinensis*.

Sunday 21.
29 6/10¼; 66½; SE.   Full moon.
Sun, sweet day.

Monday 22.
29 6/10¾; 68¾; E,   Apricots all gathered-in.
SW, W.   Sultry.
Shower, dark, distant   Wheat housed.
thunder, shower, sun.

Tuesday 23.
29 7/10½; 63; N, N.   Missel-thrushes congregate & are very wild.
Sun, cool air, hot sun,   Thistle-down floats.
sweet harvest weather.
                             Thompson, who makes this appearance a circumstance attendant
                             on his summer-evening:

"Wide o'er the thistly lawn, as swells the breeze,"
"A whitening shower of vegetable down"
"Amusive floats" . . . seems to have misapplyed it as to the season:
since thistles, which do not blow 'til the summer solstice, cannot
shed their down 'til autumn.¶

Wednesday 24.
29 7/10; 60, 66; NE.
Cold air, sun, fine.

Wheat in fine dry order.

Thursday 25.
29 3/10; 61; NE, SE,
S.
Sun, dark, dark &
spitting.

Partridges have large coveys.
Much wheat housed.

Friday 26.
29 2/10, 2/10½; 65;
SW, S, SW.
Great rain in the night,
sun & clouds, fine day,
dark clouds.

Some martins have not yet brought forth their first broods: but
then they were interrupted & retarded in their proceedings.

Saturday 27.
29 2/10, 3/10; 60; W,
SW.
Great rain in the night,
sun, heavy showers with
thunder.

The tops of the beeches in the hanger begin to be tinged with
yellow.
Young martins swarm.

Sunday 28.
29 ½/10; 59; S, NW,
SW.
Vast showers, rain, sun,
shower & lightening.

Much wheat abroad.

Monday 29.
29 4/10; 60; SW.
Cloudless, clouds,
showers & thunder,
clouds.

Gathered the first plate of peaches: ripe but not high-flavoured.
First bleached endive.

Tuesday 30.
29 4/10; 64; SW.
Rain, rain & wind,
clouds & wind.

Pulled the first Wrench's radishes: they are mild & well-flavoured:
are long & tap-rooted: bright red above ground, & milk-white
under.

Wednesday 31.

29 6/10; 64; SW.
Rain, spitting rain with
wind, wet all day.

Wheat begins to grow.
Several nectarines rot on the trees.
Peaches rot: plums burst & fall off.

SEPTEMBER 1774

Thursday 1.

29 6/10½, 6/10; 64; S,
SW.
Fog, dark & sultry, fog
& spitting.

Friday 2.

29 5/10, 6/10½; 67;
W, NE.
Thunder, dark &
spitting, sun, sweet
afternoon.

Hop-picking begins at Faringdon.
Wasps abound.

Saturday 3.

29 6/10; 58; SW, S,
SE.
Vast dew, sun, sweet
day.

Turned the horses into the great mead: there is good after-grass
considering that the field was not mown 'til July 16.
Some wheat housed.

Sunday 4.

29 4/10, 4/10¾; 60; S,
SW, W.
Sun, clouds, heavy
rain, misty.

Wood-owls hoot much.

Monday 5.

29 6/10½; 56; NW,
SW.
Vast dew, sun, fine day,
clouds, rain.

Most people at Selborne begin picking their hops.
Wheat housed all day.

Tuesday 6.

29 5/10, 6/10; 64;
SW.
Rain, rain, sun, rain,
rain.

Some grapes begin to turn colour.
Peaches & nect: much damaged by the wet.
Black caps still.

Wednesday 7.
29 7/10½; 59; NE, N, NE.
Rain all night, dark & spitting, dark & spitting.

Young swallows & martins swarm.
Hops brown, & small, & not esteemed very good. Wheat out still.

Thursday 8.
29 9/10, 8/10¼;/53; 54; NE.
Cold dew, sun, fine day, chilly evening.

Wheat housing.
White throats still seen.

Friday 9.
29 7/10; 50; NE, E.
White frost, sun, grey with sharp wind.

Mushrooms.
Hops distempered.

Field mushrooms.
Selborne.
July.

Saturday 10.
29 6/10½; 60; E, S.
Sun, sun & clouds, dark, rain.

Oats housed all day.

Swifts retire usually between the 10th & the 20th of Aug: flycatchers, *stoparolae*, which are the latest summer birds of passage, not appearing 'til the 20 of May, withdraw about the 6th of Septem!

Sunday 11.
29 5/10; 58½; SW, SW.
Sun, dark, showers, rain.

Martins do not seem to engage much this Year in second broods. Are they discouraged by the cold, wet season?

Monday 12.
29 1/10½; 57; SW, NW, SW.
Much rain in the night, sun, heavy showers, hail, great hail at Winton, bright.

Wasps abound in woody, wild districts far from neighbourhoods: how are they supported there without orchards, or butchers shambles, or grocers shops?

Tuesday 13.
29 ½/10; NE, NE.
Vast rain, heavy showers, sun, fine even.

Young swallows & martins continue to come out.

Wednesday 14.
29 4/10¾; 59; N.
Dark, sun, grey, dark
& blowing.

Ring-ouzels feed on our haws, & yew-berries in the autumn, &
ivy-berries in the spring.

Thursday 15.
29 5/10½; N, NW.
Grey, sun, & brisk air.
𝕎 *Hedera helix*.
Merula torquata.

Ring-ouzels appear on their autumnal migration. Were seen first
last year on the 30th the year before on the 11th.

Friday 16.
29 5/10; 56½; W,
NW, N.
Sun, shower, sun,
shower, fine, hard
shower.

Much barley, & oats is housed, but in poor condition.
Peaches & nect: good, but much eaten by wasps, & honey-bees.
Bees are hungry some autumns, & devour the wall-fruit.

Saturday 17.
29 6/10½ 57; N.
Grey, small shower,
showers about, grey.

Hops very brown, & distempered.

Wasps nesting far from neighbourhoods feed on flowers, & catch
flies, & caterpillars to carry to their young. Wasps make their nests
with the raspings of sound timber; hornets with what they gnaw
from decayed. These particles of wood are neaded-up with a
mixture of saliva from their own bodies, & moulded into combs.

Sunday 18.
29 7/10; N, W.
Grey, sun, dark &
spitting.

Mild & still.

Monday 19.
29 3/10; 55; SE, S.
Sun, vast dew, clouds,
rain, rain & wind.

A moor-buzzard with a white head was shot sometime ago on
Greatham-moor.

Tuesday 20.
29 4/10½; 54; W,
NW.
Sun, sun, clouds &
wind, fine even:

Wasps begin to eat the grapes as they turn.
Grapes unusually small & backward.

Wednesday 21.
29 1/10½; 54; S, S.
Rain, rain, vast rain
with wind, fine.

Swallows hawking about very briskly in all the moderate rain.
Martins about.

Thursday 22.
28 8/10; S, SE.
Sun, dark, vast
drowning rain,
thunder.

BASINGSTOKE, ALTON
The *oestrus curvicauda* is found in Lancashire: probably the
kingdom over. It lays it's nits on horses legs, flanks, &c: each one
on a single hair. The maggots when hatched do not enter the
horses skins, but fall to the ground. On what & how are they
supported?

Friday 23.
28 9/10¼; 53; S, SE.
Heavy showers, sun &
frequent showers,
thunder.

SELBORNE

Saturday 24.
29 1/10; SE.
Vast showers, vast rain,
dark & still.

Few swallows are seen.

Earth-worms obtain & encrease in the grass-walks, where in
levelling they were dug down more than 18 inches. So that they
were either left in the soil, deep as it was removed; or else the eggs
or young remained in the turf. Worms seem to eat earth, or
perhaps rotten vegetables turning to earth; also brick-dust lying
among earth, as appears by their casts. They delight in slopes,
probably to avoid being flooded; & perhaps supply slopes with
mould, as it is washed away by rains. They draw straw, stalks of
vine-leaves &c: into their holes, no doubt for the purpose of food.
Without worms perhaps vegetation would go on but lamely, since
they perforate, loosen, & meliorate the soil, rendering it pervious to
rains, the fibres of plants, &c. Worms come out all the winter in
mild seasons.

Sunday 25.
29 2/10; 54; S.
Sun, sun & heavy
clouds, mild.

Wood-lark sings.

Monday 26.
29 3/10½; 55; W.
Grey, mild & grey.

Martins abound.
Planted numbers of brown Dutch lettuces under the fruit-wall to
stand the winter.

These proved very fine the spring following.

Tuesday 27.
29 5/10¼; 60; W, SE.
Sun, sun & clouds,
sweet day.
Papilio Atalanta.

Mr Yalden mows a field of barley.
Much barley abroad.

Wednesday 28.
29 3/10; 56; SE.
Heavy rain, rain, rain,
rain, rain.

Grapes begin to ripen, but are much eaten by wasps, & bees.
All things in a drowning condition!

Thursday 29.
29 2/10; S.
Grey, dark & spitting,
rain.

Hops in some places not yet gathered.
Grapes begin to be good: the crop is scanty, & the bunches &
berries small.

Friday 30.
29 2/10; 56½; S, SW.
Dark, vast rains, bright
& mild.

Rooks begin to frequent the wallnut-trees & carry-off the fruit.

OCTOBER 1774

Saturday 1.
29 ½/10; 59; SW.
Much thunder in the
night, vast showers,
sun, great showers.

Sunday 2.
29 2/10½; 55½; SW,
NW.
Sun, showers, sun &
showers.

Some barley still standing.

Monday 3.
29 9/10; 55; N, NW.
White frost, bright sun,
warm, bright, chilly.

Gathered in the more choice pears, autumn burgamots,
chaumontels,¶ &c: a good crop.

Tuesday 4.
30, 30; 48, 54;
SW, S.
White frost, sun, sweet
day, soft, & grey.

Mr Yalden houses barley.

Wednesday 5.
30¼, 55, 59; S, S.
Sun & clouds, fresh
gale, sweet afternoon.

Mr Yalden houses barley.
No hirundines appear all this day, tho' the weather is so fine, &
the air full of insects.

Thursday 6.
29 9/10; S, SW.
Grey, showers, sun,
hot, sprinkling, grey.

One swallow.
Mr Yalden's people again have dug-out two more water-rats that
burrowed in a dry, chalky barley-field far from any water, near to
the spot where the former rat had hoarded potatoes.

Friday 7.
30 1/10; 55; W.
Shower, grey, shower,
fine.

Saturday 8.
30 2/10, 1/10½; NW,
NE.
Wh: frost, vast dew,
serene & beautiful.

Grapes good, but small.
No hirundines.

The cones of the spruce firs, which were produced Summer 1773:
are all just fallen off: so that they hung two summers & one winter
before they quitted the tree. My spruce firs produced no cones last
summer.

Sunday 9.¶
† 30 4/10, 29½ 4/10:
49, 55; S.
Great fog in the
morning, warm, bright
day.

LASHAM

Monday 10.
† 29½ 9/10¼, 3/10½;
54½; SW, S.
Dark morning, small
showers, bright
afternoon.

OXFORD

Tuesday 11.
† 29½ 4/10; 52½;
N.
Bright, bright,
dark.
Scolopax.

Began gathering apples, a large crop of some sorts. Mr Yalden
says he saw a woodcock this day.

Wednesday 12.
† 29½ 4/10¼, 4/10½;
55¾; N.
Bright sweet day, the

Hops sold at Wey-hill fair from £2:16: to £4:4: & £5:0:0: &
£5:10:0.

†Thomas White's handwriting.

sun warm, bright and
dew.

Thursday 13.
† 29½ 4/10½, 30;
51½; N.
Bright, dark &
disagreeable, dark,
bright.

Friday 14.
† 30 ¼/10; 50; N.
Dark, cold &
unpleasant, bright.

Saturday 15.
† 30 ¼/10; 29½
4/10½; 51; N.
Thick fog, white frost,
bright warm day.

Sunday 16.
† 29½ 8/10½, 3/10;
45¼; E. N.
Great fog, white
frost, bright,
bright.

Monday 17.
† 29½ 2/10½,
3/10½; 51¾; SW,
NW.
Great fog, cold,
dark & the fog laid a
long time in the
vales, bright.

Tuesday 18.
† 29½ 3/10¾,
3/10½; 54½; SW,
SW.
Dark & cold, an
small shower,
unpleasant day, dark.

Ash keys
Wool Lane
October.

Many ash-trees bear loads of keys every year; others never seem to
bear any at all. The prolific ones are naked of leaves, and
unsightly; those that are steril abound in foliage, & carry their
verdure a long while, & are pleasing objects.

Wednesday 19.
† 29½ 4/10; 53½;
SW.
Dark & cold, dark,
bright.

LASHAM

Thursday 20.
† 29½ 3/10½; 45,
50; E. Fog, &
white frost, bright &
warm, fog great.

Friday 21.
† 29½ 3/10¼; 55;
SE, SE.
Fog, white frost, fog,
bright, bright, fog,
bright.

Saturday 22.
† 29½ 2/10½,
1/10½; 56; W.
Dew, cloudy, dark
& cold, small
shower, dark.

SELBORNE

Sunday 23.
29 5/10½; NW, N.
Rain, rain, rain, dark.

Snipes begin to quit the moors, & to come up into the wet
fallows.

Monday 24.
50; N, SW.
Vast dew, bright, sweet
day.

Tuesday 25.
29 6/10½; 46; W.
Bright, fine day.

Beautiful season for sowing of wheat.
Much wet ground sown.

Wednesday 26.
29 8/10; 44; W, N.
Wh. frost, sweet day.

The air swarms with insects, & yet the hirundines have
disappeared for some time: hence we may infer that want of food
alone cannot be the motive that influences their departure.

---

†Thomas White's handwriting. GW added the note on ash trees.

Thursday 27.
29 7/10½; 42; N.
White frost, ice, sun &
clouds, fine, clouds.

Paths very dry.

Friday 28.
29 6/10½; 44; NE.
Wh: frost, sun, dark
clouds, shower, fine.

Many little insects, most of which seem to be *tipulae*, continue still
to sport & play about in the air, not only when the sun shines
warm; but even in fog & gentle rain, & after sunset. They appear
at times the winter thro' in mild seasons; & even in frost & snow
when the sun shines warm. They retire into trees, especially
evergreens.

Saturday 29.
29 3/10; 44; NE.
Fog, sun & clouds,
harsh air, bright.

Bats hunting Insects in Selborne churchyard
Early evening
October

Sunday 30.
29 1/10¾; 47; E.
Dark & harsh,
sprinkling, shower.

Monday 31.
29 ¾/10; 54; E.
Dark, rain, rain, dark
& still.

NOVEMBER 1774

Tuesday 1.
29 6/10; SE.
Dark & mild, & still.

Wednesday 2.
29 6/10; 54; NE.
Rain, rain, dark &
warm.

Rooks gather acorns from the oaks.

Thursday 3.
29 6/10½; 55; E, SE,
S.
Dark & still, sunny &
mild, fog.

Great field-fares flock on the down.

Friday 4.
29 5/10; 55; NE, E.
Fog, grey & pleasant,
dark & soft.

Grapes now delicate, & in good plenty: they had never ripened had not Oct.ʳ proved a lovely month.

The *rallus porzana*, or spotted water-rail,¶ a rare bird, was shot in the sedge of Bean's pond. This was the first of the sort that ever I heard-of in these parts. I sent it to London to be stuffed & preserved. A beautiful bird.

Saturday 5.
29; E.
Dark, dark with brisk wind, great showers.

Hen-chaffinches flock in great abundance.

Sunday 6.
28 8/10½; E.
Great showers, dark, sun, sweet mild day.

Monday 7.
NE. Dark & still.

Wednesday 9.¶
E.
Dark & still, rain, rain.

Thursday 10.
29 8/10; 40, 40; NE.
Frost, ice, sun, sun, frost.

Friday 11.
29 6/10; 38, 38; SE.
Frost, rain, snow, snow.

First day of winter.
Snow on the ground.

Saturday 12.
29 5/10; 37½; NW, W.
Frost, icicles, sun, thaw, dark & sprinkling.

Gathered-in all the grapes.
Snow on the hills.

Sunday 13.
29 9/10¼; 37; N, NW. Hard frost, sun, sharp wind.

Monday 14.
35; W.
Frost, sun.

SUTTON

Tuesday 15.
W.
Dark & mild.

Wednesday 16.
29 7/10½; 50; W.
Dark & mild, drying
wind.

SELBORNE

Thursday 17.
29 5/10½; W.
Spitting fog, sun, dark
& windy.

Trimmed, & tacked the vines: pretty good wood towards the
S:E. for next Year's bearing. The S:W vines are weak in wood.

Friday 18.
29 4/10; NW.
Rain in the night, sun
& brisk wind, shower.

Saturday 20.¶
29 5/10; 39, 39; NW.
Hard frost, harsh &
rumbling wind.

Sunday 21.¶

ALTON

Monday 22.

LONDON

When I came to town I found that herrings were out of season: but
sprats,¶ which Ray says are undoubtedly young herrings,
abounded in such quantities, that in these hard times they were a
great help to the poor. Cods & haddocks in plenty: smelts
beginning to come in.

The public papers have abounded with accounts of most severe
& early frosts, not only in the more Northern parts of Europe, but
on the Rhine, & in Holland. The news of severe weather usually
reaches us some days before the cold arrives; which most times
follows soon when we hear of rigorous cold on the Continent.

DECEMBER 1774

Friday 9.
26.
Severe frost, snow on
the ground.

Severe.

Almost continual frost from Nov.ʳ 20: & some snow frequently falling.

Mergus serratus, the Dun-diver, ¶ a very rare bird in these parts, was shot in James Knight's ponds just as it was emerging from the water with a considerable tench in it's Mouth. It's head, & part of the neck was of a deep rust-colour. On the back part of the head was a remarkable crest of the same hue. The sexes in this species, Ray observes, differ so widely, that writers have made two species of them. It appears from Ray's description that my specimen with the rust-coloured head was a female, called in some parts the sparlin-fowl; & is, he supposes, the female Goosander.

Saturday 10.
29; 30½; NE, SE.
Snow, dark, fog, rain
& fog.

SELBORNE

Sunday 11.
29 3/10; SE.
Dark, sun, mild &
blowing.

Monday 12.
29 4/10; 50; SE.
Grey, mild with brisk
air, bright.

Tuesday 13.
29 7/10; 48; SE, S.
Grey, mild & soft,
rain.

The frost seems to have done no harm.

Wednesday 14.
29 6/10; 49, 50; SE.
Dark & mild, spitting
rain, rain, rain, great
rain.

Earth-worms are alert, & throw-up their casts this mild weather.

Thursday 15.
29 8/10; 47½; W.

Much rain in the night.

Sun, sweet day.

The air abounds with insects dancing about over the evergreen trees. They seem to be of the genus of *tipula*, & *empis*.

Friday 16.
29 7/10; 43½; E.
Dark & mild.

Phalaenae come out in the evening: they seem to be hardier than the *papiliones*, appearing in mild weather all the winter thro'. Full moon.

Saturday 17.
29 7/10; 43; E.
Dark & moist, & mild.

Sunday 18.
29 9/10; 45; S.
Grey, dark, still & mild.

Rooks resort to their nest-trees.

Monday 19.
29 9/10; 45; W.
Dark, mild & still.

Tuesday 20.
29 8/10½; 43; E, N.
Deep fog all day.

Wednesday 21.
29 8/10½; 42½; N, NE.
Deep fog all day & night.

Thursday 22.
30 1/10¾; 40; NE.
Frost, bright & pleasant.

Friday 23.
30 3/10¼; 39; NE.
Grey, mild & still.

Paths very dry.

Saturday 24.
3/10½, 30 3/10¼; 37; NW.
Grey & sharp.

Vast flights of wild-fowl haunt Woollmer-pond: the water in some parts is covered with them. They are probably more numerous on account of the early severity of the weather on the continent.

Sunday 25.
30 3/10; 34; NW, N.
Hard frost, bright day.

Monday 26.
30 2/10; 37; N.
Dark, gentle thaw.

Tuesday 27.
30 2/10; 37; N.   Paths very dry.
Dark & still.

Wednesday 28.
30; 37; SW, W.
Dark, still, & moist.

Thursday 29.
30 2/10; 38.
Grey, still, bright &
frost.

Friday 30.
30; 33; E, SE.
Hard frost, very white,
serene & beautiful.

Saturday 31.
29 6/10; 30½; S.   † December 7, 1774.
Hard frost, dark &   Mrs Snooke's tortoise, after it had been buried more than a month,
thaw.   came forth, & wandered round the garden in a disconsolate state,
                          not knowing where to fix on a spot for it's retreat.

JANUARY   — 1775 —

Sunday 1.   SELBORNE
29 6/10; 37; SW, NW.
Frost, sun & thaw,
sharp & windy.

Monday 2.
29 8/10; 35; NW.   Grey & white water-wagtails¶ appear every day: they never leave
Frost, grey, frost.   us in the winter.

---

†Entry made in the first week of January, 1775.

Tuesday 3.
29 5/10; 43; W.
Wet, thaw, windy,
stormy.

Wednesday 4.
29 6/10½; 43; W.
Sun, fine day.

Thursday 5.
29 5/10; 45; SW.
Grey, soft & fine.

Friday 6.
29 8/10; 44; SW.   Thrush sings.
Bright, sweet day.   Insects swarm under sunny hedges.
                                   Primroses blow.

Saturday 7.
29 7/10; 47; SW.   Some ivy-berries half grown.
Moist & dark, &
warm.

Sunday 8.
29 7/10; 51; SW.
Soft rain, dark & mild,
soft rain.

Monday 9.
29 8/10¾; 51½, E,
SE.
Rain, mild & grey.

Tuesday 10.
29 6/10; SW.
Dark & moist.

Wednesday 11.
29 3/10; 48½;
SW.
Rain, rain, rain, &
wind.

Thursday 12.
29 4/10; 49; SW.   Insects abound in the air.
Sun, soft & mild,

showers, bright.

Friday 13.
29 4/10½; 49; SW.
Shower, bright, &
pleasant.

Insects abound.

Saturday 14.
29 3/10½; 46; SW.
Rain, showers,
showers.

The hawk *proinith*, says the new glossary to Chaucer; that is
picketh, or dresseth her feathers: from hence the word *preen*, a
term in ornithology, when birds adjust, & oil their feathers.

Sunday 15.
29 4/10½; 45½; SW.
Vast rain, dark &
blowing.

Monday 16.
29 5/10; 46; SE.
Grey, dark & mild.

Tuesday 17.
29 6/10; 45; SW, W.
Grey, rain, rain,
bright.

Wednesday 18.
29 6/10½; 40; W, N.
White frost, sun, fog,
fog.

Thursday 19.
29 5/10½; 37; E.
Frost, grey & still.

Friday 20.
29 4/10; 36½; E, NE.
Snow, snow, small rain,
dark.

Snow on the Ground.

Mr Hool's man says, that he caught this day, in a lane near
Hackwood-park, many rooks, which attempting to fly fell from
the trees with their wings frozen together by the sleet, that froze as
it fell. There were, he affirms, many dozens disabled! It is certain
that M^r H: man did bring home many rooks & give them to the
poor neighbours.

Saturday 21.
29 2/10½; E, SE.

Received two bramblings¶ from Mr Battin of Burkham. They

Thaw, hail, sun,
showers, snow gone.

are seen but seldom in these parts. Are fine shewy birds.

Sunday 22.
29 ½/10; 46; SE, S.
Rain, rain, rain.

Winter aconite, wallflowers, snowdrops blown.

Monday 23.
29 4/10; 46½; E, NE.
Grey, rain, rain, fog.

Made the seedling cucumber-bed.

Tuesday 24.
30; 35; NE.
Dark & sharp, sun,
cutting wind, hard
frost.

Icicles.

Wednesday 25.
29 6/10½; 30, 28, 28;
E.
Hard frost, dark with
sharp wind, snow.

Therm! 23 abroad.

Thursday 26.
29 4/10; 35; SW.
Sun & thaw, thaw,
bright.

Snow almost gone.

Friday 27.
29 1/10¾; 43½; SE.
Dark & windy, stormy
with much rain.

Snow melts away.

Saturday 28.
29 2/10½; 43; SW.
Bright, warm sun,
clouds, rain.

Insects abound.

Chaucer speaking of Gossamer¶ as a strange phenomenon, says,
   "As sore some wonder as the cause of thunder;"
   "On ebb, & flode, on *gosomor*, & mist:"
   "And on all thing; 'til that the cause is wist."

Sunday 29.
29 1/10½; 49; SW.
Wet & windy, stormy,
much rain.

Monday 30.
29 2/10½; 47; SW.

Titmouse begins to chirp.

Dark, sunny & soft,
dark.

Tuesday 31.
29 1/10; 49, 50; SW.
Dark, rain, sun &
wind, wind.

Much rain with stormy wind all night.

FEBRUARY 1775

Wednesday 1.
28 7/10; 51; S, SW.
Vast rain, & stormy,
windy, bright.

Much damage was done by sea & land; & on the river at
London.

Thursday 2.
29 3/10; 45; SW.
Grey, loud thunder,
hail & rain, bright.

Much damage at Portsmouth by unusual tides, & at the isle of
Wight.

Friday 3.
29 3/10; 51; SW.
Windy & wet, rain,
rain.

Hepatica blown.

Saturday 4.
28 9/10½; 50; SW,
NW. Rain & wind,
rain, great rain,
rain & stormy.

A rook should be shot weekly the year thro', & it's crop examined:
hence perhaps might be discovered whether in the whole they do
more harm or good from the contents at various periods. Tho' this
experiment might show that these birds often injure corn, &
turneps; yet the continual consumption of grubs, & noxious insects
would rather preponderate in their favour.

Sunday 5.
29 7/10¾; 45; NW.
Grey, sun, grey,
spitting.

Helleborus viridis emerges out of the ground budding for bloom.
Laurustine blooms.

Monday 6.
28 8/10; 45; SE, S.
Dark & moist, grey,
dark & spitting.

Tuesday 7.
29 5/10; 49; SW.
Grey & mild, wet &
windy.

Crocuss blow.

Wednesday 8.
29 1/10; 48½; SW, W,
SW. Rain, rain, vast
rain, dark & windy.

Many species of *muscae* come-out.
Earth-worms lie out at their holes after 'tis dark.

Thursday 9.
29 3/10½; 43½; SW,
W, NW.
Rain, rain, sun &
wind, bright.

Many species of Insects are stirring thro every month in mild
winters.

Friday 10.
29 1/10½; 44; SW, S,
SW.
Grey & mild, clouds,
great rain.

Mezereon in fine bloom.
Peter Wells's well runs over.

Saturday 11.
28 7/10; 44½; SW.
Rain, rain, grey &
mild, hail, vast shower,
thunder, bright.

Spiders, woodlice, *lepismae* in cupboards, & among sugar, some
empedes, gnats, flies of several species, some *phalenae* in hedges,
earth-worms, &c: are stirring at all times when winters are mild;
& are of great service to those soft-billed birds that never leave us.

Viola odorata.
Priory Lane.
March.

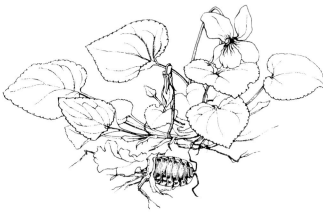

Sunday 12.
28 6/10½; 42; SW.
Showers, showers, wind
& sun., bright,
frequent lightening f^m
the S: & SE.

Sad accounts from
various parts of devastations by storms, & inundations.

Monday 13.
28 6/10¼; 44; SW.
Sun, sun & clouds,
bright.

Hazle blows.

Tuesday 14.
29 1/10½; 43; NW.
Cold dew, sunny &
still, bright.

Marsh-titmouse chirps.

Wednesday 15.
29 3/10½; 43; SW.
Great rain before day
break, bright sun, sun
& clouds, bright &
chill.

Thursday 16.
29 2/10; 44¾; S.
Dark & blowing,
chilly, great rain with
wind, bright.

A spoon-bill.¶ *platalea leucorodia* Linn: was shot near Yarmouth
in Norfolk: it is pretty common in Holland, but very rare indeed in
this island. There were several in a flock. They build, Willughby
says, like Herons on tall trees. Their feet are semipalmated. Those
birds in Norfolk must have crossed the German ocean.

Friday 17.
29 6/10½; 41; W.

† From whom did you receive this account?

Saturday 18.
29 8/10¾; 36½, 40;
NW.
Wh: frost, ice, sun with
cold wind.

Crocuss are blown.

Sunday 19.
30 ½/10; 44½; W,
NW.
Shower, blowing sun,
sweet afternoon.

Vast flocks of hen-chaffinches.
Honey-bees come forth, & gather on the Crocuss.

Monday 20.
30; 46½; W, SW.
Dark & spitting, dark
& blowing.

† A young cock chaffinch before it moults resembles much
the hen.

Tuesday 21.
29 8/10, 30 ¼/10; 45;
W, NW, W.
Rain, rain, dark &
windy, clouds, bright.

---

† Entry in an unknown hand.

Wednesday 22.
30 1/10; 43½; NW.
Wh: frost, cloudless,
bright.

Turnep-greens run very fast. Forward turneps rot.

Thursday 23.
29 8/10; 45; SW, SW.
Shower, dark &
blowing, rain.

Flocks of hen chaffinches, with some bramblings among them.
Ivy-berries near full grown: the tree blows in Octobr & Novr

Saw several empty nutshells with a hole in one side, fix'd in the
chinks on the head of a gate-post, as it were in a vice, & pierced, as
I suppose, by a nut-hatch, *sitta europaea.* Vid: Willughby's
Ornithol:¶

Friday 24.
29 8/10; 48½; SW.
Wet, wet, blowing, &
dark.

Daiseys blow.
Daffodils blow. Willow blows.
Appleshaw river runs.

Saturday 25.
29 7/10; 49; S.
Sun, clouds, soft &
spring-like.

Honey-bees, & many dipterous insects ¶ abound.
Frogs croak in ponds.

A pair of house-pigeons, which were hatched at Mich: last, now
have eggs, & sit. An instance of early fecundity!

Sunday 26.
29 7/10½; 47; SE.
Wh: frost, fog, sun &
sweet day.
✾ *Viola odorata.*

Ivy berries begin to turn black.

Monday 27.
29 7/10¾; 42½, S,
SE. White frost, sun &
sweet day.

Crocuss in great splendor.

Tuesday 28.
29 7/10; 43, 50, 47; S.
Wh: dew, sun, sweet
day.
✾ *Ficari verna.*
Papilio urticae.

Humble-bees, & many *muscae* appear. Spiders shoot their webs
from clod to clod.

MARCH 1775

Wednesday 1.
29 5½/10; 49; S.

Cucumber-plants throw out their tendrils.

Sun, hollow wind with
clouds, rain.
༓ *Tussilago farfara*.

Great titmouse sings.
Hedge-sparrow sings.

Thursday 2.
29 4/10; 49; SW, W.
Rain in the night, dark,
sunny & soft, clouds to
the west.

Apricot, & peach-trees begin to blow.

Friday 3.
29 4/10; 43; W.
Rain, sun & clouds,
hail, & showers,
bright.

Rooks begin to build.
They began the same day at Fyfield.

Saturday 4.
29 7/10½; 45; SW.
Rain, rain, sun, rain,
much rain.

Swine & sheep, for such large quadrupeds, become prolific very
early; since a sow at four months old requires the boar: & ram-
lambs, which fall in Jan: & Feb: if well kept, will supply the wants
of their own dams by the following Octobᵉ & beget lambs for the
next year. Horses & kine seldom procreate 'til they are two
years old.

Sunday 5.
29 1/10; 45; NW.
Rain, dark, sun &
clouds, bright.

Monday 6.
29 2/10; 49; SW.
Showers, showers, sun.

Tuesday 7.
SW.
Sun, dark clouds, heavy
showers, fine.

FYFIELD
Broᵣ Harry's strong beer, which was brewed last Easter monday
with the *hordeum nudum*, is now tapped, & incomparably good: it
is some what deeper-coloured than beer usually is in this country,
not from the malt's being higher dryed; but perhaps from the
natural colour of the grain. The barrel was by no means new, but
old & seasoned. Wheat, it seems, makes also high-coloured beer.

Wednesday 8.
29 3/10; SW.
Rain, rain, sun &
clouds.

Thursday 9.
SW.
Rain, rain, rain,
& wind, rain,
blowing.

Sad season for the sowing of spring corn. Just such weather this
time twelve months.

Friday 10.
W. Shower, sun,
showers about.

Rooks are very much engaged in the business of nidification: but they do not roost on their nest-trees 'til some eggs are lain.

Saturday 11.
29 1/10½; SW.
Dark, rain & wind,
vast rain.

This rain must occasion great floods.
The trufle-hunter came this morning & took a few trufles: he complains that those fungi never abound in wet winters, & springs.

Sunday 12.
29 7/10½; W.
Dark, sun, hail storm,
bright.

Rooks are continually fighting, & pulling each other's nests to pieces: these proceedings are inconsistent with living in such close community. And yet if a pair offers to build on a single tree, the nest is plundered & demolished at once. Some rooks roost on their nest-trees.

Monday 13.
29 9/10, 30 2/10; N.
Sun & showers, sun &
clouds, bright.

Tuesday 14.
30 3/10; 26 abroad;
NW.
White frost, ice, sun,
bright.

Bat appears.

Wednesday 15.
30 2/10; 25; NW.
Hard frost, hot sun.

Sheltered the fruit-wall
bloom with boughs
of ivy & yew.

Thursday 16.
30 1/10¼; 31; NW.
White frost, sun, grey
clouds, bright.

Ephemerae bisetae come
forth.

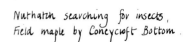

Nuthatch searching for insects,
Field maple by Coneycroft Bottom.

Friday 17.
29 8/10; 45; NW.
White frost, sun &
clouds, fine.
Ⓥ *Anemone nemorosa.*

SELBORNE
Nuthatch brings out & cracks her nuts, & strews the garden-walk with shells. They fix them in a fork of a tree where two boughs met: on the Orleans plum-tree.

Saturday 18.

The twigs which the rooks drop in building supply the poor with brush-wood to light their fires.*
    Some unhappy pairs are not permitted to finish any nest 'til the

Oakhanger Stream
6 November.

Priory Lane.
9 March.

29 3/10; 48; W,
SW.
Sun, dark &
spitting rain.
🌱 *Adoxa moschatellina.*

rest have compleated yʳ building; as soon as they get a few sticks together a party comes, & demolishes the whole.
*Thus did the ravens supply the prophet with necessaries in the wilderness.

Moschatel
Hollow lane to Alton.
2 April.

Sunday 19.
29 3/10; 45; NW, N.
Sun, & clouds, showers
& hail.

As soon as rooks have finished their nests, & before they lay, the cocks begin to feed the hens, who receive their bounty with a fondling, tremulous voice, & fluttering wings, & all the little blandishments that are expressed by the young while in an helpless state. This gallant deportment of the males is continued thro' the whole season of incubation. These birds do not copulate on trees, nor in their nests, but on the ground in open fields.

Monday 20.
29 5/10¼; 42; N, W.
Sun & clouds,
drying air.
🌱 *Caltha palustris.*

† I have observed this also when the Cock Canary bird feeds the hen in a cage.

Tuesday 21.
29 7/10½; 49; W, N.
Sun, grey & mild, soft
even:
🌱 *Cucumis sativus.*

Mʳˢ Snooke's old tortoise came out of the ground, but in a few days buried himself as deep as ever.
Earth-worms lie out, & copulate.

Wednesday 22.
29 7/10¼; 49; NW.
Sun, sun & clouds, fine
weather.
Bombylius medius,
Papilio rhamni.

Snake appears: toad comes forth. Frogs spawn. Horse-ants¶ come forth.

---

† Entry in an unknown hand.

Thursday 23.
29 8/10; 49; N, NW.
Sun, bright & pleasant.

Earthworms travel about in rainy nights, as appears from their sinuous tracks on the soft muddy soil, perhaps in search of food.

Friday 24.
29 6/10½; 53; NW, W.
Cold air, dark & windy.

The apricot-bloom, which came-out early seems to be much cut by the late frosts.
Peaches & Nect: now in fine bloom.

Saturday 25.
29 4/10; 49; W, NW, N.
Sun, dark with harsh wind, spitting.

Planted a raspberry bed.

Sunday 26.
29 4/10; 43¼; W, NW, NE.
Sun, clouds, hail & sleet.

Monday 27.
29 5/10; 37; NW, W.
Hard frost, ice, storms of hail & sleet, dark & windy.

The creeper,¶ a pretty little nimble bird, runs up the bodies & boughs of trees with all the agility of a mouse. It runs also on the lower side of the arms of trees with it's back downward. Stays with us all the winter.

Tuesday 28.
29; 41; W, NW, N.
Dark, rain, rain, sun, snow.

Wednesday 29.
29 2/10; 34½; W, NW, W.
Fierce frost, thick ice, froze within.
Sun, flights of snow & hail.

Ground covered with snow.

Thursday 30.
29 5/10; 39; N, NW.
Hard frost, sun, flights of snow, frost.

Horse-ants retire under the ground.
Wheat-ears appear.

Friday 31.
29 5/10; 25 abroad;
NW.
Hard frost, sun, flakes
of snow, bright.

MIDHURST
Birds eat ivy-berries, which now begin to ripen: they are of great
service to the winged race at this season, since most other berries
ripen in the autumn.
Roads are much dryed.

APRIL 1775

Saturday 1.
29 7/10; 44; NW.
White frost, sun, dark
clouds.

SELBORNE
The shell-less snails, called slugs, are in motion all the winter in
mild weather, & commit great depredations on garden-plants, &
much injure the green wheat, the loss of which is imputed to earth-
worms; while the shelled snail, the φερεσικις,¶ does not come
forth at all 'til about April the tenth; & not only lays itself up pretty
early in autumn, in places secure from frost: but also throws out,
round the mouth of it's shell, a thick operculum formed from it's
own saliva; so that it is perfect secured, & corked-up as it were
from all inclemencies. Why the naked slug should be so much
more able to endure cold than it's housed congener I cannot
pretend to say.

† The slug is cover'd with a much thicker slime.

Sunday 2.
29 8/10¾; 46½; NW,
W.
Frost, ice, sun, clouds,
bright.

Bees resort to the hot-beds tempted by some honey spread on the
leaves, & blossoms of the cucumbers. When bees do not frequent
the frames, the early fruit never sets well: therefore this expedient
is very proper for early melons, & cucumbers.

Monday 3.
29 7/10¾; 43; W.
Frost, bright sun, dark
& still.

Tuesday 4.
29 7/10½; 48½; W,
NW, W.
Grey, dark, small rain,
bright.

Cucumbers begin to swell.

Wednesday 5.
29 9/10; 50; N, NE.
Frost, bright sun, grey
& mild.
Turdus torquatus.

The ring-ouzel appears on it's spring migration.

---

† Entry in an unknown hand.

Thursday 6.
29 8/10¾; 50; N.
Frost, bright &
pleasant, dark, spitting.
Oedicnemus.

Sowed cucumber seeds of the large white sort. Stone-curlew appears & whistles.

Friday 7.
30; 51; NE, N.
Dark, sun, harsh wind.
❦ *Prunus spinosa.*

The black-thorn begins to blow. This tree usually blossoms while cold NE: winds blow: so that the harsh, rugged weather obtaining at this season is called by the country people, blackthorn winter.
Roads dry, & dusty.

Saturday 8.
30; 49; NE.
Dark & harsh.

Sunday 9.
30; 45; NE, N.
Dark, sun with harsh
wind, bright.
Hirundo domestica.

Swallow appears.
Young thrushes.

Monday 10.
29 8/10½; 49; N.
Dark & harsh, dark &
mild.

Cut the first cucumber; a large fruit.
Curlews whistle.

Tuesday 11.
29 8/10; 47½; W,
NW.
Grey, dark & mild.
Two swallows. Black
snail.

Some few apricots, which escaped the frost seem to be set. Some peach & nect: bloom not destroyed. The trees were stuck full of ivy-boughs, which seem to have been of service against the severe cold.

Wednesday 12.
29 8/10¾; 54; NW,
W.
White frost, fog,
summer day, sweet
even.
White butterflies.

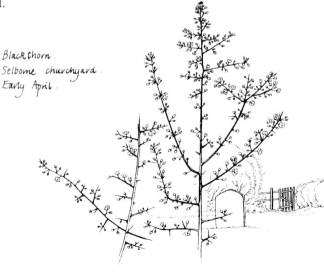

Blackthorn.
Selborne churchyard.
Early April.

Thursday 13.
29 9/10; 52½; NW,
N.
Wh: frost, sweet
summer weather.
Several swallows.

The barley-season goes-on briskly. Hops are poling.
Curlews clamour.

Friday 14.
29 6/10; 53½; SE, S.
Mist, grey, sun,
clouds.
*Conops calcitrans.**

Cut a brace of fine cucumbers.
*Stinging-fly appears.

Saturday 15.
29; 50; W, NW.
Soft rain, sun & clouds,
sun & brisk air.

A brace of fine cucumbers.

The Saxon word *hlithe,* with the h aspirate before it, signifies
clivus: hence no doubt two abrupt steep pasture-fields near this
village are called the short, & long *lithe.* Much such another steep
pasture at about a mile distance is also called the *lithe. Steethe* in
Saxon signifies *ripa,* a perpendicular bank: hence *steethe swalwe,*
riparia hirundo.

Sunday 16.
29 3/10½; 52½; W,
SW. Fine rain, sun &
clouds, brisk air.

Monday 17.
29 3/10½; W.
Sun.
Regulus non cristatus.

LASHAM
Cut two brace of fine cucumbʳˢ.
Mʳˢ Snooke's tortoise came out of the ground the second time, for
the summer.

Tuesday 18.
29 3/10; 53; NW.
Luscinia, Cuculus, Jynx.

OXFORD
Brace & half of cucumbers.

Wednesday 19.
29 3/10½; 51; NW.

Began mowing the walks.

Thursday 20.
29 7/10; 50; S.

Thomas kept a journal of incidents during my absence.
  Worms, when sick, seem to come out of the Ground to die:
under the same circumstances some amphibiae quit the water.

Friday 21.
29 4/10; 51; SE.

Saturday 22.

LASHAM
Cut five brace of fine cucumbers.
Several beeches in the hanger begin to leaf.
Black snails abound.

Sunday 23.
29 6/10½; 52½; W.
Sun & clouds, showers
& thunder, sun &
clouds.

SELBORNE
Swallows abound; but no house-martin or black-cap. No swift.

Monday 24.
29 8/10½; 55; W,
NW.
Rain, hot sun, soft &
cloudy.
Musca vomitoria,
Ruticilla.*

Pears & cherries well blown. *Redstart.
Some few apricots & nect?

Tuesday 25.
29 8/10½; 56½; S.
Dark & spitting, sun,
springlike, dark.

Ivy-berries fall off dead-ripe.
Titlark sings.

Wednesday 26.
29 7/10½; 56, 62; SE.
Sun, hot & summer-
like, bright.
*Atricapilla.**

*Black-cap whistles.
The house-snail, φερεσικος, ¶ begins to appear.

Thursday 27.
29 7/10; 67½.
Great dew, sun, sultry
in the sun, sweet even.
*Hirundo urbica.**

Apple tree blows. Early tulips blow.
*A pair of house-martins appear, & frequent the nest at the end
of the house; a single one also wants to go in. These must be of the
family bred there last year. The nest was built last summer.¶

Bank-martins abound on short-heath: they come full as soon as
the house swallow. Two swans inhabit Oakhanger-ponds: they
came of themselves in the winter with three more. Pulled down
many old house-martins nests; they were full of rubbish, & the
exuviae of the *hippobosca hirundinis* in the pupa-state. These
insects obtain so much sometimes in yⁱʳ nests, as to render the place
insupportable to the young, & to oblige them to throw themselves
out on the ground. The case is the same sometimes with young
swifts.

Friday 28.
29 7/10; 70¾! S, SE.
Sun, sultry, fierce heat,
midsum! evening.
Hirundo apus.

The sun scorched 'til within an hour of setting.
Swift appears at Manchester: at Fyfield.
One single swift. They usually arrive in pairs.
Parhelia, or odd halo round the sun.¶
Described since in *Gent: mag:*

Saturday 29.

29 6/10½; 71!; SW.
Rock-like clouds, sun,
fierce heat!
Some thunder-like
clouds, summer
evening, distant
lightening.

The martins throw the rubbish out of their nest.
The hanger almost in full leaf.

Sunday 30.

29 7/10½; 61; SW,
W.
Sun, brisk air, dark
with blue mist,
thunder, dark, fine
rain.
White throat.*

Gardens much injured by the heat.
Cut several brace of cucumbers.
*Appears, & whistles, using odd gesticulations in the air when it
mounts above yᵉ hedges.

MAY 1775

Monday 1.

29 9/10½; 69; NW.
Sun, brisk air, sun.
Caprimulgus.

The fern-owl returns & chatters very early!
Sowed two boxes of polyanth-seed from London.
Sowed a large bed of carrots which could not be sowed before on
account of long dry season.
Ground still dry, & harsh.

Tuesday 2.

30; 64; NW, SW, W.
Sun, bright, & summer
day.

Grasshopper lark whispers.
Several peaches, & nectarines seem to be set. Swift, & house
martins gone again.
Tulips in bloom, & make a good show.

Wednesday 3.

29 8/10; 62¼; SE.
Sun, summer's day.
Gryllo-talpa.

One swift at Bramshot; one at Selborne.
*Mole-cricket churs.
Several ponds are dry.

Thursday 4.

29 5/10½; 68; S, SW.
Sun, summer's day,
clouds.

May 1. Some oaks, & ashes half in leaf. The beeches in the hanger
in full leaf. Trees more than a fortnight forwarder than they have
been for some years past. Apple-trees blow well.
    At Blackburn in Lancashire swallows first seen April 15: swifts
April 28: house-martins May 4ᵗʰ Cuckow sings April 28: laughing
wren sings Apr: 17.

Friday 5.
29 4/10; 55; SW, NW.
Sun, dark, fine shower, bright.
♆ *Lantana viburnum.*
Turtle dove.

No martins: One swift.
House snails abound now; scarce any have appeared before on account of the long drought.

Saturday 6.
29 7/10¾; 51, 59; NW, SW.
Cold air, sun, hot sun & chilly air.

Brown-Dutch-lettuce, that stood the winter under the fruit-wall, now in fine order, & well loaved.

Sunday 7.
29 7/10; 58; SW.
Sun, clouds, brisk & cold wind.

At Lyndon in Rutland the first swallow was seen April 14: first swift April 29: first H: martin May 6.

Monday 8.
29 7/10¾; 58; SW, NW.
Sun, strong cold wind, wind.
♆ *Crataegus oxyacantha.**

*White-thorn blows.

Tuesday 9.
29 7/10; 61½; SW.
Sun, dark & windy, sun.

The long rows of tulips make a gallant show.

Wednesday 10.
29 8/10; 56; W, NW.
Sun, drying harsh wind.

Pair of swifts.

Thursday 11.
29 8/10; 50; NW, N, SW.
Cold dew, sun, hot sun, dark & still.
Musca meridiana.

3 pairs of swifts.
Gardens much dryed-up.

Friday 12.
29 6/10¾; 54; SE,

House martins begin to abound.

NW, NE.
Hail, sun & clouds,
showers, small showers
about.

Fern-owls chatter in the highwood, & hanger.

Saturday 13.
29 8/10½; 53; NE, N.
Sun, sun & blue mist,
sun & clouds.
Papilio Atalanta.*¶

*This is an autumnal fly, & therefore must appear at this season
by accident.

Fine rains about the kingdom; but little to the advantage of our
district.

Sunday 14.
29 8/10¾; 59; NE,
SW, NW. Sun, sun
& bright weather.

Two pairs of nightingales in my fields.
The country strangely dryed-up.
Fine showers about last friday.

Monday 15.
29 7/10½; 60; W, N.
Sun, summer day.

Began to tack the new shoots of the vines.
S^t foin is in full head, but not blown.
Tulips make a show still.

Tuesday 16.
29 4/10¾; 53; NW,
SW.
Sun, bright weather,
dark & louring.

Ivy-berries all ripe, & dropped-off.

Wednesday 17.
29 6/10; 53; W, NE.
Sun, sun & brisk air,
bright.
Stoparola.*

*Fly-catcher appears: this is invariably the latest summer-bird of
passage. When this bird comes summer is established.
Ponds fail.

Thursday 18.
29 7/10¾; 50; NW.
Cold white dew, sun
with harsh air.
Sphinx filipendulae.

Watered away hogsheads on the garden, which is burnt to
powder.

Friday 19.
29 6/10; 49; NW, N.
Dark & harsh, small
showers.
*Regulus non cristatus
stridet voce locustulae.**

No chafers appear as yet: in those seasons that they abound they
deface the foliage of the whole country, especially on
the downs, where woods & hedges are scarce.

*This bird, the latest & largest willow-wren, haunts the tops of the tallest woods, making a stammering noise at intervals, & shivering with it's wings. – Bank martins abound over the ponds in the forest: swifts seldom appear in cold, black days round the church. Finished tacking ye vines.

Saturday 20.
29 8/10½; 48; N.
Harsh air, sun &
clouds, bright & cold.

Some heads of S^t foin begin to blow.
No martins build yet.

Sunday 21.
29 8/10¾; 47½; N.
Sun, sun & clouds,
showers about.

Rooks are about in flocks with their young.
Mr Yalden's tank is dry.

Monday 22.
29 8/10½; NE.
Sun, blue mist, sun &
sweet even.
Apis longicornis.

This bee begins to frequent the hard-trodden walks, in order to bore holes for it's nidification.

Tuesday 23.
29 7/10; 54; E.
Grey, dark & mild, &
still.

Tulips still in good bloom.
Dutch-honeysuckle in fine bloom.

Wednesday 24.
29 5/10; 60½; NE,
W.
Mist, sun, sprinklings
with hail, thunder, vast
clouds in horizon.

Bank martins abound at the sand-pit at Short-heath. Thrushes now, during this long drought, for want of worms hunt-out shell-snails, & pick them to pieces for their Young. My horses begun to lie abroad.

Honeysuckle.
Selborne Common.
Late May.

Thursday 25.
29 6/10; NW.
Sun, drying winds,
bright.
Hippobosca equina.

Friday 26.
29 8/10; 56; NW.
Sun, drying air, dark
clouds, bright.

We are obliged to water the garden continually. Some wells dry.

Saturday 27.
29 9/10; NW, N.

No thoro' rain in this district since the 9. 10. & 11 of March.

Thrush breaking snail shells
Selborne churchyard
24 June

Sun, dark & cool, distant showers, soft & still.

The small ponds¶ in the vales are now all dryed up, while the small ponds on the very tops of hills are but little affected. Can this difference be accounted-for from evaporation alone, which certainly is most prevalent in bottoms: or rather have not those elevated pools some unnoticed recruits by condensation, or some other secret means in the night time, so as to draw supplies to themselves from dews & mists, especially where trees over-hang? Without a constant supply the cattle alone must soon drink them. It must be allowed that in these parts the upland ponds have the most clayey, & holding bottoms: yet this advantage alone can never occasion the difference, the circumstance of cattle considered.

Sunday 28.
30 ¼/10; 61; SE, N, SW.
Sun, grey & still.

Monday 29.
30; 61½; NW, W, N.
Sun, sultry, dark & mild.

Grass on the common burnt very brown.
Tulips decay. No dews for mowing in common.

Tuesday 30.
29 9/10½; 67½; NE, SE, S.
Sun, sultry, sweet evening.

Hawthorns in beautiful bloom.
Seven pairs of swifts.
House-martins do not build as usual: perhaps are troubled to find wet dirt.

Wednesday 31.
29 9/10; 64; SW, NE, SW.
Sun, sultry, sweet even.

Bees swarm.
Severe heat in the lanes in the middle of the day.

JUNE 1775

Thursday 1.
29 9/10; 62½; NE.
Sun, sultry, brisk gale, dark & cool.

Grass very short, large dew.
Martin begins to build at the end of the brewhouse.

Friday 2.
29 8/10; 67; NE.
Dark, strong harsh

Began to plant-out annuals.
House-martins seem to abound again.

wind, sun, sweet even: Swift's nest has two eggs, fresh laid.

Saturday 3.
29 7/10¾; 67½; NE.   Dusty beyond comparison. Watered away five hogsh: of water.
Sun, hot sun, & brisk   *Stoparola* has five eggs.
gale, sweet even.   Rooks live hard: there are no chafers.
Barley & oats do not come up; the fields look naked.

Some pairs of swifts always build in this village under the low
thatched roofs of some of the meanest cottages: & as there never
fails to be nests in those particular houses, it looks as if some of the
same family still returned to the same place.
Very few house-martins at present.

† Cut of[f] a claw of one of them caught in its nest – Observe
then whether the same bird does not return next year.

Sunday 4.
29 7/10½; 60, 64;   Wheat-ears begin to peep.
NE.   Glow-worms abound.
Sun, sun, strong gale,   Roses begin to blow: pinks bud: fraxinella blows.
sweet even.   Garden burnt to powder.

Monday 5.
29 7/10; 72½; NE, E,   Pinks blow. *Elder blows. Corn-flag blows.
NE.   Diurnal birds suffer for want of worms: thrushes seem to live on
Sun, hot sun & brisk   snails.
air, clouds, sweet even.
⚘ *Sambucus nigra.**

Tuesday 6.
29 5/10¼; 71½; E, S,   Swifts abound; near 15 pairs; they seem to come from other
E. Dark & sprinkling,   villages. H: martins now abound, & build briskly.
sultry, sun, dark
sprinkling, showers
about.

Wednesday 7.
29 4/10; 67, 71; E.   *Jakes-fly appears.
Fog, distant thunder,   The vine blows very early: it did not blow last year 'til about the
short but smart shower,   26.
distant showers.
⚘ *Vitis vinifera.*   Watered the wall-trees well this evening with the engine: the leaves
*Musca tenax.**   are not blotched & bloated this year, but many shoots are
shrivelled, & covered with aphides. Plums & pears abound;

---

†Entry in an unknown hand.

moderate crop of apples with me. Vine-shoots very forward.

Thursday 8.
29 5/10¾; 66, 70; E,
S.
Short but brisk shower,
dark & spitting, dark
& moist, fine even.
🌱 *Digitalis purpurea.***

*Foxglove blows.
St foin about half out of bloom.

Friday 9.
29 5/10; 70; E, NE.
Fog, dark & spitting,
dark, fine shower,
lightening.

Cut my S⸰ foin, a fine crop, notwithstanding the dry season. The
eighth cutting.

Thrushes do great service in hunting out the shell-snails in the
hedges, & destroying them: the walks are covered with their shells.

Saturday 10.
29 4/10¾; 65; S, S.
Dark & louring,
shower, mild & moist,
fine even.

Shower in the night.
Planted-out vast quantities of annuals both in the borders, &
basons; both in the fields, & gardens.

Sunday 11.
29 5/10; NE, S.
Dark & louring,
thunder, fine rain,
dark.

The autumn-sown brown lettuces, which stood the winter, still
continue good. The season last friday morning had lasted just
3 months: the 9: 10: & 11 of March were very wet.

Monday 12.
29 5/10¾; 61; SW, S.
Dark, shower, hot sun,
sweet even.

The autumn-sown spinage just going off: a fine crop.
The thrushes have done service by destroying so many shell-
snails.

Tuesday 13.
29 6/10¼; 70; SE.
Sun, sultry, sweet even,
vast dew.

Red kidney-beans begin to climb their sticks. Mulberry-tree in
full leaf.
Snails copulate.
Planted-out cabbages & annuals.

Wednesday 14.
29 6/10; 69; NE, E,
NE.
Sun, sultry, great
shower, continual
distant thunder, sun.

Stopped-down the vines; they are much in bloom. We had just
the skirts of a vast thunder-storm.

Thursday 15.
29 6/10¾; 67½; NE,
N.
Fog, grey, sun, rock-
like clouds, sweet even.

Wheat in ear in general.
Tremendous thunder, & vast hail yesterday at Bramshot &
Hedley, with prodigious floods. Vast damage done. The hail lay
knee-deep.

Friday 16.
29 6/10; 70; N, NW.
Great dew, sun, sultry,
sweet even.

Finished tacking the vines, & wall-trees; the vines have fine
wood; but the wall-trees have their leaves much curled.

Saturday 17.
29 3/10½; 72; N, SW.
Sun, sultry, distant
thunder, sweet even.
🌱 *Triticum sativum,
Spiraea ulmaria.*

Wheat in fine bloom.
S! foin well got-up.

The shell-snail has hardly appeared at all this season on account of
the long dry time. Snails copulate about midsumʳ & soon after
deposit their eggs in the mould by running their heads & bodies
under ground. Hence the way to be rid of them is to kill as many as
possible before they begin to breed. In six weeks after wheat is in
ear, harvest usually begins, unless delayed by cold, wet, black
weather.

Sunday 18.
29 6/10; 71; NW, N.
Cloudless, hot sun with
air, sweet even.

Young partridges & pheasants abound.
Wheat looks well.
Phallus impudicus stinks.

Monday 19.
29 7/10; 62½; NE, N,
NE.
Dark, dark & still,
sweet even.

Great honey-dew.
Began cutting my meadow-grass. Grass very short.

Tuesday 20.
29 6/10¾; 71¼; W,
NW.
Great dew, bright,
showers about, sultry,
sweet even.
🌱 *Agrimonia eupatoria.*

Barley shoots into ear.
Meadow-grass very short indeed.

Wednesday 21.
29 7/10½; W,
NW, W.
Fine dew, sun, fresh
air, brisk cool gale.

Hay makes at a vast rate.
Rasps begin to ripen.
Vast crops of plums, currants, & goose-berries.
House-martin, which laid in an old nest, hatches.

Thursday 22.

29 7/10; 73; W, W.
Grey, sun, sultry with
brisk wind, clouds
about.

Pines begin to ripen at Hartley.
I have not seen the great species of bat this summer. Ricked y^e
meadow-hay in delicate order; about half a crop: it is very short
& fine.

Friday 23.

29 4/10½; 65; W,
SW, W.
Sun, hot, dark &
windy, dark & spitting.

The *oestrus curvicauda*, the Insect which lays it's nits on the flanks
& legs of horses appears in the forest; it seems to abound most in
moist moorish places, tho' sometimes seen in the uplands.

Saturday 24.

29 3/10; 61½; W,
NW.
Bright, dark, soft rain
for hours, grey & mild
& still.

Teals breed in Woolmer forest: jack-snipes breed there also no
doubt, since they are to be found there the summer thro': – A
person assures me, that Mr Meymot, an old clergyman at North
chappel in Sussex, kept a cuckow in a cage three or four years; &
that he had seen it several times both winter & summer. It made a
little jarring noise, but never cryed *cuckow*: It might perhaps be an
hen. He did not remember how it subsisted.

† Is Mr Meymot or any of his family alive who might confirm
this account?

Sunday 25.

29 5/10¼; 59; W,
NW.
Sun & strong gale,
cool, sun & sultry,
sweet even.

Wheat in general out of bloom. After so kind a blowing time we
may from the heat of the summer expect an early, & plentiful
wheat-harvest.

Monday 26.

29 5/10; 64; NE, W,
SE.
Sun, hot, sweet even.

Saw the first young swallows, flyers.
Some dark clouds about.

Tuesday 27.

29 3/10½; 61; E, NE,
N.
Sun, dark, & louring,
showers.
☿ *Geranium pratense*,
Carduus palustris.

More young swallows come out, & perchers.
Thistles blow late for want of showers.

---

† Entry in an unknown hand.

Wednesday 28.

29 2/10; 64; NE, E, S, W.
Many hard showers, hot sun.
🌼 *Tilia europaea.*

House martins have young in the old nests.
The lime blows, & smells sweet.
Ground well moistened.

Thursday 29.

29 4/10; 64; W, SW.
Smart shower, sun & clouds, showers about.
🌼 *Monotropa hypopithys.*

Young minute frogs migrate from the ponds this showery weather, & fill the lanes, & paths: they are quite black.

Friday 30.

29 5/10½; 62; NW, N, S, NW.
Sun, hot, thunder, smart shower with hail.

Began to cut large white cucumbers.
Moist & growing.

JULY 1775

Saturday 1.

29 6/10; NW, W.
Shower, hot sun, shower, bright & mild.

On the 28 of June a large quantity of trufles were found near Andover: near two months sooner than the common season. So these roots are in season nine months at least.

Sunday 2.

29 4/10; 59; SW, SE.
Rain, dark & blowing, rain, rain.

House-martins, which breed in an old nest, get the start of those that build new ones by 10 days, or a fortnight.

Monday 3.

29 5/10; 65; W.
Sun, brisk air, dark rain, clouds & bright.

House-snails seem to be so checked by the drought, & destroyed by the thrushes, that hardly one annual is eaten, or injured.

When earth-worms lie-out a nights on the turf, tho' they extend their bodies a great way, they do not quite leave their holes, but keep the ends of their tails fixed therein; so that on the least alarm they can retire with precipitation under the earth. Whatever food falls within their reach when thus extended they seem to be content with, such as blades of grass, straws, fallen leaves, the ends of which they often draw into their holes. Even in copulation their hinder-parts never quit their holes: so that no two except they lie within reach of each others bodies can have any commerce of that kind: but as every individual is an hermaphrodite, there is no difficulty in meeting with a mate, as would be the case were they of different sexes.

Tuesday 4.
29 7/10; W.
Sun, sun & clouds,
sweet even.

Whortle-berries ripe.

Wednesday 5.
29 6/10; 64; SW, S.
Sun, grey & soft.

Grapes swell.

Thursday 6.
29 2/10; 65; SE, NE,
W, NW.
Dark, showers, heavy
showers with thunder,
dark.

Wasps begin to come.
Growing weather.

Friday 7.
29 4/10½; 63; NW.
Dark & showery, moist
air.

Saturday 8.
29 4/10½; 63; S, SE,
S.
Sun, warm, dark &
spitting.

Sunday 9.
29 4/10¾; 65; S, S,
SW.
Rain, rain, sun, fine.

Mown hay begins to take damage.

Monday 10.
29 5/10; 64; S, SW.
Showers, showers, fine.

Mushrooms begin to appear.

Tuesday 11.
29 5/10; 65; S, SW.
Showers, sun &
showers.

Destroyed a wasp's nest which was grown to a considerable bulk,
& had many working wasps.

Wednesday 12.
29 3/10¼, 63; SW.
Sun & soft showers.

Five young kestrils, or windhovers almost fledge are taken in an
old magpie's nest.

Thursday 13.
29 5/10¾; 63; SW.
Sun, grey, showers,
showers, showers.

Friday 14.
29 4/10½; 64; SW,
NW.
Showers, heavy showers
all day, distant showers.

Hay much damaged: many meadows not cut.
This dripping season, which hurts individuals in their hay, does
marvelous service to the public, in the spring-corn, after grass,
turneps, fallows, &c.

Saturday 15.
29 5/10¾; 63; NW,
N.
Showers, showers,
sweet sun, dark &
mild.

Oats are much recovered, & brought-on. Wheat begins to
change colour, is not lodged.

When a person approaches the haunt of fern-owls (*caprimulgi*) in
an evening, they continue flying round the head of the intruder; &
striking their wings¶ together above their backs, in the manner that
the pigeons called smiters are known to do, make a smart snap:
perhaps at that time they are jealous for their young; & this noise
& gesture are intended by way of menace.

Sunday 16.
29 5/10¾; 59; NW.
Sun, dark, shower,
sweet even:

Some of the forwardest birds of some broods of martins are out,
the more backward remain in the nest.

Monday 17.
29 7/10; 61½; NW.
Grey, dark clouds,
sweet afternoon.
Scarabaeus solstitialis. *

*In this month the great support of fern-owls.
Some martins are building against Mr Yalden's windows.
Turneps grow well.
Young martins perchers on the battlements of the tower, where
the old ones feed them.
Swallows continue to come out.

Tuesday 18.
29 8/10; 66; N, E, S.
Bright with vast dew,
heavy clouds, sweet
even.

Wednesday 19.
29 7/10½; 68; SW, S.
Sun, summer day,
sweet even.

Pease are hacked.
Wheat harvest about Winton.
Five wasps nests destroyed this evening: two before.

Thursday 20.

29 6/10½; 67; SW.
Sun, sultry, heavy
clouds, sweet even.

Wasps still abound.
The solstitial chafer seems only to obtain on upland, chalky soils.

Friday 21.

29 5/10; 69; SE. Sun,
sultry, dark & blowing.

Young swallows & martins continue to come-out.

Saturday 22.

29 4¾; 66½; NE,
NW.
Dark & louring, sultry,
red even: distant
thunder.

Opened the crop of a swift, & found it filled with the wing-cases
& legs, &c. of small *coleopterae*.¶ Hence it is plain the *coleopterae*
soar high in the air. Swifts seem encreased in number: and their
young flown.

The young martin becomes a flyer¶ in about sixteen days from the
egg: most little birds come to their ηλικια,¶ or full growth, in
about a fortnight: for were they to be a long time in the nest in a
helpless state few would escape; some mischief or other would
destroy the whole breed.
   Destroyed the 8th wasp's nest.
   Tho' swifts are so fledge before they quit the nest that they are
not to be distinguished from their dams on the wing; yet from the
encrease of their numbers, & from their unusual manner of
clinging to walls & towers one may perceive that several are now
out. And no wonder that they should begin to bestir themselves,
since they will probably withdraw in a fortnight.

Sunday 23.

29 4/10; 74½, 81
abroad; NE, SW.
Distant thunder, bright
sun, sultry, very
ripening weather, heavy
clouds about, sweet
even with brisk air.

Birds are much influenced in their choice of food by colour: for
tho' white currans are a much sweeter fruit than red; yet they
seldom touch the former 'til they have devoured every bunch of
the latter.

†May they not like the more pleasant acid of the red?

The male & female ants of the little yellow, & little black sorts,
leaving their nests fill the air. The females seem big with eggs. They
also run about on the turf, & seem in great agitation. The females
wander away, & form new colonies when pregnant.

Monday 24.

29 5/10; 68; S, S.
Red morning, louring
& black, small showers,
sweet even.
🜊 *Humulus lupulus.*

Swifts abound: young seem to be all out; above 30.
Hops throw-out good side shoots, & blow.
Some few hills have perfect hops. A sealark shot at Newton-pond.

---

†Entry in an unknown hand.

Tuesday 25.
29 5½/10; 65; S, S.
Sun, hot ripening
weather, sweet even.
❦ *Clematis vitalba.*

First apricot. Swallows begin to abound.
Swifts seem to be gone in part.

Wednesday 26.
29 4/10½; 70; SW,
SW.
Sun, sun & clouds,
sweet even.

Only 3 or four swifts.

Swifts all appear again.

Thursday 27.
29 4/10½; 70; W,
SW.
Shower, hot ripening
weather, sweet even.

Sowed a crop of spinage to stand the winter.
Many swifts morning & evening: a pair or two only all day. The
former probably have all their young out; the latter perhaps have
still nestlings to attend.

Friday 28.
29 3/10; 65; SE, E,
W.
Cloudy, rain, thunder,
rain, dark.

Swifts still. Ten nests of wasps have been destroyed just at hand:
they abound & are plowed-up every day.

Saturday 29.
29 4/10½; 64; SW,
SW.
Showers, & sun, distant
thunder, showers.

Swifts still.

Sunday 30.
29 7/10; 62½; W,
NW.
Dark & louring, sun &
clouds, sweet afternoon.

By this evenings post I am informed, by a Gent: who is just come
from thence that the hops all round Canterbury have failed: there
are many hundred acres not worth picking.

Monday 31.
29 6/10; 66; W, SE.
Sunny, sultry, sweet
afternoon.

Horses at plow so teized by flies as to be quite frantic.*
Wheat harvest this day becomes general.

*Horses are never tormented in the manner 'til after midsum! the
people say it is the nosefly that distracts them so. I can discover
only such flies as usually haunt the heads of horses. Perhaps at this
season they lay their eggs in the nose & ears. I never can discern
angaes on these days; only swarms of small *muscae.*

AUGUST 1775

Tuesday 1.
SW. Small rain, sun &
clouds.

CHILGROVE

Wednesday 2.
SW.
Dark, spitting rain,
fine afternoon.

RINGMER

Wheat harvest is general all along the downs: when I came just
beyond Findon I found wheatear traps which had been open
about a week. The shepherds usually begin catching about the last
week in July.
Female viper taken full of young, 15 in number: gaped &
menaced as soon as they were cut out of the belly of the dam.

Thursday 3.
SW.
Sweet harvest day,
sultry.

Friday 4.
SW.
Sun, smart shower,
sweet afternoon.

Little wheat housed. Wheat is very fine in general.
A young cuckow is hatched every year in some part of M^{rs}
Snooke's out-let, most usually by red-breast.

Saturday 5.
SW.
Sun, small shower,
sweet afternoon.

No cross-bills this year among Scotch-pines. They usually appear
first about the beginning of July. No fern-owls.

Sunday 6.
NW.
Vast dew, sun, sultry
with a blue mist &
thundrous clouds, sweet
afternoon.

Lovely harvest weather.
Multitudes of young swallows of the first brood cluster on the
scotch-firs.
The swifts, for the bulk of them, departed from Fyfield, about
this day.

Monday 7.
Rising; NW.
Fog, sun, sultry, sweet
afternoon.

Timothy, Mrs Snooke's old tortoise, which has been kept full 30
years in her court before the house, weighs six pounds three
quarters, & one ounce. It was never weighed before, but seems to
be much grown since it came.

† Pray let it be weighed every year.

---

†Entry in an unknown hand.

Tuesday 8.
NW, W. Sun, hot,
sultry, sweet even:

Brood of flycatchers come out.

Wednesday 9.
SW, NW.
Dark, rain, dry & fair.

Cimices lineares are now in high copulation on ponds & pools. The females, who vastly exceed the males in bulk, dart & shoot along on the surface of the water with the males on their backs. When a

Thursday 10.
NW, W.
Vast dew, sun, sun &
clouds

female chuses to be disengaged she rears & jumps & plunges like an unruly horse; the lover thus dismounted soon finds a new mate. The females as fast as their curiosities are satisfyed retire to an other part of the lake, perhaps to deposit their foetus in quiet: hence the sexes are found separate except where generation is going-on. From the multitudes of minute young of all gradations of sizes these insects seem without doubt to be viviparous.

Friday 11.
SW.
Dark, rain, rain, sun &
clouds.

One single swift, the last, was seen at Fyfield.

Saturday 12.
W.
Sun, sun, wind, clouds
& showers, fine.

Full moon. High tides frequently discompose the weather in places so near the coast, even in the dryest, most settled seasons, for a day or two.

Sunday 13.
W.
Dark, sweet day.

Black cluster grapes begin to turn colour.

Monday 14.
W.
Sweet harvest weather.

Two great bats appear. They feed high: are very rare in Hants, & Sussex. Low fog.

Tuesday 15.
SW.
Dark & still, chilly.

Dark & still.
Some little farmers have finished wheat-harvest.

Wednesday 16.
SW.
Sun, shower, soft sun.

Generation seems to be pretty well over among *cimices lineares*. Minute young abound.

Thursday 17.
S.
Dark, driving rain,
dark & foggy.

FINDON
Rabbits make incomparably the finest turf; for they not only bite closer than larger quadrupeds; but they allow no bents to rise: hence warrens produce much the most delicate turf for gardens. Sheep never touch the stalks of grasses.

Rabbits on Nore Hill.
Late August.

Friday 18.
SW.
Grey, sweet afternoon.

CHILGROVE

Saturday 19.
29 5/10; 62, 65; NE,
W.
Sun, dark clouds, sweet
afternoon.
Papilio Atalanta.

SELBORNE
Wheat-harvest in general seems to be finished, except where there
is turnep-wheat.

Fifteen wasps nests have been destroyed round the village: yet
those plunderers devour the plums, & eat holes in the peaches &
nectarines before they are ripe: & will soon attack the grapes.
Grapes begin to turn colour: they are forward this year. Harvest
weather was much finer at Ringmer than Selborne. Some wheat a
little grown at Newton.

Sunday 20.
29 5/10; S, SW.
Sun, showers, windy,
fine.

China-asters begin to blow.
Hops are uneven; some grown large, & some just blown.

Monday 21.
29 3/10½; 61½; S, S.
Dark, showers, small
showers, dark.

Young swallows continue to come-out.
Young broods of Martins in their nests.

Tuesday 22.
29 5/10½; 62; W.
Much rain in the night,
wind & clouds, bright
& chilly.

Wednesday 23.
29 7/10; W.
Sun, hot sun, fine.

Sixteen wasps nests destroyed.

Thursday 24.
29 7/10, 6½; 60, 64;
W, NE, SE.

Wasps abound, & destroy the fruit.
Clouds about.

Sun, hot sun, fine even.

Friday 25.
29 5/10; 64; SE, S.
Vast dew, sun,
thundrous clouds, sweet
afternoon.

Saturday 26.
29 4/10; 63½; S, W.
Sun, clouds, showers,
bright.

Sunday 27.
29 4/10; 63; SW, S.
Sun, dark, driving
rain.

Monday 28.
29 4/10; S, S.
Rain, rain, rain, sun,
grey.

Tuesday 29.
S.
Sun, showers & sun.

Wednesday 30.
S.
Sun, showers, bright.

Thursday 31.
S.
Great rain, showers,
bright.

SEPTEMBER 1775

Friday 1.
29 5/10; 60; S, W, SE.
Sun, showers, much
rain.

Worms copulate.

Sr Simeon Stuart begins to pick his hops.
Wasps have begun on the Grapes.
Seventeen wasps nests destroyed.
Peaches are gathered every day, being injured by the wasps: they
are not full ripe.

Young swallows of the second brood come out every day.
Swallows & martins congregate in vast flocks.

Twaite, in Saxon is ground cleared from wood, & plowed.
Woddan is not a way, but the verb *to go*:
wud is wood in Saxon.

8 more wasps-nests; in all 25 have been destroyed round the
village.

Hop-picking becomes general.
Worms copulate.

MEONSTOKE

Wasp feeding on a windfall,
Bakers Hill
27 August.

SELBORNE
Barley begins to be injured.
Many fields of barley, green & not mowed.

Saturday 2.
29 6/10; 61; SW.
Rain, rain, rain, red
evening.

Gathered first grapes: they look well; & are large; but not highly
flavoured yet.
Sad hop-picking: a large crop in this district.
Barley in the suds.¶

Sunday 3.
29 7/10; 60; SW.
Rain, rain, rain,
bright.

Great rain. Hops sadly washed.
Destroyed the 26th wasps nest, a vast colony.

Monday 4.
29 6/10½; 61; SE, E.
Bright, fine morn:,
dark & mild.

Linnets congregate. Wasps swarm about the Grapes, tho' so
many nests have been destroyed.

Tuesday 5.
29 ½/10; 69½; E.
Grey, spitting, bright
& sultry, dark &
sultry, distant
lightening.

Wasps swarm.

Wednesday 6.
29 5/10; 65; E.
Grey, sun, sweet day,
grey, distant thunder.

Wasps abound not only in neighbourhoods, but in lone fields &
woods: how subsisted there?
Grapes good, but much gnawed, & defaced by wasps.

Thursday 7.
29 3/10; 66; E.
Grey, sprinkling, dark
& sprinkling.

In the dusk of the evening when beetles begin to buz, partridges
immediately begin to call: these two circumstances are exactly
coincident.

Friday 8.
20 1/10½; 66; SW, S.
Dark, sprinkling, dark,
sprinkling.

Wasps abound, & mangle the grapes.
We have, I should think, destroyed 50000.

On Friday Sepr 8th at 10 at night a considerable shock of an
earthquake was felt at Oxford, Bath, & several other towns.

Saturday 9.
29 3/10½; SE, S, SW.
Sun & showers,
showers, showers.

Wasps somewhat abated.

The day & night insects occupy the annuals alternately: the
papilios, muscae, & *apes* are succeeded at the close of day by
phalenae, earwigs, woodlice, &c.

Sunday 10.
29 2/10; SW.
Great rain, sun,
thunder clouds, vast
rain.

My tallest beech measures in girth at three feet from the ground six feet & four inches. It grows at the S:E end of Sparrow's hanger, & appears to be upwards of 70 feet high.

Monday 11.
29 5/10; 54½; NW,
W, NW.
Sun, vast showers,
thunder, bright.

Much barley abroad, most of it standing: what is cut lies in a sad way. Hop-picking much interrupted: hops become brown.

Tuesday 12.
29 4/10; 51, 56; NW,
W, S.
Sun, bright & pleasant,
rain, rain.

Put 50 fine bunches of grapes in crape bags to secure them from wasps.

Wednesday 13.
29 3/10; 54; W.
Sun, showers, clouds &
cold showers.

Good grapes every day, but not delicate.
Baged more grapes.

Thursday 14.
29 5/10; 55; NW.
Dark, wet & cold, sun,
cold & dark.

Little barley housed towards Winton, & Andover. Many crops not ripe.

Friday 15.
29 3/10; 56; NW.
Miserable cold rains!

Saturday 16.
29 5/10; 56; NW, W.
Rain, cloudy, clearing,
bright.

Wasps begin to
abate.

Sunday 17.
29 4/10; 56; SW, W.
Sun, bright, pleasant
clear evening.
❀ *Hedera helix.*

Ivy begins to blow.

Monday 18.
29 3/10; 61; SE, SW,

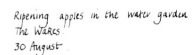

Ripening apples in the water garden
The Wakes
30 August

SE.
Showers, cloudy & fair,
violent drowning rain.

Tuesday 19.
29 5/20; 66; S.
Dark & spitting rain,
rain, dark.

Wednesday 20.
29 3/10; 67; SE, E.
Dark, shower, sun,
sultry, lightening.

Clouds of *muscae, apes, vespae,* &c. resort to the Ivy-bloom. Ivy is that last bloom that insects enjoy: it blows on thro' Octobᵣ & Novemᵣ

On Wednesday 20 there was a violent storm of thunder & lightening at Fyfield between ten & eleven at night.

Thursday 21.
29 4/10; SW.
Showers, showers, sun
& showers, rainbow,
bright.

BASINGSTOKE, SELBORNE
Barley in a sad condition about Basingstoke.
Rams begin to pay court the [to] the ewes.

Friday 22.
29 6/10; 61, 60; SE,
E.
Sun, sultry, sweet day.
Merula torquata.

Ring-ouzels appear on the common on their autumnal migration.

Saturday 23.
29 5/10; 68; SE.
Fog, sun, sweet day.

Apples begin to ripen.
My grapes are now delicate.

The large female-wasps begin to come in a door, & seem as if they were going to hide, & lay themselves up for the winter. The common wasps are much abated in number.

Sunday 24.
29 4/10; 68; E, SE.
Fog, sun, sweet day.

Monday 25.
29 3/10½; 67; SE.
Fog, vast dew, sun,
sweet day.

Gathered-in the swan's eggs, autumn-burgamot-pears: a [vast?] crop of the former.
Much barley housed this day.

Tuesday 26.
29 3/10½; 67; SE.
Great dew, soft, sunny,
vast clouds & distant
thunder, sweet even.

Much rain to the N:W: & N.
Much barley housed.
Gathered in the golden-rennets.¶ Apples are too large from much wet.

Wednesday 27.
29 5/10; 61; W.
Grey, sun, sweet day.

Gathered-in the royal russets, & knobbed russets.¶
Tyed-up endive. Winter-garden-crops in vast vigour.

Thursday 28.
29 5/10; 57; SW.
Grey, spitting, dark &
mild.

Swallows at present seem to be gone. Saw only one the whole day.

Friday 29.
29 5/10; S, NW.
Grey, spitting, sweet
mild afternoon.

No hirundines.

Saturday 30.
29 8/10; 52; N, NE.
Cold dew, sun & sweet
day.

No hirundines.

My *Arundo donax,*¶ which I received from Gibraltar, is grown this year eight or nine feet high: I therefore opened the head of one stalk to see what approaches it had made towards blowing after so hot a summer. When it was cut open we found: a long series of leaves enfolded one within the other to a most minute degree but not the least rudiments of fructification: so that the plant must have extended itself many feet before it could have attained to it's full stature: & must have required many more weeks of hot weather before it could have brought any seeds to maturity.

OCTOBER 1775

Sunday 1.
29 6/10; 59½; NE.
Heavy fog, sweet day.

Two swallows appear.

Monday 2.
29 2/10½; 58; NE, E.
Heavy fog, dark &
mild, rain, great
shower.

The barom! falls with great precipitation.

Tuesday 3.

29 1/10½; N, NW, S.
Grey, heavy clouds,
sparkling, halo round
the moon, fog.

No *hirundo*.
Some ring-ouzels.

Wednesday 4.

29 4/10½; 53½; W.
Grey, bright day, clear
& chilly.

One swallow. What can this bird be doing behind by itself? Why might not they have all staid, since this individual seems brisk, & vigorous?

Thursday 5.

29 4/10¾; 49; W.
White frost, bright &
sharp, sun, cold &
bright.

Here & there a straggling swallow. Curlews clamor.

Friday 6.

29 4/10¼; 53; S, W,
NW. Grey, great
rain, sun, grey.

Just before it was dark a flight of about 12 swallows darted along over my House towards the hill: they seemed as if they settled in the hanger.

Saturday 7.

29 5/10½; 51½; W,
NW.
Vast showers, sun,
bright & chilly.

Now several house-martins appear under the hanger.

An oak in Newton-lane¶ near the Cross by the condensation of the fogs on it's leaves has dripped such quantities for some nights past, that the water stands in puddles, & runs down the ruts. Why this tree should drip so much more than it's neighbours is not easy to say. No doubt this is one of the means by which small upland ponds are still supplyed with water in the longest droughts; & the reason why they are never dry. What methods of supply upland ponds enjoy, where no trees over-hang, may not be so easy to determine. Perhaps their cool surfaces may attract a fund from the air when it is loaded with fogs & vapors, especially in the night time. That they have some never-failing stock at hand to counter-balance evaporation & the waste by cattle, is notorious to the meanest observer. For on the chalks no springs are ever seen on the tops or sides of hills, but in the bottoms alone.

Sunday 8.

29 6/10; 49; W, S.
White frost, bright sun,
clouds & cold air, rain.

30 or 40 martins appear under the hanger, & about the village.

Monday 9.

29 6/10¼; 61; W.

*Woodcock returns.

Rain, rain, sun,
shower, grey, bright.
Scolopax. *

Saw one swallow.
Rooks frequent wall-nut trees, & carry off the fruit.

Tuesday 10.
29 7/10; 57; W.
Bright, grey, soft, red
evening.

Several swallows, & h: martins about.
Woodcock killed this day.

Wednesday 11.
29 6/10¾; 58.
Rain early, sun,
sprinkling, grey &
mild.

Swallows & martins.
Lowered the flower-bank in the garden, & laid it on a gentle
slope, & filled it with flowers of various sorts.

Thursday 12.
29 5/10; 61; SW.
Spitting fog, rain, rain,
dark & warm.

Martins. In moist dark weather black snails are out & feeding all
day long.
Toads are still about.

Friday 13.
29 6/10½; 55.
Sun, brisk gales, clouds
& sun, bright.

Many martins. Hops were a drug¶ at Weyhill-fair; unusual
quantities were exposed for sale.

Saturday 14.
29 7/10; 52½; SW, W.
Bright, sun with rock-
like clouds, bright.

Many people sow wheat: the ground works well.
No hirundines all day.

Sunday 15.
29 7/10, 29 9/10½; 49,
51; W, NW.
Bright, grey, clear &
cold air, bright.

BASINGSTOKE
No hirundines.
Mr Barker writes word that in Sep: last there fell in the county of
Rutland near six inch: & ½ of rain.

Monday 16.
29 8/10; 51; W.
Fog, sweet day.

OXFORD
The beeches on the hanger, & the maples in my fields are now
beautifully tinged, & afford a lovely picturesque scape, very
engaging to the imagination.
No hirundines this morning.

Tuesday 17.

Wednesday 18.

Thursday 19.
28 8/10

This storm occasioned much damage at sea, & in the river thames.
Vast rain with stormy wind.
This storm damaged my trees & hedges.

Friday 20.

BASINGSTOKE
One swallow near Wallingford.
Strong wind. Acorns abound; the hogs in the lanes & woods seem to be half fat.

Saturday 21.
29 4/10; W.
Sun, brisk gale, sun, bright.

SELBORNE
The storm on thursday night tore all the remaining flowers to pieces.

With us the country people call coppice, or brush-wood *ris*, or *rice*: now *ɦƿıꞅ* in Saxon signifies frondes, & is no doubt the word whence our provincial term originates. *ɦꞃæð ɦƿıꞅ* is frondes celeres: hence probably *Red Rice*, the name of a hunting-seat standing in the midst of a coppice near Andover.

Sunday 22.
29 4/10; 47: W, NE, N.
Miserable, cold rains.

My autumn-crop of spinage this year runs much to seed.

Monday 23.
29 8/10½; 45; NW.
Sun, sun & clouds, dark.

No hirundines.
Many large *muscae* on the asters: the air full of insects, & floting gossamer.

Tuesday 24.
29 7/10; W.
Sun, bright, dark, rain.

The berries of the early-blowing Ivy-trees near half-grown. The berries in the spring, when they ripen, are a noble provision for birds.

Wednesday 25.
29 8/10½; 44; NW.
Frost, sun & pleasant.

The *arbutus* casts it's blossom & discloses the rudiments of it's fruit. In these two instances fructification goes on the winter thro'.

Thursday 26.
29 9/10¼; 39; NW.
Wh: frost, ice, bright & sharp.

Three martins in the street.
Gossamer on every bent.¶

Friday 27.
29 8/10½; 45; NW.

Many *muscae, tipulae.* &c &c.

Wh: frost, still, grey &   Gossamer abounds.
pleasant.
Papilio Atalanta.

Saturday 28.
29 6/10; 47; W.   Fine season for sowing of wheat.
Grey, mild, still &   Bat appears.
pleasant.

                            Βγηξ̄εδε Bynstede, the name of a parish near us, signifies *Locus
                            cultus, vel habitatus.* ¶ This parish abuts on a wild woodland
                            district. which is a royal forest, & is called the Holt. This parish
                            was probably cultivated when all around were nothing but
                            woodlands, & forests.

Sunday 29.
29 7/10½; 47; N.   Redwings on the hawthorns.
Grey, sun, sweet,   Bat appears.
cloudless day.
Turdus iliacus.

Monday 30.
29 8/10; 44; N, SW.   Flocks of large field-fares.
Wh: frost, ice, sun,   Celeri finely blanched.
sweet day, grey.
Turdus pilaris.

Tuesday 31.
29 3/10½; 48; S.   Leaves fall very fast.
Rain, rain, rain.   The hangers begin to lose their picturesque beauties.

NOVEMBER 1775

Wednesday 1.
29 3/10½; 53; SW.   Hogs come so fat out of the stubbles & woods, that they die very
Much rain in the night,   good pork.
soft rain, dark & mild.

Thursday 2.
29 4/10¾; E, NE.   One swallow remains.
Sun, sun & sharp air.   *A flock of wood-pigeons: these are usually the latest winter-birds
*Columba oenas.**¶   of passage that appear. They do not abound as formerly. Where
                            they breed seems to be a secret.

Friday 3.
29 4/10½; 43; E.   The wheat-sowing pretty well finished in very good order.
Frost, sun & sharp air.

Saturday 4.
29 3/10¼; 43; NE.
Grey & pleasant.

Grapes are delicate still; especially those that are bagged in crape; those that are, are shivelled, & vapid.

Sunday 5.
29 3/10⅔; 44; E.
Cold, rain, dark & cold.

The great month for spring migration is April: tho' the wryneck, one species of willow-wren, & the upland curlew are seen in March: in this month also the winter-birds retire. In Sept: most of the short-winged summer birds withdraw; & in Oct: the woodcock, redwing, & fieldfare return. The hirundines are most irregular in their retreat: for the Swift disappears in the beginning of Aug: the rest of that Genus not 'til Oct: In Nov: the wood-pigeons, & wild fowls return. We have found at times, in the parish of Selborne alone, about 120 species of birds, which are more than half the number that belong to Great Britain in general; & more than half as many as Linnaeus can produce in the kingdom of Sweden. Mr Pennant enumerated 227 species in Gr: Britain,¶ & Linnaeus about 221 in his native country.

Monday 6.
29 ½/10; 44; NE.
Rain, rain, dark & damp.

Yellow-water-wagtail.

Tuesday 7.
29½/10; NE, N.
Dark & moist, dark & still.

Phalenae out near hedges.

Wednesday 8.
29 3/10; 46; N.
Grey & pleasant.

Thursday 9.
29 6/10; N.
Grey & mild, bright.

Friday 10.
29 6/10; 39; N, NW, E, SE, W.
Frost, ice, sun, grey & mild.

Saturday 11.
29 3/10½; 44; NE.
Rain, rain, dark, rain.

Trees begin to be naked.

Sunday 12.
29; 54; S, SW.
Rain, rain, dark, rain.

Monday 13.
28 2/10; W. Vast rain,
grey & warm.
Charadrius pluvialis.

Green whistling plovers appear: they come in the autumn to us, but do not breed here. They haunt downs.

Tuesday 14.
29 5/10; 40; W, NW.
Bright, sun & wind,
bright & sharp.

Saw yesterday a considerable flock of gulls flying over the hanger to the S: W.
Gulls very seldom appear in this district; except some times on the forest ponds.

Wednesday 15.
29 2/10; 39; W, SE.
Frost, dark, cold, sleety
rain.

Thursday 16.
29 6/10½; 38; W,
NW.
Bright & frosty, sun &
sharp air, frost.

When horses, cows, sheep, deer, &c: feed in wind, & rain, they always keep their heads down the wind, & their tails to the weather: but birds always perch, & chuse to fly, with their heads to the weather to prevent the wind from ruffling their feathers, & the cold & wet from penetrating to their skins.

Friday 17.
28 9/10; 47; SW.
Rain, rain, rain,
bright.

Saturday 18.
29 4/10; 42; NW.
Dark, spitting, sun,
bright.

Sunday 19.
29 8/10½; 38; N,
NW.
Frost, sun, serene.

Monday 20.
29 8/10; SE.
Dark, rain, rain, dark
& spitting.

Tuesday 21.
30; SE, E. Grey,
spitting rain, spitting.

Began trimming the vines: the wood of last summer is well-ripened, but neither long nor large.

Wednesday 22.
30 ½/10; 36½; NE.
Hard frost, icicles, sun,
grey.

Thursday 23.
29 8/10; N, NE.
Rain, rain, wet fogs,
wet.

The high glass brings no good weather: Barom.ˢ usually dote, ¶ &
are mistaken about this time of year.

Friday 24.
29 8/10; 39; NE.
Grey, dark & spitting,
dark.

A flight of woodcocks about in the country.

Saturday 25.
29 7/10; 40; NE.
Dark & still.

Many *phalaenae* appear. Strange that those nocturnal *lepidopterae*
should be so alert, at a season when no day-papilios appear, but
have long been laid-up for the winter!

Trees will not subsist in sharp currents of air: thus after I had
opened a vista in the hedge at the E: corner of Baker's hill, no tree
that I could plant would grow in that corner: & since I have
opened a view from the bottom of the same field into the mead, the
ash that grew in the hedge, & now stands naked on the bastion, is
dying by inches, & losing all it's boughs.
   Phalaenae appear about hedges in the night time in mild
weather the winter thro'.

Sunday 26.
29 6/10½; 39½; NE.
Dark & spitting, dark
& still.

Very dark season: dark within doors a little after 3 o'clock in the
afternoon.

Monday 27.
29 5/10½; NE.
Grey, & still.

Arrangement of parts is both *smell* & *colour*: thus a sweet, &
lovely flower when bruized both stinks & looks ugly. We may
add that arrangement of parts is also *flavor*: since *muddled* liquors
& *frozen* meats immediately lose it.

Tuesday 28.
29 4/10; 42; E.
Dark & still, rain, rain.

Wednesday 29.

29 4/10; 48; SE, SW.
Rain, rain, rain, stars.
*Corvus cornix.**

*The grey-crow, a bird of winter-passage, appears. It is as rare at Selborne, as the carrion-crow is in Sweden. This is only the third bird that I have seen in this district. They are common on the downs near Andover, & Winton.

Thursday 30.

29 7/10; 54; SW.
Wet, dark with driving rain.

The air unusually damp, with copious condensations on the walls, wainscot, looking-glass, &c of houses, in many places running in streams.

DECEMBER 1775

Friday 1.

29 8/10¼; 55; S.
Grey, sun & sweet mid-day, grey & soft.

Many species of flies come forth.
Bats are out, & preying on *phalaenae*.
The berries of Ivy, which blowed in the end of Sep: now half grown. A noble & providential supply for birds in winter & spring! for the first severe frost freezes, & spoils all the haws, sometimes by the middle of Nov! Ivy-berries do not seem to freeze.

Saturday 2.

29 8/10; 53; SW.
Grey & soft, mild & spring-like, dark & spitting.

White butterfly appears.

Large, grey, shell-less cellar-snails lay themselves up about the same time with those that live abroad: hence it is plain that a defect of warmth alone is not the only cause that influences their retreat.
The rudiments of the arbutus-fruit swell, & grow. Laurustines continue to blow.

Sunday 3.

29 8/10½; 52½; SW.
Grey, sun, soft & spring-like, dark & still.

Hepaticas blow.
Crocuss spring. Grass grows.

Monday 4.

29 9/10¾; 52; W.
Grey, mild, & spring-like, dark & still, spitting fog.

Furze blows.
Colds & feverish complaints obtain in this neighbourhood. In London, Portsmouth, & other places colds & coughs have been general: in Dublin also.

Tuesday 5.

30, 30; 49; W.
Dark & spitting, mild & still, dark, clearing.

Wednesday 6.
30 ¾/10, 30 1/10; 48;
NW, N.
Sun, sweet day, some
clouds, mild, bright.

Paths quite dry.
Spring-like weather.

Thursday 7.
30 1/10; 44; N, NW.
Grey, dark & mild,
dark & still.

Phalaenae about.

Friday 8.
30; 46; NW.
Grey, gleams of sun,
grey, bright.

Fogs on the hills.
Spring-like: more like Feb: than Dec!

Saturday 9.
30 1/10; 40; NW.
Wh: frost, sun, bright,
frost.

Finished the trimming & tacking of the fruit-trees: they are put
in good order.

Ravens in their common mode of flying have a peculiarity¶
attending them not unworthy of notice: they turn-over in the air
quite on their backs, & that not now & then, but frequently; often
every two or 300 yards. When this odd attitude betides them they
fall down several fathoms, uttering a loud crow, & then right
themselves again. This strange vacillation seems to be owing to
their scratching when bitten by vermin: the thrusting-out of their
leg destroys their equipoize, & throws their wings out of the true
centre of gravity. Ravens spend their leisure-time over some
hanging wood in a sort of mock fight, dashing & diving at each
other continually; while their loud croakings make the woody
steeps re-echo again.

Sunday 10.
30 1/10¾; 36; NW.
Frost, bright & still,
hard frost.

This epidemic disorder falls heavier on adults than children.
Hen chaff-finches in vast flocks.

Monday 11.
30 1/10; 35; SW.
Hard frost, sun, thaw,
dark & still.

Tuesday 12.
30; 38, 38; S, SE.
Small frost, sun, sweet
day, frost.

Ivy-berries more than half grown.
The fruit of the *arbutus* grows.

Wednesday 13.
29 9/10; 33; SW.
Hard frost, sun, thaw,
dark & moist.

Ice bears: boys slide.

Thursday 14.
29 9/10½; 45; 46½;
W, NW, N.
Grey & still, mild,
dark & still.

Thaw.

Friday 15.
29 9/10½; 44; E.
Dark, mild, & still.

Fieldfares, & red-wings in vast flocks.

Saturday 16.
30 ⅓/10; E.
Fog, sun, sweet day.

Sunday 17.
30 1/10¾; 36, 35; E.
Hard frost, sun, grey
with thaw, hard frost.

People recover from the epidemic disorder.

Monday 18.
30 ¼/10; 33, 34; E.
Hard frost, sun, sun,
hard frost.

Ice bears.

Tuesday 19.
29 8/10½; 32½; E.
Hard frost, sun, grey
& still, dark.

10 or 12 large gulls sailing high in the air over comb-wood pond.

Wednesday 20.
29 5/10; 36; E.
Dark with thaw, sun,
frost.

Thursday 21.
28 9/10, 28 9/10; 44;
SE, S, SW.
Rain, rain, sun, dark &
raw, stars.

People fall with colds.
Dry weather for near three weeks, 'til the ground was very free
from water.

Friday 22.
29 3/10; 43, W, SW.
Sun, grey, mild.

Saturday 23.
28 8/10; 47; SW.
Great rain, sun, grey & mild.

Sunday 24.
28 3/10; 43; S, SW.
Great showers, rain, rain, sun, rain, bright.

Monday 25.
28 8/10; 41; SW.
Sun, sun, showers, bright.

Tuesday 26.
29 3/10; 42; SW.
Rain, sun, pleasant day.

Wednesday 27.
29 6/10; 39; SW.
Frost, sun, mild, shower, frost.

Thursday 28.
29 4/10; 35; S.
Hard frost, rime, shower, sun, thaw, grey.

Friday 29.
29 6/10; 39; W, NW.
Rain, sun, sweet day, frost.

Saturday 30.
29 5/10½; 40; SE.
Frost, thaw, sun, shower, bright.

The country-people, who are abroad in winter-mornings long before sun-rise, talk much of hard frost in some spots, & none in others. The reason of these partial frosts is obvious: for there are, at such times, partial fogs about: where the fog obtains little or no frost appears; but where the air is clear there it freezes hard. So the frost takes place either on hill or in dale; where ever the air happens to be clearest, & freest from vapour.

The barom.ʳ at 28 3/10, & yet no great rain or wind.

On every sunny day the winter thro', clouds of insects usually called gnats (I suppose *tipulae* & *empedes*) appear sporting & dancing over the tops of the ever-green-trees in the shrubbery, & frisking about as if the business of generation was still going on. Hence it appears that these *diptera* (which by their sizes seem to be of different species) are not subject to a torpid state in the winter as most winged Insects are. At night, & in frosty weather, & when it rains & blows they seem to retire into those trees. They often are out in a fog.

ⱨyⱣⱨ. *cornu vel angulus*: whence our Faringdon Hyrn, or hern as we pronounce it, is the corner-field of the parish. ⱨeaⱨe *Humilis*: hence perhaps our honey-lane. Our Gally-hill, is perhaps gallows hill, from Ɫalȝa *crux*. Does not domesday book, among other privileges, say that Priors &c: were allowed Fareas, gallows? By,

Exposed beech roots,
Dorton

Sunday 31.
29 7/10; 42; SE.
Hard frost, sun,
sun, fog.

habitation: from whence yᵉ adjective **Byn** as Binsted &c. **Deopʒuɲ**
saltus: hence no doubt our Dorton, a wild, bushy common just
below the village. Deerton, a place where deer were kept. **Eoρδδ**
Ovile: hence perhaps our field called the Ewel? **Ymbhɑɲʒeρ** the
winding hanger: we have places so named. **Rodc** coux: hence our
Rode-green near the priory, where probably a cross was erected.
Fyρδ a ford: also a *camp*, hence probably our high common-field
to the N:W. is called the fordown. **Eδeρ** *sepes*: the top border that
binds down our hedges, & keeps them together is called by our
hedgers the *ether* to this day: the wickering the top along they call
ethering. **ᚱᚱᚨᚤᚾ** (Gothic) *Salutatio*: hence perhaps our word
Golly, a sort of jolly kind of oath, or asseveration much in use
among our carters, & lowest people.

Eoρδ ριcʒa *blatta terrena*: hence our absurd word, not peculiar
to this district, *Earwig.* ¶

Monday 1.
29 2/10; SE.
Dark & chilly, rain,
rain.

SELBORNE

Tuesday 2.
29 4/10; W, NW.
Rain, grey, mild, dark.

Grey & white wagtails appear every day: they never leave us.

Wednesday 3.
29 7/10½; 39; E.
Grey & harsh.

Thursday 4.
29 1/10; 40; S, W.
Rain, rain, rain, rain.

Friday 5.
29 1/10½; 45; SW,
NW.
Grey, shower, soft &
bright.

Wagtail.
Oakhanger Stream.
20 January.

Saturday 6.
29 1/0; 41; SW, E.
Frost, sun, partial fogs,
dark, rain, rain.

Sunday 7.
29; 37; NE, N.
Snow, driving snow all
day, snow.

Monday 8.
29 2/10; 34; N.
Snow on the ground,
icicles, dark & still.

Tuesday 9.
29 3/10½; 32; NE.
Rime, snow lying, dark
& freezing.

Wednesday 10.
29 3/10¾; 32½; N.
Dark & still, snow
frozen.

Thursday 11.
28 9/10; 35; E, SE, E.   Some lambs fall.
Snow, thaw with some
rain, snow.

Friday 12.
28 8/10; 33; E, NE.   A very deep snow.
Snow all night, snow,   Poor birds begin to be distress'd, & to come in a door: hares do
small snow.   not stir yet.

Saturday 13.
29; 32, 31; N.   The snow is drifted up to the tops of gates & the lanes are full.
Deep snow with wind,   Poultry do not stir-out of the hen-houses: they are amazed, &
dark & heavy.   confounded in snow, & would soon perish. Hares lie-by at first,
          'til compelled to beat-out by hunger.

Sunday 14.
29 2/10½; 29½; N.   Rugged, Siberian weather. The narrow lanes are full of snow in
Driving, drifting snow   some places, which is driven into most romantic, & grotesque
all day.   shapes. The road-waggons are obliged to stop, & the stage-
          coaches are much embarrassed. I was obliged to be much abroad
          on this day, & scarce ever saw it's fellow.
Monday 15.
29 3/10¾; 28½; N.
Grey & light, dark with
snow.

Tuesday 16.
29 3/10½; 28½; 30;
N. Snow, snow, snow.

The brambling appears in farmyards among the chaffinches. It is rare in these parts.

Wednesday 17.
29 4/10; 30, 31; NE,
N. Small snow, dark &
still.

Rooks come to dunghills close to houses. Skylarks resort to farm-yards.

Thursday 18.
29 5/10½; 32; N.
Deep snow, no thaw,
dark & still.

Cats catch all the birds that come-in for shelter from the cold. Wagtails retire to brooks, & rivulets; there they find the *aureliae* of water-insects. Titmice pull the mosses & lichens off from trees in quest of grubs, &c: Nut-hatches do the same.

Friday 19.
29 4/10; 23 abroad,
25; E.
Snow falling, grey &
light, dark & still.

Saturday 20.
29 3/10½; 28, 28;
NW, E.
Fierce frost, sun: none
since the snow fell,
grey, clouds fly some
from the NW, some
from the E.

Hares, compelled by hunger, come into my garden, & eat the pinks. Lambs fall, & are frozen to the ground.
What drops from horses is immediately eaten by crows, & rooks: so strict an economist is Nature, that the most refuse matters are turned to some use; nothing is wasted.

Sunday 21.
29 1/10½; 20, 33
abroad; NW, W.
Frost, sun, grey, sleet.

Flocks of wild-geese pass-over.
Snow lies very deep.

Monday 22.
29 ½/10; 30; E.
Grey & still.

Went to FARNHAM.

Tuesday 23.
Therm: in London
areas: 20.

LONDON
The ground covered with snow, & every thing frozen-up.

Wednesday 24.

Thursday 25.

Friday 26.

Snow very thick on the roofs & in areas.

Saturday 27.
Snow all day, fierce
frost at night.

Sunday 28.
S. Lambeth: abroad 11.
Fierce frost: ice under
people's beds & cutting
winds.

Therm.ʳ at Selborne: ¶ abroad, 7.

Monday 29.
7.
Intense frost, ice under
people's beds.

6. As intense frost usually befalls in Jan: our Saxon forefathers
call'd that month with no small propriety the wolf-month:
because the severe season brought down those ravenous beasts out
of the woods among the villages.

Tuesday 30.
6. Fierce frost, sun.

10.

Wednesday 31.
6.
Fierce frost, sun.

32 deg: below the freezing point, below zero!! At eleven it rose to
16½. Rime. A most unusual degree of cold for S: England: 32
deg: below freezing point!

FEBRUARY 1776

Thursday 1.
Fierce frost, thaw &
some rain.

Snow now lying on the roofs for 26 days! Thames frozen ¶ above
& below bridge: crouds of people running about on the ice.
The streets strangely encumbered with snow, which crumbles &
treads dusty, & looks like bay-salt. Carriages run without any
noise of clatter.

Friday 2.
Thaw.

Thaws, I have observed, frequently take place immediately from
intense freezing, as men in sickness often begin to mend from a
paroxysm.

Saturday 3.

Now swarms of little *tipulae* frisking at S: Lambeth. How did
these minute insects escape from being frozen?

Sunday 4.
Wind & rain.

At Selborne the frost was more violent than at any other place that
I could hear of with any certainty: tho' some say the therm: in
some place in Kent was 2 deg: below zero, 34 deg: below the
freezing point! Severe frost seems to run in currents: for at the
same time the therm.ʳ at Lyndon in Rutland was at 19: & at
Blackburn in Lancashire at 19: & at Manchester at 21: & 20: 18.
Thus does some unknown circumstance strangely over-balance
latitude.

Monday 5.
Thaw, hot sun,
springlike.
Much snow under
hedges.

Made the seedling cucumber-bed.

Tuesday 6.

Part of the snow gone at Selborne. It lay for many weeks in deep
hollow lanes.

Wednesday 7.

Great rains, & vast floods thro' the month of February.

MARCH 1776

Thursday 7.

Made the bearing cucumber-bed with 8 loads of hot dung.

Friday 22.
29 5/10½; 54; S.
Fog, sweet day.

LONDON, SELBORNE
Came from London to Selborne. Hot sun: summer-like weather.

When I arrived in Hants I found the wheat looking well, & the
turneps little injured. My laurels & laurustines somewhat injured:
but only those that stood in hot sunny aspects. No ever-greens
quite destroyed; & not half the damage sustained that befell in Jan:
1768. Those laurels that are some what scorched on the S: sides
are perfectly untouched on their N: sides. The care I took in
ordering the snow to be shaken from the branches whenever it fell,
seems greatly to have availed my laurels. Mr Yalden's laurels facing
to the N: untouched. Portugal laurels not hurt.

Saturday 23.
29 5/10½; 55; SE.
Sunny, summer.
Bombylius medius.

Many species of *muscae* come forth.

Sunday 24.
29 7/10; 57; SE.
Sun, sweet day, clouds,
sprinkling.
*Regulus non cristatus
minor.*

Least willow-wren chirps: usually the first summer-bird of
passage.

Monday 25.
30; E. NE.
Soft rain, grey, sweet
afternoon.
*Charadrius
Oedicnemus.**

Tuesday 26.
29 8/10½; 48; NE.
Frost, ice, hot sun, &
cold air.

Wednesday 27.
29 6/10½; 42; NE.
Hard frost, sun,
London-smoke, grey &
mild.

Thursday 28.
29 7/10; 46; N.
Sun, dark & harsh air.
*Hirundo domestica!
Hirundo agrestis!*

Friday 29.
29 9/10; N.
Dark & harsh, sun,
grey & still.

Saturday 30.
30; 49; N, NW.
Wh: frost, sun, grey &
mild.
🌱 *Cucumis sativus* mas.

Sunday 31.
30 ¾/10; NE.
Sun, sweet day.

*Stone-curlew returns, & clamors.

Flocks of fieldfares remain: no redwings are seen. No song-thrushes are heard; they seem to be destroyed by the hard weather.
Some wagtails survive.
Peaches, Nect: & apricots in full bloom. Blackbirds are mostly destroyed by shooters. Hardly any rain since the beginning of the month.

On the 28: Farmer Tredgold saw five hirundines at Willey-mill near Farnham playing about briskly over the mill-pond: four, he says, were house-swallows, & the fifth an house-martin, with a white rump. These birds are very early!
Some few bank-martins haunt round the skirts of London, & frequent the dirty pools in St George's fields, & near White-chappel: they build perhaps in the scaffold-holes of some deserted house; for steep banks there are none.

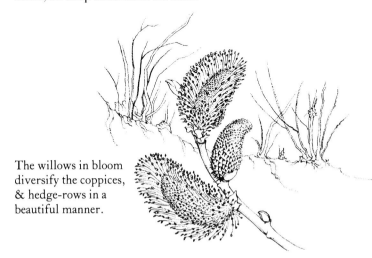

The willows in bloom
diversify the coppices,
& hedge-rows in a
beautiful manner.

APRIL 1776

Monday 1.
30; NW, N.
Sun, sweet summer
weather.

Spider's webs abound on the surface of the ground: Gossamer floats.
Wood-larks hang suspended in the air, & sing all night.

Tuesday 2.
29 9/10; 58; SE, S.
Vast dew, sun, summer
weather.
🌿 *Cucumis sativus* fem.

Wheat looks well.
Stems of the cucumber-fruit drawn by the heat of the weather.

Wednesday 3.
29 8/10½; 58; SW,
NW.
Wh: frost, sun, hot sun,
sweet day.

Peaches & nectarines in bloom make a glorious show.
Thomas began this day mowing the grass-walks.¶

Thursday 4.
29 8/10½; 55; N.
No dew, sun, harsh,
sun & clouds.
Hirundo riparia.

Apricots begin to set & swell.
Bank-martins at Oakhanger.
No rain since the beginning of March. The ground dry & harsh.

Friday 5.
29 8/10; 50; N.
Dark & harsh, sun,
sun.
Atricapilla.

Black-cap whistles.¶
Ivy berries are now black & ripe & seem to have sustained no damage from the severe winter. So hardy are those plants which providence has destined to be in a state of fructification the winter thro'!

Saturday 6.
29 7/10; 49; SE, S,
NW.
Dark, moist & spitting,
grey, clear.

The Bombylius medius abounds. It is an hairy insect like an humble-bee, but with only two wings, & a long straight beak, with which it sucks the early flowers, always appearing in March. The female seems to lay it's eggs, as it poises on it's wings, by striking it's tail on the ground, & against the grass that stands in it's way in a quick manner for several times together.

Sunday 7.
29 6/10; NW.
Dark & harsh, sun,
dark.

Linnets, & chaffinches flock still; so are not paired. Some few sky-larks survive.

Monday 8.
29 2/10½; 49; NW.

Men begin to sow barley.

Dark windy & harsh, showers of snow, & hail.

Cucumbers swell.

Tuesday 9.
29 4/10½; 43; N.
Sun, dark & cold, showers of sleet.

READING
Young geese; & ducks.
Four swallows at Alton.

Wednesday 10.
NE.
Frost, ice, sun & cold air.

OXFORD
One swallow at Wallingford.

Oak logs.
Selborne High Wood.
April.

Thursday 11.
NW.
Dark.

Friday 12.
NW.
Clouds & sun.

Oaks are felled: the bark runs.

Saturday 13.
29 5/10; NW.
Dark, sun.

OXFORD, SELBORNE
Two swallows at Shillingford-bridge.
Rain is much wanted.

At Fyfield; *charadrius oedicnemus* returns & clamors April 14: first swallow April 16: nightingale Apr: 16: cuckow Ap: 20: swifts first seen Apr: 26: came to their nesting place May 8. At Lyndon in Rutland, first swallow Apr: 16: first swift May 6th.

Sunday 14.
29 4/10; 55; W. SW.
Grey, dark, sun, clouds.
Second willow-wren; laughing wren.

Several beeches in the hanger in leaf.
House-snails begin to come-forth.

Monday 15.
29 3/10½; 52; SW.
Grey, sun & clouds, bright.

Swallow appears at Selborne.
Cucumbers swell.

Tuesday 16.
29 1/10½; SE.
Sun, dark, rain, dark.

First swallow at Fyfield.
Swallows. Young turkies.

*Hirundo urbica.**   *House-martin appears.

Wednesday 17.
29 3/10½; 59; S.
Moist, dark, sun, sweet
even: warm.

Tulips bud. Polyanths, sown last year, blow very finely.
Swallows, several. Black snails.

Thursday 18.
29 5/10; 52; W.
Heavy shower, dark,
sun & clouds, sweet
even.
Luscinia.

Mowed all round the garden.
Cut the first brace of cucumbers: they were well-grown.
Nightingale sings.

Friday 19.
29 6/10½; W, S.
Much dew, sun with
clouds, sweet day,
clouds.
Grass-hopper-lark
whispers.

The *bombylius medius* is much about in March & the beginning of
April, & soon seems to retire. It is a very early insect. *Bombylius*
still: seems to be laying it's eggs by striking it's tail against
grasses. Many house-martins appear.
Pulled-down the old martins nests against the brewhouse &
stable: they get foul & full of vermin. These abounded with fleas,
& the cases of *Hippoboscae hirundinis.*
Besides while these birds are building they are much more
in sight, & are very amusing.

Saturday 20.
29 8/10; 55; SW, W.
Large dew, sun &
clouds, summer, some
showers about.
Redstart whistles.

Sunday 21.
29 9/10; 55; N.
Wh: frost, sun, sweet
day.
White-throat. Cuckow.

Pears, plums, & cherries blow finely: apricots swell, peaches &
Nect: set.

Monday 22.
29 8/10½; 59; NW.
Sun, summer weather.

Codlings blow.
Cut a brace of cucumbers.
Hot-beds want rain to make them ferment.

Tuesday 23.
29 7/10; 61½; E.
Wh: frost, hot sun,
cold air.

Early tulips blow: common tulips much stunted for want of rain.

Wednesday 24.
29 5/10; 64; NE.
Fog, hot sun with brisk
air, sweet even:
Musca vomitoria, the
flesh-fly appears.

Hot-beds never do so well in long dry fits of weather: they do not
ferment enough.
The hot dry weather hurries the flowers out of bloom.

Thursday 25.
29 6/10½; NW, W.
Wh: dew, hot sun,
distant thunder, brisk
breeze, sun & clouds,
dry & cold.

The wolf-fly appears in windows, & pierces other flies with his
rostrum: is of a yellow hue: an *asilus* of Linn:
Many sand-martins down at the forest-side. One thrush & one
blackbird is heard from my fields.

Friday 26.
29 6/10½; NW.
White frost, sun &
clouds, harsh.
Gryllo-talpa, mole
cricket churs.

Gardens suffer for want of rain.
Pheasants crow. Ring-doves coe. Nect: & peaches swell.
Hops are poling.

Saturday 27.
29 9/10½; 52, 54;
NW.
White frost, sun &
clouds, harsh.
Musca meridiana.

Rain much wanted. No rain since the second week in March.

The latest summer birds of passage generally retire the first: this is
the case with the *hirundo apus*, the *caprimulgus*, & the *stoparola*.
Birds are never joyous in dry springs: showery seasons are their
delight for obvious reasons.

Sunday 28.
29 8/10; W, N.
Sun, summer weather,
clouds, harsh.

Apple-trees blow well. Vines shoot & shew the rudiments of
much fruit.
The bud of the mulberry hardly swells yet.

Monday 29.
29 8/10¼; 56½; N.
Sun, with harsh wind,
clouds with some sleet,
bright.

The hanger pretty much in leaf.
Peaches & Nect: swell: the fruit is somewhat sheltered by the
leaves.

Tuesday 30.
29 8/10½; 47; N.
White frost, sun &
harsh wind, bright &
still.
Acer majus in bloom.*

Birds silent for want of showers.
*The sycamore, when in bloom affords great *pabulum*¶ for bees
& sends forth an honey-like smell. All the maples have saccharine
juices.

MAY 1776

Wednesday 1.
29 8/10½; 44; N.
White frost, ice, sun,
cold air, sun & clouds,
still & grey.

The grass crisp with white frost.
Tulips hang their heads in the morning, being pinched with the frost.

Thursday 2.
29 7/10; 49; W, S,
SW.
Dark, sun & clouds,
wind & dark, strong
wind.

Tulips very short; & many not blown at all. Some missle-thrushes on the down above us: black birds & thrushes mostly destroyed.

Friday 3.
29 4/10; 56; W, S,
NW.
Shower in the night,
sun & clouds, strong
harsh wind.
*Regulus non cristatus
major.**

*This bird shivers with it's wings, & makes a sibilous noise on the tops of the tallest beeches.

Saturday 4.
29 1/10½; W, SW.
Sun, strong wind, misty
rains.
*Gryllus campestris,
Libellulae.*

Field-crickets shrill.
Snipes in the forest. The forest quite burnt-up. Small reed-sparrow sings: young ring-doves fledge.

Hay is now risen to four pounds per ton: No grass in the fields, & great distress among the cattle.

Sunday 5.
28 9/10; W, NW.
Showers all day with
hail, & wind.

The ground is pretty well moistened.

Monday 6.
29 4/10½; 38 abroad;
NW.
Sun, sun & clouds,
harsh.
⚘ *Lathraea
squammaria.*

Tuesday 7.
29 3/10; 59; NW, SW, NW.
Grey, clouds with harsh air, sleet, showers.
*Hirundo apus.**

*One swift appears at the forest:
Three swifts round the church. Swifts are late this Year.

Wednesday 8.
29 4/10; NW.
Dark, frequent showers with hail, grey.

Apple-tree loaded with bloom.

Thursday 9.
29 5/10½; N, NE.
Shower, cold, showers, hail, cold.

The ground moist.
Swifts scarce appear.

Friday 10.
29 8/10; 49; NE, SW, S.
Sun, sun & clouds, sun, & soft air, showers about.
*Apis longicornis.**

Swifts are seen again.
*This bee appears but does not bore nests in the ground yet.

Saturday 11.
29 9/10: NE.
Wh: dew, sun, sun, heavy clouds at a distance, soft even.

Oaks loaded with bloom; particularly my single oak in the great mead.
Young rooks fledge.

Field Maple in flower.
Footbridge by Dorton Cottage.
18 May.

Sunday 12.
30; 57½; W.
Grey, sprinkling, sun,
sweet even.

The sycamore or great maple is in bloom, & at this season makes a beautiful appearance, & affords much *pabulum* for bees, smelling strongly like honey. The foliage of this tree is very fine, & very ornamental to outlets. All yᵉ maples have saccharine juices.¶

Monday 13.
30 1/10; NW.
Bright, hot sun.

FYFIELD

Tuesday 14.
30; N.
Grey, sun.

Spring-corn in a sad state, not half come up.

Wednesday 15.
N.
Sun, spitting rain.

Rooks, young, are perchers, but have not left their nest-trees.

Thursday 16.
N.
Sun & clouds, harsh.

Friday 17.
N.
Sun & clouds, harsh.

Saturday 18.
N.
Sun & cold showers.

Sunday 19.
NE.
Dark, soft gentle rain
for many hours.

Monday 20.
Soft, soft rain.

Wheat on the downs begins to spindle for ear.

Tuesday 21.
NE.
Sun, cold wind, sun &
clouds.

Medlar blows: this is the most uncouth tree in it's growth, the boughs never continuing streight for two feet together.

Wednesday 22.
29 9/10; NE.

Apis longicornis begins to bore it's nests in the ground.

Cold dew, sun.

Nightingale continues to sing.

Thursday 23.
29 8/10; N.
Dark & very harsh.

Female wasps abound.
Young rooks venture-out to the neighbouring trees.

Friday 24.
NE. Cold dew,
hot sun, soft even.
*Stoparola.**

WINTON
*The fly-catcher, the latest summer bird of passage, appears.

Saturday 25.
29 8/10; 56; NE, W,
SW.
Frost, ice, hot sun,
chilly.

SUTTON-BP'S, SELBORNE
The frost has killed the tops of the wallnut-shoots, & ashes; & the
annuals where they touched the glass of the frames; also many
kidney-beans.
The tops of hops, & potatoes were cut-off by this frost: Tops of
laurels killed.
The wallnut trees promised for a vast crop, 'til the shoots were
cut-off by ye frost.

Sunday 26.
29 7/10½; W, SW.
Sun, dark & mild.
Caprimulgus.

Tulips still in bloom.
Fern-owl first seen: a late bird of summer passage.

Monday 27.
29 7/10; N, NE, SE.
Still & grey, dark &
mild.

Fly-catcher.
Thinned the peaches, & nectarines, & pulled-off many
hundreds.

Tuesday 28.
29 6/10½; 62; S, SE.
Fog, sun, brisk air,
sweet day, cloudless.
Scarabaeus melolontha
Chafer.

Cucumbers thrive very poorly, & scarce make any progress.
Annuals in a poor state. Fern-owl chatters.

Wednesday 29.
29 5/10½; 67; SE, S.
Sun, soft & cloudy,
sweet even.

Laburnums in beautiful bloom.
Hawthorns blow finely.

Thursday 30.
29 4/10¾; 62½; SE.
Rain, fine rain, dark &
windy.

Strawberries blow well.
The first effectual rain after a long dry season.

Friday 31.

29 5/10; 62; S.
Grey, sun & clouds,
shower, sweet even:

Grass grows.

No one that has not attended to such matters, & taken down remarks, can be aware how much ten days dripping weather will influence the growth of grass or corn after a severe dry season. This present summer 1776 yields a remarkable instance: for 'til the 30th of May the fields were burnt-up & naked, & the barley not half out of the ground; but now, June 10th, there is an agreeable prospect of plenty.

A very intelligent Clergyman assured me, that hearing while he was a young student at the University of toads being found alive in blocks of stone, & solid bodies of trees; he one long vacation took a toad, & put it in a garden-pot, & laying a tile over the mouth of the pot, buryed it five feet deep in the ground in his father's garden. In about 13 months he dug-up the imprisoned reptile & found it alive & well, & considerably grown. He buried it again as at the first, & on a second visit at about the same period of time found it circumstanced as before. He then deposited the pot as formerly a third time, only laying the tile so as not quite to cover the whole of it's mouth, but when he came to examine it again next year, the toad was gone. He each time trod the earth down very hard over the pot.

JUNE 1776

Saturday 1.

29 3/10½; SE.
Steady, soft rain all day,
dark & still.

Dames violets, double,¶ blow finely: roses bud: tulips gone: pinks bud.
Bees begin to swarm. Tacked the vines the first time.
Began to plant-out annuals in the basons in the field. Ponds & some wells begin to be dry.

Sunday 2.

29 6/10; 62; NE, SW.
Fog, grey, sun, sultry,
& heavy clouds, smell
of sulphur in the air.
Full moon.

Paid for near 20 wasps;¶ several were breeders; but some were workers, hatched perhaps this Year.

Monday 3.

29 5/10; 62, 76 abroad;
SE.
Sun, sultry, clouds
about, soft rain, distant
lightening.
Glowworm.

Grass & corn much improved by the rain already. The long-horned bees bore their holes in the walks.

Tuesday 4.
29 5/10; 65; S.
Sun, hot, clouds, sun &
clouds, shower &
rainbow.

Continue to plant-out annuals. The ground in a fine state for
vegetation being both warm & moist. Continue to plant-out
annuals.

Wednesday 5.
29 3/10½; S, SW.
Dark, rain, rain, dark.

Boys bring me female-wasps.
Apis longicornis bores it's nests & copulates.

Thursday 6.
29 2/10; 57, 54; SW.
Showers, showers,
showers.

S! foin large, & in bloom, & wanting to be cut.
No swarms of chafers: I have seen but one.

Friday 7.
29 3/10; 54; SW.
Cold showers, with
some hail.

Fly-catcher builds.
Farmers cut clover for their Horses.

Saturday 8.
29 4/10; 55; SW.
Great rain, showers,
showers, fine.

Elder begins to blow.
Many hundreds of annuals are now planted-out, which have
needed no watering.
Wheat begins to shoot into ear.

Hardly any shell-snails are seen: they were destroyed, & eaten by
the thrushes last summer during the long dry season. This year
scarce a thrush, they were killed by the severe winter.

Sunday 9.
29 6/10; SW.
Showers, showers,
showers, fine.
*Hippobosca equina**

*Forest-fly begins to appear.
Grass & corn grow away.

Monday 10.
29 5/10; 57; S.
Dark, sprinkling rain,
dark.

St foin in bloom, & wants to be cut.
Trimmed, & tacked the peaches, & Nectarines: the trees are full
of fruit.

Tuesday 11.
29 2/10; SE.
Much rain in the night.
Sun, clouds, great
showers, bright.

Sweet williams, pinks, fraxinellas, orange-lilies begin to blow.
Ground full of water.

Wednesday 12.
29 2/10½; 59; S.
Showers, bright, sweet
day.

Drones abound round the mouth of the hive that is expected to swarm.
Sheep are shorn.
Planted-out annuals.

Thursday 13.
29 3/10¾; 63; S, SW.
Fog, sun, vast clouds,
soft & still.
❧ *Serapias latifolia,
Cardui.*

Martins begin building at half hour after three in the morning.
Thistles begin to blow.

Friday 14.
29 5/10; 62; S, SW.
Sun, summer weather.
❧ *Digitalis purpurea.*

I saw two swifts, entangled with each other, fall out of their nest to the ground, from whence they soon rose & flew away. This accident was probably owing to amorous dalliance. Hence it appears that swifts when down can rise again.

Saturday 15.
29 5/10; 62; SW.
Shower in the night,
spitting rain, sun, soft
even:

Took-up the tulip-roots: planted more annuals. A brood of young swallows appears; very early indeed: probably the dams bred in an old nest, & so lost no time in building. They usually do not come forth 'til the end of the month.
Swifts seen only morning & evening: the hens probably are engaged all the day in the business of incubation; while the cocks are roving after food down to the forest, & lakes. These birds begin to sit about the middle of this month, & have squab young before the month is out.

Sunday 16.
29 4/10; 62; SE, E,
W.
Rain, rain, sun &
clouds, chilly air.
New moon.

Monday 17.
29 7/10; SW.
Sun, cold air, clouds,
showers, grey, chilly
air.

Snails begin to engender, & some few to lay eggs: hence it is matter of consequence to destroy them before midsummer.

Tuesday 18.
29 8/10½; 64; SW,
NE.

Tacked & trimmed the wall-trees.
The early brood of swallows flie strongly.

Sun, clouds, & sultry
sun, sweet even:

Martagons blow; & cornflags.

Wednesday 19.
29 9/10; 65; NE, E,
SE.
Sun, sultry, sun, sweet
even:

Wood-strawberries begin to come.

Thursday 20.
29 7/10; 66; S, SE.
Sun, sultry, sweet even:
*Libellula virgo, sive
puella.**

Cut my S^t foin; a large burden: rather over-blown; the nineth
crop.
*Dragon-fly with blue upright wings.

Friday 21.
29 5/10; 62; SW.
Dark, grey & warm,
dark & threat'ning.

Roses blow.
White throat whistles.
Portugal-laurel blows.

Saturday 22.
29 6/10; W, SW.
Dark, sun & clouds
with brisk cool wind.

Hay makes very fast.

Sunday 23.
29 5/10; 60; SW, S.
Grey, clouds &
blustering wind,
spitting rain.

As the way-menders were digging for stones in a bank of the street,
they found a large cavern running just under the cart-way. This
cavity was covered over but by a thick stratum of rock: so that if
the rock had given way under a loaded waggon, considerable
damage must have ensued.

Monday 24.
29 6/10½; 57; W.
Grey, sun & strong,
cold wind.

Hay makes well.
The wind bangs the hedges & flowers about.

Tuesday 25.
29 6/10¾; 55; W.
Sun & clouds, summer.
⚘ *Vitis vinifera,
Triticum sativum.*

BRAMSHOT
Vine just begins to blow: it began last year June 7: in 1774 June
26.
Wheat begins to blow.
Thomas's bees swarm, & settle on the balm of Gilead fir: first
swarm.

Wednesday 26.
NW.

Ricked the S^t foin. Hay in fine order. No young partridges are

Sun, grey & soft.

flyers yet: but by the deportment of the dams it is plain they have chickens hatched; for they rise & fall before the horses feet, & hobble along as if wounded, to draw-off attention from their helpless broods.

Thursday 27.
NW, NE.
Mist, rain, rain, rain.

*Flowers in the Wakes garden.
Late June.*

Friday 28.
29 5/10; NE, N.
Dark, rain, soft,
shower, dark.

SELBORNE
Finished stopping, & tacking the vines. Turned out the white cucumbers from under their hand-glasses, which could no longer contain them: some fruit set.
Flowers in the garden make a gaudy appearance.
*A vast insect; appears after it is dusk, flying with an humming noise, & inserting it's tongue into the bloom of the honeysuckle: it scarcely settles on the plants but feeds on the wing in the manner of humming birds.¶

Saturday 29.
29 6/10¾; 59; NW.
Dark & still, gleams of
sun, grey & mild.
Sphinx forte ocillata? *

Omiah, who is gone on board the *Resolution*, is expected to sail this week for Otaheite with Capt: Cook.¶

Sunday 30.
29 6/10½; 61; W,
SW, W.
Grey, sun, dark, sweet
even:

Wheat generally in bloom.
The beards of barley begin to peep.

JULY 1776

Monday 1.
29 6/10; 60; W, SW,
S.

Began to cut my meadow-hay, a good crop, one 3rd more than

Grey, cloudy & still,
spitting rain, dark &
mild.
Full moon.

last year.
Cherries begin to ripen, but are devoured by sparrows.

Tuesday 2.
29 7/10; 63; W, NW.
Grey, dark & warm,
sprinklings, dark &
still.

The early brood of swallows are active & adroit, & able to
procure their subsistence on the wing. Fresh broods come forth
daily.

Wednesday 3.
29 6/10; 65; W, SW.
Grey, grey, gleams of
sun, scattered clouds.

Hay makes very slowly.
The early broods of martins begin to peep out of their nests: these
were hatched in nests ready built.
Black-caps are great thieves¶ among the cherries.

Thursday 4.
29 4/10¾; 70¾; SW.
Grey, sun, sultry, sweet
even:
 ⚘ *Monotropa
hypopithys*.

The flycatcher is a very harmless, & honest bird, medling with
nothing but insects.
Hay in small cock: it makes slowly.
The vine bloom smells sweetly!

Friday 5.
29 3/10½; 66; E, SE.
Heavy shower early,
gleams of sunshine,
great rain with distant
thunder, dark &
still.

By their numbers the swifts seem to have brought-out some of
their young: if this is the case, they are very early.
Field-crickets are pretty near silent: they begin their shrilling cry
about the middle of May.

Saturday 6.
29 1/10¼: SE, SW.
Rain, rain, rain, sun &
clouds, it threatens for
more rain.

The bees that have not swarmed lie clustering round the mouths
of the hives.
Took-off the frames from the cucum^rs those under the
handglasses begin to shew fruit.
Hay lies in a sad state.
Chrysanthemums, & marigolds begin to blow.

Sunday 7.
29 5/10; 61.
Sun, showers, vast
drowning shower,
sun, clouds in the
horizon.

Frogs, young ones, migrate from ponds this showery weather.
Hay sadly washed.

Monday 8.
29 6/10½; 59.
Sun, clouds,
sprinkling, sun, distant
showers, fine.

Mr Grimm, my artist,¶ came from London to take some of our
finest views.
Second swarm of bees on the same bough of the balm of Gilead
fir.
Turned the hay-cocks which are in a bad state.
Cherries delicate.

Tuesday 9.
29 6/10; 65.
Fog, dark, sun, heavy
clouds about, sweet
afternoon.

The bees are very quarrelsome, & sting me.
Swifts abound.
Put the hay into large cock.

Wednesday 10.
29 5/10; 63¾; SW,
SE.
Sun, sun & clouds,
dark & soft, & still.

Some of the little frogs from the ponds stroll quite up the hill;
they seem to spread in all directions.
Rick'd part of the meadow-hay: it has lost much of it's colour &
smell.

Thursday 11.
29 4/10½, 5/10; 66;
SW, SE.
Vast rain in the night,
sun, sweet weather, fine
even, clouds, & mist.
❀ *Tilia Europaea.**

Swifts abound: their young are certainly out.
*The lime blows, smells very sweetly, & affords much *pabulum*
for bees.

Friday 12.
29 4/10¾; 63; SW, S.
Dark, grey, sun,
clouds, small rain &
fog.
❀ *Geranium pratense.*

Swallows abound: many broods out.
Wheat still in bloom.
Housed the last load of hay in the great mead in tollerable order.

Saturday 13.
29 5/10; 69; W, W.
Grey, sun, sultry, vast
showers with hail, sweet
even:

Cut the first cucumber under the hand-glasses. Grapes begin to
set.
A pair of martins begin to build, at the NW: end of my house.

Bees come & suck the cherries where the birds have broke the skin:
& on some autumns I remember they attack'd & devoured the
peaches & Nect: where the wasps had once made a beginning.

Sunday 14.
29 4/10¾; 65; W, S.

Young frogs migrate, & spread around the ponds for more than a
furlong: they march about all day long, separating in pursuit of

Grey, sun, small
shower, pleasant day.

food; & get to the top of the hill, & into the N: field.
Turneps come up finely.

Monday 15.
29 3/10; 63; S. S.
Dark, spitting rain,
dark & moist, rain.

Tuesday 16.
29 3/10½; 64; S. S.
Dark, rain, bright,
shower, dark & still.

Hay in a bad way.
Large white cucumbers bear.
Bees, when a shower approaches, hurry home.

Wednesday 17.
29 4/10; 68½; SW,
SW.
Small shower, sun,
brisk air, sultry, fine
even:
Scarabaeus solstitialis.

One hive of bees does not swarm: the bees lie in clusters at the
mouth of the hive. The *apis longicornis* still continues to bore it's
nests.

Thursday 18.
29 4/10¾; 71; SW, S.
Sun, & clouds, hot sun
with air, summer
weather, sweet even.

Rasps are ripe.
Two young martins are come forth; the dams feed them on the
ridge of the house: the more forward ones come-out to make
room for the rest.

Friday 19.
29 3/10¾; 62¾; SE,
SE.
Grey, sun, hot, sweet
afternoon, vast showers
about.
𝇋 *Sambucus ebulus.* *

Young swallows abound.
Finished cutting my tall hedges.
*Dwarf elder blows.
Fungi begin to appear.

Saturday 20.
29 5/10¼; 67; W,
NW, SW.
Grey, sun, sweet
summer's day, dark in
the west.

Many young martins begin to peep out of their nests.
Much hay housed in good order.

Sunday 21.
29 4/10¾; 62; S, SE.
Dark, rain, rain, rain,

Missle thrushes bring forth their broods, & flock together.

great rain.

Monday 22.
29 5/10½; 67; SE, SW.
Grey, clouds, sun, & sultry, sweet even.

No hay housed.
Creeping fog in some meadows.
Bees swarm: the swarm of a swarm, which swarmed itself the beginning of June. A neighbour has had nine swarms from four stalls; two apiece from three of them, & three from one.

Tuesday 23.
29 6/10¼; 65; SW, S.
Vast dew, sun, sweet noon, dark, rain.

Walnuts abound, but are rather small & spotted.

Wednesday 24.
29 7/10¾; 60; S, SW.
Grey, dark & spitting, sun, sweet even:

Young martins continue to come forth.
Solstitial chafers abound on chalky uplands.

Thursday 25.
28 8/10¾; 67½; W. SW.
Sun, sultry, sweet afternoon, brisk gale.

Bees that have not swarmed kill their drones.
Apis longicornis still works.

Friday 26.
29 8/10; 71; S, SW.
Sun, hot sun, sweet summer day.

Cut the grass in the little meadow.
Hay makes well.
Hops fill their poles, & throw-out lateral shoots.

Saturday 27.
29 7/10; 70; S, SE, NW.
Sun, sultry, dark clouds, sweet even:

Wheat begins to turn colour.
Ricked the hay & finished the rick.
Fern owls chatter, & curlews clamor.

Sunday 28.
29 8/10½; 68; NW.
Sun, sweet summer weather.

Barley begins to smell, & wheat to turn colour.
Cucumbers abound in the hand-glass-crop.

Monday 29.
29 9/10, 8/10; 66; W, SW, W.
Grey, no dew, dark, dark & spitting.

Fine hay ricked.
Trufle-hunter begins to take trufles at Fyfield in Bro: Henry's grove.

Tuesday 30.

29 9/10; 70; NW, N.
Bright, cloudless, sweet
day, cloudless.
Total eclipse of the
moon.

Peacocks begin to moult, & cast their splendid train.
Young wagtails abound.

Wednesday 31.

29 9/10; 71; N, E, S.
Bright, cloudless,
sultry, sweet even:
⚘ *Humulus lupulus*.

Hops blow.
Young martins begin to congregate, & play round the weather-
cock, & tower.

AUGUST 1776

Thursday 1.

29 8/10; 74; E, E.
Sun, cloudless, brisk
air, sultry, sweet even.

Much hay housed in most delicate order.
We destroyed a strong wasp's nest, consisting of many combs:
there were young in all gradation from fresh-laid eggs to young
wasps emerging from their *aurelia* state, many of which came
forth after we had kept the combs 'til the next day.

Friday 2.

29 7/10½; 79; SE,
SW.
Sun, cloudless, sultry,
clouds in the horizon,
lightening.

Where a martin's nest was broken that contained fledge young;
the dams immediately repaired the breach, no doubt with a view
to a second brood.

Saturday 3.

29 7/10½; 72½; W.
Fog, sun & clouds,
sweet summer weather.

Much cow-grass well-housed.
Hay all finished-off in most delicate condition.

Sunday 4.

29 6/10½; 72; NW, S.
Sun, hot ripening
weather, dark clouds in
horizon.

Corn turns very fast.

Monday 5.

29 4/10¾; 72; SW.
Sun, fog, hot &
ripening, clouds & rain
bow.

M.r Grimm the artist left me.
Began to gather apricots.
Put out two rows of celeri: the ground dry, & harsh.

Tuesday 6.
Sun, sultry, distant
showers.

MEONSTOKE
Wheat-harvest begun at E: Tisted & West meon.

Wednesday 7.
Sun, sultry, showers
about.

Thursday 8.
Great rain with wind,
hot sun, showers.

One swift appears.

Friday 9.
Rain, rain, rain.

Saturday 10.
29 4/10; 61.
Showers, sun, showers,
showers.

SELBORNE
Hay not housed at Meonstoke & Warnford.
Swifts seem to be gone.

Sunday 11.
29 3/10; 59½; SW.
Grey, rain, rain, rain.

No swifts.
Apricots good.

Monday 12.
29 3/10; 60; S.
Dark, rain, rain,
wind, vast rain with
wind.

Grapes swell.

Tuesday 13.
29 5/10; 61; W.
Sun, clouds, &
showers, fine.

No swifts: our swifts departed between the 6 & the 10 of this
month.
Flowers & fruit-trees injured by the wind.
Corn bent down.

Wednesday 14.
29 6/10; 62; W, S.
Sun, fine, dark.

Wheat-harvest pretty general.
One straggling swift.

Thursday 15.
29 5/10; SW.
Sun & clouds, sultry,
showers about.

CHILGROVE

Friday 16.
W, SW.
Showers, sun & clouds,
heavy showers.

RINGMER

Saturday 17.
N, W, S.
Sun & clouds, heavy
showers, sun.

Wheat housed in a wet condition.

Sunday 18.
Sun, clouds, wet
afternoon.

Wind wavering.

Monday 19.
Rain, great rain, dark.

Many swifts seen for the last time at Blackburn in Lancashire.
They staid much longer than in Hants. See back.¶

Tuesday 20.
Sun, some showers.

Wheat housed.
Timothy the tortoise weighs just six pounds three quarters & two
ounces & an half: so is encreased in weight, since Aug: 1775, just
one ounce & an half.

Wednesday 21.
Fog, sun, showers
about, sweet day.

Much wheat housed.

Thursday 22.
Fog, sun, sweet day.

Swallows abound, & congregate. Young swallows continue to
come forth.

Friday 23.
N.
Sun, clouds, showers
about.

Saturday 24.
N.
Sun, dark & still.

Stoparola, & yellow-wrens abound.

Sunday 25.
N.
Sun, dark & still.

Monday 26.
SE.
Shower, dark & still.

While the cows are feeding in moist low pastures, broods of wagtails, white & grey, run picking round them close up to their noses, & under their very bellies, availing themselves of the insect flies that settle on their legs; & probably finding worms & *larvae* that are roused by the trampling of their feet. Nature is such an œconomist, that the most incongruous animals can avail themselves of each other! Interest makes strange friendships.

Tuesday 27.
E. Grey, sun, sweet day.

ISFIELD, RINGMER

Wednesday 28.
E.
Sun, still, sweet day,
fleecy clouds.

The tortoise eats voraciously: is particularly fond of kidney-beans.
Vast halo round the moon.

Thursday 29.
Great rain, rain, fine
afternoon.
Full moon.

FINDON
The rams begin to pay court to their ewes.

Friday 30.
29 3/10; 65; SW.
Sun, heavy showers,
sun & clouds, fine even.

CHILGROVE
Mʳ Woods of Chilgrove thinks he improves his flock by turning the east-country poll-rams among his horned ewes. The east-country poll-sheep have shorter legs, & finer wool; & black faces, & spotted fore legs; & a tuft of wool in their foreheads. Much corn of all sorts still abroad. Was wetted thro' on the naked downs near Parham-ash. Some cuckoos remain.

Saturday 31.
29 1/10½; S.
Sun, sun & clouds, fine
harvest day.

SELBORNE
Some corn housed.

N.B. From Lewes to Brighthelmstone, & thence to Beeding-hill, where the wheat-ear traps are frequent¶ no wheat-ears are to be seen: But on the downs west of Beeding, we saw many. a plain proof this, that those traps make a considerable havock among that species of birds.

SEPTEMBER 1776

Sunday 1
29 1/10; SW.
Great showers, sun,
sun, great showers,
lightening.

The barley coming-up unequally is not yet ripe.
Hops promise to be very small.

Monday 2.
28 4/10.
Great showers, sun,
vast shower with hail.

Plums, & wall-fruit much injured by continual rains.
Turned the horses into the great mead.
Much grass.
On this day last year I began to gather grapes: but now they show but little tendency towards turning their colour. A part of the orchard, where I laid the earth which came out of the garden, was sown in April with rye-grass, & hop-trefoil, & has been mown already three times.

Tuesday 3.
29 1/10¾; 60.
Stormy with heavy
showers, sun & wind.

Some few wasps. Fruit rots on the trees. The tops of the beeches begin to be tinged with a yellow hue.
The season for shooting is come; but scarce any partridges are to be found: the failure of breed is remarkable.

Wednesday 4.
29 2/10½; 57½; W.
Sun, vast clouds, heavy
showers with thunder,
bright.

Grapes but just begin to colour, here & there a bunch: are very backward & small.

Thursday 5.
29 4/10½; 54; W.
Sun, showers about,
sprinklings, great
shower, bright.

Some wasps on the wall-fruit. Where the wasps gnaw an hole, the honey-bees come & suck the pulp.
All fruits are backward, watry & bad. Hop-picking begins.
Hops are small, & distempered.

Friday 6.
29 6/10½; W. Sun,
sun & clouds, fine day.
Papilio Atalanta.

Wheat housed.
House martins do not deal in second broods so much as usual: & yet it should seem that they are not influenced by the cold wet summer, since the swallows seem to be as prolific as ever. Bees injure the wall-fruit in bad autumns; because they are hindered from gathering honey.
Wheat housed.

Saturday 7.
29 3/10; 60; E, S.
Dark, rain, sun &
clouds, showers.

Sunday 8.
29 3/10; NW.
Showers, showers, sun
& showers.

A sharp, single crack of thunder at Faringdon: the air was cold, & chilly.

Monday 9.
29 7/10; 53; N.
Cold dew, sun,

Hirundines flock & cluster on roofs.
Corn housed.

pleasant, clouds, &
shower, bright.

Peaches, some few well-flavoured. Grapes turn color very fast.

Tuesday 10.
29 7/10½; 59; N.
Deep fog, sun,
fine day.

China asters blow but slowly.
Corn housed all day.

Wednesday 11.
29 7/10½; 63; W.
Fog, grey, sweet soft
day.

Stoparolae still remain.
Young swallows continue to come forth.
Much corn housed.

Thursday 12.
29 7/10; 62; SW.
Fog, sun, dark, soft,
sweet day.

The wasps, tho' by no means numerous, plunder the hives, & kill
the bees, which are weak & feeble, this wet autumn: . . . *"asper
craebro imparibus se emiscuit armis."*¶

Friday 13.
29 6/10; 62½; S.
Fog, spitting, dark,
sun, still & soft.

My muscle-plums are this year in much more perfection than any
other fruit.
Corn housed.

Saturday 14.
29 5/10½; 67; S, SW.
Fog, sun, still, sweet
day, soft air.

Swallows cluster, & hang about in a particular manner at this
season of the year.
Much corn housed.
Honey-bees swarm by thousands, & devour the peaches, &
nectarines.
Stoparolae still appear.

Sunday 15.
29 5/10; 60;
NE, N.
Fog, dark, spitting,
rain, rain.

Swallows catch at walls as they flie about.
Much distant thunder, & lightening.

Monday 16.
29 6/10; W, SW.
Fog, sun, shower, dark
& still.

Stoparolae still.
Distant lightening.

Tuesday 17.
29 5/10; 58; SE, NW.
Rain, rain, rain, rain.

Great quantities of after-grass.
Hops damaged by wind & wet.
Much barley still out.

Wednesday 18.
29 6¾; N.
Rain, rain, bright.

The ground full of water.
Wagtails join with hirundines, & pursue an hawk high in the air:
the former shew great command of wing on the occasion.

Thursday 19.
29 8/10; 50; NE.
Sun, clouds, heavy
showers, bright.

BASINGSTOKE, SELBORNE
Much barley out round Basingstoke; some standing: & many
fields of oats.
Green wheat up.

Friday 20.
29 9/10; 49; N.
White frost, sun,
showers & hail, bright.
✿ *Hedera helix.* *

*Ivy begins to blow.
Swallows & Martins still abound.
Peaches, & nect: rot. Wasps are busy still.

Saturday 21.
30; 48; NE.
White frost, sun, vast
clouds, bright.

Grapes very backward.
Much barley housed.

Large earth-worms now abound on my grass-plot, where the
ground was sunk more than a foot. At first when the earth was
removed, none seemed to remain: but whether they were bred
from eggs that were concealed in the turf, is hard to say. Worms do
not seem to inhabit beneath the vegetable mould.

Sunday 22.
29 8/10; 48¼; NE, E.
White frost, sun, sun &
clouds, chill air.
Merula torquata. *

*The ring-ouzel appears on it's autumnal visit.

Monday 23.
29 6/10; 54½; E.
White frost, sun, sun &
clouds, red even:

Wasps still go into the hives.
Gathered-in some of the early pippins: fine baking apples.

Tuesday 24.
29 5/10; 52; NE, S.
Sun, soft sweet day,
rock-like clouds in the
horizon.

Much barley housed at Newton.
Gathered the first grapes: they are small but good.

Wednesday 25.
29 1/10½; 60; SE, S.
Sun, sweet day, dark &
still.

Fine young clover & fine turneps about the country.

Thursday 26.

28 4/10½: 60; S, W.
Grey, showers,
showers, grey & still.

Some swallows remain.

Friday 27.

29 3/10½; 57; SW,
W.
Vast dew, sun, sweet
day, soft & still.
Full moon.

Martins abound: few swallows to be seen.
Planted a row of lettuces under the fruit-wall to stand the winter.

Sloes in a hedgerow.
Selborne.
Late September.

Saturday 28.

29 4/10; 56; SW, SW.
Rain, sun, showers,
sweet even:

Some swallows.
Martins abound.

The quantities of haws, & sloes this Year are prodigious. Those hives of bees that have been taken have proved very deficient in wax, & honey. In shady wet summers bees can scarce procure a store sufficient to carry them thro' the winter: if not fed they perish.

Sunday 29.

29 6/10½; 57; NW,
N.
Bright, sweet soft day.

Nothing left abroad but seed-clover, & a few beans.

Monday 30.

29 6/10½; E.
Fog, sun, sweet, soft
day.

Martins, but no swallows.
Bat appears.

OCTOBER 1776

Tuesday 1.

29 6/10¼; 58; E, NE.
Fog, sun, dark, rain,
rain, dark.

Swallows & martins, before they withdraw, not only forsake houses, but do not frequent the villages at all; so that their intercourse with houses is only for the sake of breeding.

Wednesday 2.

29 8/10; 61; N. NE.
Fog, sun, sweet day,
bright, fog.

Wasps seem to be quite suppressed; yet butterflies, & *muscae* remain.
Some swallows above the hanger.

Thursday 3.

29 8/10¼: 59; NE, N.
Fog, dark & still.

Beautiful wheat-season for the wet fallows.
The buzzard is a dastardly bird, & beaten not only by the raven, but even by the carrion crow.
Gathered baking-pears.

Friday 4.

29 6/10; 59; N.
Dark & still, hot sun,
grey & still.

Beans are housed.
One swallow. Apples are gathered.
Ivy continues to blow. Bat is out.

Saturday 5.

29 5/10; 55; W, NW,
N.
Vast dew, sun, dark, &
spitting rain.

Black snails are more sluggish than in summer; but in sight all day at this season of the year.
Rooks steal wallnuts off the trees. Some wallnut trees naked of leaves. Saw one hornet.

When mice eat nuts, they perforate a round hole in the shell: but squirrels split their nuts in halves at the little end, as a man does with his knife. The nut-hatch sometimes splits the shell, & sometimes picks an irregular hole in it's side.

Sunday 6.

29 5/10; 51½; NW.
Vast dew, sun & clouds,
agreeable day, bright.

Numbers of swallows & martins playing about at Faringdon, & settling on the trees. If hirundines hide in rocks & caverns, how do they, while torpid, avoid being eaten by weasels & other vermin?

Monday 7.

29 2/10½; 54½; W,
SW.
Sun, grey, rain &
wind.

Gathered some keeping apples.
The intercourse between tups & ewes seems pretty well over. Ewes go, I think, 22 weeks.

Tuesday 8.

29 5/10; 56½; S, SW,
W.
Sun, grey, rain, rain,
bright.

One swallow.

Wednesday 9.

29 8/10½; 52; W.

Nuts fall very fast from the hedges.

Sun, bright day, soft
even:

Thursday 10.
29 8/10½; 60: W.
Grey, windy, soft &
agreeable.

Now my grapes are delicate notwithstanding the summer was so
wet & shady.

Friday 11.
29 9/10; 59; W, NW.
Sun, sweet day.

The red breast entertains us with his autumnal song.
Two swallows.
Wallnut trees naked.

Saturday 12.
29 9/10½; 57; NW,
NE.
Grey, still & mild.

The hanging beech-woods begin to be beautifully tinged, & to
afford most lovely scapes, very engaging to the eye, &
imagination. They afford sweet lights & shades. Maples are also
finely tinged. These scenes are worthy the pencil of a Reubens.

Sunday 13.
29 8/10½; 56; W.
Grey, grey & mild.

Swallows withdrew at Lyndon in Rutland. Some swallows remain
at Faringdon: in appearance a young brood not long flown: they
were very brisk.
Bat out.

Monday 14.
29 8/10; 56; W, SW.
Grey, mild & still.

Woodcock seen.
Many house martins flying over the village. They have not been
seen for some time. Redbreast whistles.

No more swallows 'til the first of Novemʳ
No more Martins seen afterwards.

Tuesday 15.
29 6/10½; 55; S, SE.
Grey, still & mild, sun,
bright.

My largest wallnut-tree produced four bushels & an half of nuts;
many bunches contained 8, 9 & on to 15 wallnuts each.

Wednesday 16.
29 5/10; 52; S.
Sun, dark & louring.

The redbreast's note is very sweet, & pleasing; did it not carry
with it ugly associations of ideas, & put us in mind of the
approach of winter.

Thursday 17.
29 4/10½; 57; S, NW,
W.

Rain, rain, sun, fair.

Friday 18.
29 8/10½; 50; W,
SW, S.
White frost, bright,
clouds & shower, fine
even:

Many butterflies about.

Saturday 19.
29 4/10; 54; S.
Dark & windy, rain,
rain, sun, strong wind.

Leaves fall very fast.
Butterfly.

Sunday 20.
29 6/10½; S, NW.
Grey, showers,
showers, dark.

Black snails are still about, tho' the shell-snails have withdrawn for some time. Slugs keep-out all the winter in mild weather. It seems strange that naked snails should be more hardy than those that have houses to their backs.

Monday 21.
29 6/10½; 53; S.
Fog, sweet noon, grey
& mild.

Butterflies appear, tho' the hirundines seem to be gone.
A cock-pheasant flew over my house, & across the village to the hanger.

Tuesday 22.
29 7/10; 58; S.
Grey, sweet, still soft
day.

The nuthatches are busy rapping with their bills about the wallnut-trees; & as I find wallnuts fallen down with holes picked in their shells; no doubt they are made by those birds.

Wednesday 23.
29 7/10¾; 56½; N.
NE.
Deep fog, dark & still,
spitting fog.

Thursday 24.
29 7/10½; 57; NE.
Dark, heavy dark
weather, spitting.

The weather has been so mild that the tender annuals continue in full vigor.

Friday 25.
29 5/10½; 54; E.
Dark, sun, sweet
afternoon, dark.

Butterflies.
One bunting in the northfield: a rare bird at Selborne.

Saturday 26.
29 5/10; 52; NE, N.
Grey & still, sun, grey.

The leaves fall fast. The hanger begins to look bare.

There is this year a remarkable failure of mushrooms: & the more to be wondered at, since the autumn has been both moist & warm. There is a great failure also of trufles in my Brother's outlet at Fyfield, notwithstanding in simular weather they abounded last year. So that some secret cause influences alike these analogous productions of nature.

Sunday 27.
29 6/10¼; 48; N, NE.
Fog, grey, sun & grey,
grey & still.

Larks frolick much in the air: when they are in that mood the larkers catch them in nets by means of a twinkling glass: this method they call <u>daring</u>.

Monday 28.
29 7/10; 45; N, SE.
White frost, sun, dark
& soft, showers.

BP'S SUTTON
The month of Oct: has been very dry: mill-ponds begin to want water.
Sheep frolick.

Tuesday 29.
29 6/10½; SE.
Dark, showers,
showers, dark & still.

FYFIELD
Grey crows return. These are winter-birds of passage, & are never with us in the summer. The flocks are feeding down the green wheat on the downs, which is very forward, & matted on the ground.

Wednesday 30.
29 5/10½; 49; SE.
Grey & mild, sweet
mild, still weather.

They sow wheat on the downs sometimes as soon as the end of July provided that season is showery.

Thursday 31.
29 5/10; 7/10; S.
Rain, rain, sun, dark.

The rooks visit their nest-trees in vast clouds.

NOVEMBER 1776

Friday 1.
29 4/10; SE.
Grey & mild, rain.

Saturday 2.
SW.
White frost, sun, rain,
sun & clouds.

My Brother's turkies avail themselves much of the beech-mast which they find in his grove: they also delight in acorns, wallnuts, & hasel-nuts: no wonder therefore that they subsist wild in the woods of America, where they are supposed to be indigenous. They swallow the hasel-nuts whole.
Four swallows were seen skimming about in a lane below Newton. This circumstance seems much in favor of hiding,¶ since the hirundines seemed to be withdrawn for some weeks. It looks as if the soft weather had called them out of their retirement.

Sunday 3.
29 8/10½. N.
White frost, sun, sweet
day.

M.ʳ Cannings has now 48 acres of barley abroad either standing or
in cock: it was not sown 'til the rains came in the beginning of
June. Nov.ʳ 4 He is now ricking one field: the other is standing. The
grain is lank, & the cocks cold, & damp.

Monday 4.
8/10½; 53; SW.
Wh: frost, sun, grey &
pleasant.

The trufle-hunter was here this morning: he did not take more
than half a pound, & those were small.

Tuesday 5.
29 8/10½; SW.
Grey, sun, sweet day.

Farmer Cannings has fine weather for his barley harvest.

Wednesday 6.
29 8/10; 35; W, SE.
White frost,
sun, cloudless
sweet day.

Flies abound: They stay long after the hirundines are withdrawn.
Tipulae sport in the air.

Thursday 7.
29 6/10¾; S.
Deep fog, sun, sweet
afternoon.

The great fieldfare appears.
Beetles abound every evening.
Farmer Canning's new barley-ricks smoke & ferment like
hotbeds already.

Friday 8.
29 6/10¾; SE.
Fog, most sweet
sunshine.

BP'S SUTTON
Infinite quantities of haws, & Sloes.
Nothing could be more lovely than the ride from Andover to
Alresford over the Hants downs. The shepherds mow the
charlock growing among the wheat.

Saturday 9.
29 6/10; 49; SE.
Grey, clouds & sun,
sweet day.

SELBORNE

I saw no fieldfares all thro' my Journey. If they come, as Ray says
they do, *"ventis vehementer spirantibus"*;¶ they can have had no
advantage of that kind; for the autumn has been remarkably still.
Magpies sometimes, I see, perch on the backs of sheep, & pick the
lice & ticks out of their wool; nay mount on their very heads; while
those meek quadrupeds seem pleased, & stand perfectly still, little
aware that their eyes are in no small danger; & that their assiduous
friends would be glad of an opportunity of picking their bones.

Sunday 10.
29 6/10¼; 52; SE,
SW.
Rain, rain, sun &
clouds,
deep fog.
Redwings.

These birds begin to appear at last.

Monday 11.
29 6/10; SE.
Rain, dark & dismal,
rain.

Leaves fall very fast.
My grapes are delicate, & in great abundance still.

Tuesday 12.
29 8/10; 48; W.
Frost, sun, fine day.

Fieldfares flock.
Flesh-flies still about.

Wednesday 13.
29 8/10½; 50; SW,
SW. Frost, sun, soft
still day.

Nuthatches rap about on the trees.
Crocuss begin to sprout.
The leaves of the medlar-tree are now turned of a bright yellow.

Thursday 14.
29 8/10¼; 53; W.
Spitting rain, grey,
spitting, starry.

One of the first trees that becomes naked is the wallnut: the
mulberry, & the ash especially if it bears many keys, & the Horse-
chestnut come next. All lopped trees, while their heads are young,
carry their leaves a long while. Apple trees & peaches remain green

Friday 15.
29 7/10; 53; W.
Grey, brisk, blowing
wind, dark, starry.

'til very late, often 'til the end of Nov: Young beeches never cast
their leaves 'til spring, 'til the new leaves sprout & push them off:
in the autumn the beechen-leaves turn of a deep chestnut color.
Tall beeches cast their leaves towards the end of Oct.ʳ

Saturday 16.
29 5/10; 55; W.
Showers, brisk wind,
sunny & warm.

Began trimming the vines: the new wood is not very well ripened
for want of sun last summer.

Sunday 17.
29 6/10; 48; W.
Bright, strong wind,
cloudless.

Phalaenae still flie under hedges of an evening.

Monday 18.
29 4/10; 45; W.
Sun, brisk drying
wind, clouds &
sprinkling.

The stock-dove, or wild pigeon seems to be come: this the last
winter-land-bird of passage that appears with us.

Tuesday 19.
29 2/10; 54; SW.
Rain, rain, rain, grey.

This afternoon the weather turning suddenly very warm
produced an unusual appearance; for the dew on the windows was
on the outside of the glass, the air being
warmer abroad than within.

Wednesday 20.
29; 52; W. Strong
wind; stormy with
showers, wind, bright.

Mʳˢ Snooke's old tortoise at Ringmer went under ground.

Thursday 21.
29 6/10; 42; W, NW.
Frost, sun with sharp
wind, bright.

The thatch is torn by the wind.

Friday 22.
29 4/10; 39; W, S.
Frost, sunny & mild,
great rain.

The ground now covered with snow at Buxton in Derbyshire.

Saturday 23.
28 9/10; 43; SE, S, W.
Great fog, sun, shower,
bright.

Sunday 24.
29 7/10½; 41; NW.
Grey, sun, sharp wind,
grey & mild.

Monday 25.
29 9/10; 36½; NW.
Hard frost, thick ice,
bright sun, bright.

This is the first great frost.
Gathered in all the grapes.
Grapes are good.

Tuesday 26.
29 9/10½; 32; E.
Great rime, hard frost,
sun, frost.

We continue to tack the vines, & peaches &c.
A man brought me a common sea-gull alive: three crows had got
it down in a field, & were endeavouring to demolish it.

Wednesday 27.
29 5/10; 31½, 32; E.
White frost, grey, frost
all day, grey, frost.

Thursday 28.
29; 33; SE.
Dark & still, hard
frost, dark with some
thaw, dark & heavy.

The nuthatch hunts for nuts in the hedges, & brings them to the
forked bough of a certain plum-tree, where it opens them by
picking a ragged irregular hole in the small end of the shell. It
throws the empty shell on the walk.

Friday 29.

28 7/10; 44; SE, S,
SE.
Rain, rain, grey, sun,
rain.

Forward ivy-berries are grown to near one-third of their size.

Saturday 30.

29 1/10¾; 44; W,
SW, S.
Sun, fair & warm,
louring, great rain.

Hen chaffinches begin to congregate.

DECEMBER 1776

Sunday 1.

29 5/10; 45; S, SW,
SW.
Grey, sun, &
strong wind, shower,
bright.

Monday 2.

29 6/10; 49, 50; SE.
Fog, rain, grey, sun,
still & mild.

When the thermʳ is at 50 flies & *phalaenae* come-out, & bats are
often stirring.
Beetles flie.

Tuesday 3.

29 6/10; 49; SE, E.
Deep fog, dark, still &
warm.

Worms lie-out very thick on the walks, & grass-plot; many in
copulation. They are very venereous, & seem to engender all the
year.

Wednesday 4.

29 7/10; 49, 53; S, W.
Fog, grey, still & soft.

Vast condensations on walls & wainscot, which run in streams;
these things are colder than the warm wet air.

Thursday 5.

29 7/10; 55; W, SE.
Dark, dark & spitting.

Friday 6.

29 6/10; 52; S, SE,
NE.
Fog, dark & mild.

Few worms lie-out on the common.

Saturday 7.
29 7/10; 44; NE.
Fog, dark & still.

Sunday 8.
29 7/10½; 48; NE,
SE. Fog, dark,
still, & mild.

Monday 9.
29 8/10⅓; 46; E.
Fog, sun, dark & still.

Tuesday 10.
30; 48; E, SE.
Fog, grey, sun, soft &
still.

Rooks repair their nests.

Wednesday 11.
30 [?]/10; 52½; W.
Sun, soft & sweet, dark
& mild.

Song-thrush sings much.
Summer-like: the air full of gossamer, & insects.

Thursday 12.
30; 15; W.
Still, dark & spitting,
deep fog.

When the barom! gets very high, it is often attended with a black
spitting weather.

†Friday 12[13].
29 9/10¾; 50; W.
Dark & spitting.

Missle-thrush sings merrily every morning.
Song thrush very loud.

†Saturday 13[14].
29 8/10¾; 49; W.
Fog, dark & spitting.

A new magpie's nest near finished was found in a coppice; this
soft season reminds birds of nidification.

Sunday 15.
29 7/10; 45; SE.
Dark & moist, grey.

Monday 16.
29 4/10¾; 41½; N.
NW.

---

†GW's error in dating.

Great rain, sun &
clouds, shower.

Tuesday 17.
29 3/10; 39, 37; NW.   Young lambs begin to fall.
Frost, some snow, sun,
grey, sun, frost.

Wednesday 18.
29 1/10; 34; NW, SW.   The song-thrush sings very loud.
Hard frost, sun, fleecy
clouds, snow, rain.

Thursday 19.
29 1/10; 38; W.
Much rain, frost, sun
& strong wind, bright
& sharp.

Friday 20.
29 4/10; S, NE.
Frost, rain, rain,
bright.

Saturday 21.
29 5/10½; 49; S. W.   The shortest day: a truly black, & dismal one.
Rain, rain, rain,
bright.

Sunday 22.
29 5/10; 52; SW.
Dark, grey, sun, grey
& mild.

Monday 23.
29 5/10; 48; SW, NW.   Vast condensations on walls.
Grey, sun, mild,   Strong N: auroras tho' the moon was very bright.
bright.

Tuesday 24.
29 2/10½; 40; W,
NW.
Shower, sun & brisk
wind, flight of sleet &
snow, frost.

Wednesday 25.
29 6/10; 37; NW.
Frost, sun, pleasant,
frost.
Full moon.

Thursday 26.
29 6/10; 34; NW.   Fieldfares abound.
Hard frost, sun, dark
& louring.

Friday 27.
29 6/10; 37; NNW.
Dark & frosty, grey &
thaw, some snow, snow
on the ground.

Saturday 28.
29 7/10; 36; NW.
Snow on the ground,
grey, sun, louring &
still.

Sunday 29.
29 3/10; 31, 34; W,
NW.
Hard frost, grey,
spitting, dark, bright &
freezing.

Monday 30.
29 2/10½; 34, 29; W,
N.
Severe frost, sun, snow.

Tuesday 31.
29 5/10½; 23 abroad;   A gross-beak was shot near the village. They sometimes come to
W, N.   us in the winter.
Severe frost, sun, still.

JANUARY   — 1777 —

Wednesday 1.   LASHAM
N.

Steady frost, snow on
the ground.

Thursday 2.
N.
Dark & harsh.

Friday 3.
N.
Frost, flights of snow.

Saturday 4.   SELBORNE
29 5/10½; 33; NW.   Larks congregate.
Dark & thawing, frost,   Roads hard, & beaten.
snow on the ground.

Sunday 5.
29 4/10½; 31; NW.
Snow in the night,
frost, bright sun, keen
frost.

Monday 6.
NW.
Hard frost, dark &
still.

Tuesday 7.
29 3/10; 18 abroad; N,   Ground still covered with snow.
W.
Hard frost, bright sun,
frost.

Wednesday 8.
29 2/10½; 15¾; N.   Bottles of water frozen in chambers.
Intense frost, snow in   Haws frozen on the hedges & spoiled so as to be no longer of any
the night, bright sun,   service to the birds.
severe frost.

Thursday 9.
29 3/10; 22; SW, W.   Water-bottles frozen in chambers.
Fierce frost, sun, frost.   Ground covered with snow.

Friday 10.
29 1/10; 37, 34¾;   *Tipulae* are playing about as if there had been no frost at all.

SW, S, SE, E.
Thaw, fog, spitting
rain.

Saturday 11.
29 1/10½; 42; S, W.   The dew all day lies on the outsides of the windows, because the
Swift thaw, fog & rain,   air is warmer without than within.
sun, snow gone, dark &
still.

Sunday 12.
29 1/10¾; 49;   Vast condensations on wainsots [wainscots] & walls.
SW, S.   Warm air.
Rain, rain, driving
showers.

Monday 13.
29 2/10; 48; S, SE, S.
Showers & strong
wind.

Tuesday 14.
29 3/10¾; 47½; SE,
S.
Thunder, hail, & rain,
sun, grey, rain.

Wednesday 15.
29 6/10; 48; S, SE.   Flies & gnats out, & moving.
Dark, mild & wet.

Thursday 16.
29 6/10; 48¾; SE.   Bees, & flies moving: air full of insects: spiders shoot their webs:
Grey, sun, sweet   butterfly out.
day.

Friday 17.
29 7/10½; 46; W,   Daiseys, winter-aconite, & hepaticas blow.
NE, E.   Crocuss swell for bloom.
Fog, sun, soft & mild,
fog.

Saturday 18.
29 7/10; 48; E.   Warm & still.
Fog, grey, fog.

Sunday 19.
29 6/10½; 42¾; E.
Fog, dark & still, deep
fog.

Monday 20.
29 4/10; 39; E.
Dark & harsh.

Tuesday 21.
29 3/10; 37; NE.
Frost, sun, grey &
harsh.

Wednesday 22.
29 3/10½; 37; N.
Grey & still, cold air.

Thursday 23.
29 5/10; SW, S.
Sun, snow, rain.

Friday 24.
45; W, NW.
Sun, dark & brisk
wind.

Saturday 25.
29 9/10½; 39; N.
Grey & still, cold air.

Sunday 26.
29 7/10; 36; N, SE.   Rooks resort to their nest-trees.
Hard frost, sun,
clouds, sun, clouds.

Monday 27.
29 4/10; S.   Made the seedling cucumber bed.
Fog, wet fog, rain,
rain.

Tuesday 28.
29 5/10; NW.
Grey, sun & clouds,
dark & still.

Wednesday 29.
29 4/10; 36; N, W.
Hard frost, sun, thaw,
dark, small snow.

Thursday 30.
29 7/10; 36; NE, NW.
Hard frost, bright sun,
clouds, stars bright.

Friday 31.
29 8/10½; 33; NW,
SW. Hard frost,
sun, grey & mild.

FEBRUARY 1777

Saturday 1.
29 4/10; 41; S.
Wet, wet, rain with
wind.

Sunday 2.
29 1/10¾; 41; SW,
W.
Frost, ice, sun, shower,
sun, strong gale.

Monday 3.
29 4/10½; 40; W,
NW.
Sun, brisk wind, vast
clouds, hail, frost.

The Planet Mercury is now to be seen every evening:¶ it is nearer to the horison than Venus, & more to the right hand setting somewhat S: of the W: about six in the evening. Will be visible about six days longer.

Tuesday 4.
29 6/10; 33; NW.
Hard frost, sun, cutting
wind, frost.

Wednesday 5.
29 6/10; 33½; NW.
Snow in the night, hard
frost, cutting wind,
snow, snow.

Snow-drops blow.

Thursday 6.
29 5/10; 29 abroad;
NW, W.
Hard frost, some snow,
sun & clouds, frost.

Friday 7.
29 7/10⅓; 32½; NW,   The garden-quarters are very dry, & dig finely.
SE, S.
Hard frost, bright &
still, frost.

Saturday 8.
29 6/10¼; 31¼; E.
Severe frost, sun, flisky
clouds, hard frost.

Sunday 9.
29 6/10; 32¼; NE.   Very harsh day.
Severe black frost,   The fieldfares now feed on sloes, which abound on the hedges.
dark, cutting wind,   'Til now I never observed that any birds touched the sloes.
snow, snow covers the
ground.

Monday 10.
29 6/10½; 29 abroad;   Cucumber-plants come-up well.
NE.
Black frost, snow on the
ground, dark with
rime, fog & rime.

Tuesday 11.
29 6/10; 31 abroad;
NE.
Dark & harsh, some
snow, dark & raw, fog,
sharp wind.

Wednesday 12.
29 3/10½; 35; N, NE.   Turneps rot very fast.
Snow, snow, snow,   Snow covers the ground.
sleet.

Thursday 13.
29 4/10½; 35; NE.   Thrushes hunt for shell-snails in the hedges, & eat them.

Snow, snow, snow,
deep snow.

Friday 14.
29 4/10; 36; N, W.
Grey, sun & still, grey,
frost.

The snow is about five inches deep.

Saturday 15.
29 1/10; 39; W, N.
Snow, grey, sun, thaw,
snow, bright, hard
frost.

Sunday 17[16].
29 1/10; 33; NW.
Severe frost, bright
sun, bright, over cast.

Ground covered with snow.

Monday 18[17].
28 9/10½; 35; S.
Frost, sun.

LONDON

MARCH 1777

Wednesday 26.

Thursday 27.

Two sultry days: Mrs Snooke's tortoise came forth out of the
ground; but retired again to it's hybernaculum in a day or two, &
did not appear any more for near a fortnight. Swallows appeared
also on the same days, & withdrew again: a strong proof this of
their hiding.

On March 26, & 27, two sunny, sultry days, swallows were seen at
Cobham in Surrey.
Therm^rs were at that time in London up at 66 in the shade.
   A swarm of bees came forth at Kingsley, & were hived. From
that day to April the 10th harsh, severe weather obtained, with
frequent frosts & ice, & cutting winds. How are these bees to
subsist so early in an empty hive?

APRIL 1777

Thursday 3.
Charadrius oedicnemus.

Black-cap whistles.
Stone-curlew returns, & whistles.

Thursday 10.

GUILDFORD
Two swallows in the King's field.

Friday 11.
29 6/10½; 55; SE,
SW, S.
No frost, dark &
lowering, grey.
Hirundo domestica,
Luscinia, Regulus non
crist: medius, & minor.

Returned from LONDON to SELBORNE
The smallest uncrested wren, & the laughing D? are heard.¶
One swallow seen near Farnham, & three at Selborne.
Nightingale.

Saturday 12.
29 4/10; SW.
Fine rain, sun &
clouds, dark & *mild.*

Some cucumbers set. The ground is finely moistened.

Sunday 13.
29 5/10¾; 53¼; NW.
Wh: frost, sun, dark,
sweet afternoon.
Cuculus canorus.

Cuckow sings.

Monday 14.
29 8/10½; 49; NE, N.
Clouds, sun & clouds,
dark, shower.
Turdus torquatus.

Some ring-ousels appear on their spring-migration.
Cucumbers swell.

Tuesday 15.
29 9/10; 47¾; NE.
Dark, shower, dark &
spitting,
D?　　　　　　D?

Apricots seem to be cut-off by the late severe frosty mornings.
Peaches still in bloom.

Wednesday 16.
29 7/10½; 47; NE.
Dark, moist, ground
wet, misty, dark, moist,
sweet even, grey, bright.

The grass-walks begin to be mown.
The cucumber-beds are earthed-out.
Cut the first cucumber.

Thursday 17.
29 3/10¾; 47, 50;
NE.
Frost, fog, dark, sun,

Cucumbers swell.

sweet afternoon, chilly.
Bombylius medius.

Friday 18.
29 2/10½; 42; NE.
Dark with cutting
wind, snow, hail,
cutting wind, bright &
sharp.

The golden-crested wren frequents the fir-trees, & probably
builds in them.

Saturday 19.
29 5/10⅓; 39; NE, S.
Frost, thick ice, bright
sun, & sharp wind,
dark & milder.

No bank-martins appear yet at Short-heath.
Cut a fine cucumber.

Tho' the spring has been remarkably harsh & drying, yet the
ground crumbles, & dresses very well for the spring-crops. The
reason is the driness of the winter: since the ground bakes hardest
after it has been most drenched with water.

Sunday 20.
29 5/10; 40; SE.
White frost, harsh
wind, dark, small
shower.

Winter-like: yet many sorts of flowers blow daily.
The house-snail, φερισικος,¶ begins to appear: the naked black-
snail comes forth much sooner. Slugs, which are covered with
slime, as whales are with blubber, are moving all the winter in
mild weather.

Monday 21.
29 2/10; 53; SW.
Rain all night with
wind, rain, rain.

Cut a brace of cucumbers.

Tuesday 22.
29 3/10½; 55; SW.
Showers, sun &
showers, soft air,
cloudy.
*Hirundo urbica, Alauda
trivialis.*

The black-cap appears.
The cuckow sings all day in the hanger.
Grass-hopper lark.

Wednesday 23.
29 1/10¾; 56½; W,
SW.
Showers, showers, sun
& clouds, dark & mild.
Ruticilla.

Redstart. House-martin.
House-martins abound under the hanger.

Thursday 24.
29 5/10¾; 47; W,

The cock green-finch begins to toy, & hang about on the wing in

NW, W.
Bright sun, & brisk
wind, showers & hail.
Whitethroat.

a very peculiar manner. These gestures proceed from amorous propensities.

Friday 25.
29 8/10½; 42; W, W.
Sharp air, sun, cold
wind, showers & hail,
bright & cold.

The titlark rises, & sings sweetly in it's descent. The Ring-dove hangs on it's wings, & toys in the air.

Saturday 26.
29 9/10; 51; W.
Wh: frost, sun,
summer-day, sweet
afternoon.

Wheat-ears appear on the common. They are not seen there in the winter.
No swift to be seen yet.

Sunday 27.
29 8/10; 47; E, SE.
Wh: frost, sun, sharp
air, bright & sunny.

Notwithstanding the dry winter & spring, the pond on the common is brim full.
Cucumbers swell very fast.

Monday 28.
29 5/10¾; 47; E, SE.
Grey, cold air, sun, fine
day.

Cut seven brace of fine cucumbers.

Tuesday 29.
29 3/10⅓; 50; SE.
No dew, dark & still,
soft rain, rain.

Beeches begin to leaf in the hanger.
The bark of oak now runs; & I am felling some trees. When trees are sawn off, & thrown, a rushing sound is heard from the but, often attended with a little frothing & bubbling-out of the sap. This rushing or hissing is occasioned by the motion of the air escaping thro' the vessels of the wood.

Wednesday 30.
29 2/10½; 51; SE, S,
SW.
Fog, dark, hot sun,
dark & mild.

No swift seen yet.

MAY 1777

Thursday 1.
29 ½/10; 58; SE.

The churn-owl chatters.

Mist, dark, sun, sweet afternoon.
Caprimulgus.

Cut 4 brace of cucumbers.
Vines very backward, & just sprouting.

Bank-martins appeared in Rutland about May 1st: the first swallow March 29: house-martins April 26: swifts May 1st.

Friday 2.

28 9/10½; 60;
Dark, rain, sweet afternoon.

Growing weather.
Vast clouds about.

Saturday 3.

29 1/10¼; 57.
Showers, sun & showers with wind.
Hirundo apus.

A pair of swifts appear at last: they usually come in pairs.
Cucumbers abound.

Sunday 4.

29 2/10¾; 54; SW.
Showers, sun & showers.

The ground is well moistened, & corn & grass grow finely.

Monday 5.

29 5/10½; 54½; SW.
Showers, sun & showers.

No swifts in sight.
Polyanths make a fine show.

Tuesday 6.

29 4/10; 54; SW.
Rain, rain, showers with wind.

Began cutting some grass for the horses in the orchard.
No swifts appear.
Tulips begin to blow.

Wednesday 7.

29 7/10; 52½; SW, NW.
Bright sun, rain, rain, sun, bright & cool.

The ground is well wetted.

Thursday 8.

29 8/10, 7/10; 51; W, S. Bright sun, grey & mild, dark & mild.

Planted-out the large white cucumbers under the hand-glasses.
Five swifts appear.

Friday 9.

29 3/10¾; 54, 58; W, SE, NE.

8 swifts appear: house-martins in abundance.

Dark, shower, mild,
thunder, showers,
thunder.

Apple tree in blossom.
Selborne Village.

Saturday 10.
29 7/10½; 54; N, NE.
Vast rain all night,
bright sun, sweet
afternoon.

The scenes round the village are beautifully diversified by the
bloom of pear-trees, plums, & cherries. A great flood on the
Thames in consequence of the rain on friday-night.

Sunday 11.
29 6/10¾; S, N, W.
Bright sun, heavy
clouds, showers about.
Musca vomitoria.

Cut 14 cucumbers.
Fleshfly appears.

Monday 12.
29 7/10; 50; NW.
Bright sun, clouds &
sun, some showers,
bright even.
Muscicapa grissola,
Scarabaeus melolontha.

The flycatcher, the latest summer bird of passage, appears.
Chafer appears.

Tuesday 13.
29 3/10; 51; S, SW.
Bright sun, sun &
clouds, cold wind, rain
& wind.

Vine shoots are very backward.
The hanger is in full leaf.
8 pairs of swifts about the church.

Wednesday 14.
29 2/10, 29 1/10; 50;
SW. Bright sun, cold
dew, clouds, showers
& hail, cold air.

Cut 10 cucumbers.
Tulips blow out.

Thursday 15.
28 9/10¾; 50; S, W,

Cut ten more cucumbers.

N, E.
Bright, fog, clouds, soft
with clouds, rain, rain.

Friday 16.
29 2/10¼; 51; NE.   The roads are full of water.
Rain & hail in the
night, dark, showers,
dark.

Saturday 17.
29 4/10; 49;   Most vivid rainbow.
NE, NW.
Sun, fine day, showers.

Sunday 18.
29 4/10⅓; 49; NW, S,   Apple-trees are in fine bloom.
SW.
Cold white dew, bright,
clouds, shower, bright
& cold.

Monday 19.
29 2/10¼; 51; E.   Swallows begin to collect dirt from the road, & to carry it into
Bright sun, fine day,   chimneys for the business of nidification.
clouds, rain.

Tuesday 20.
29 4/10; 53; N, NE.
Great rain, dark & wet,
rain, rain.

Wednesday 21.
29 6/10; 51; NW, S,   Mulberry-trees but just begin to bud. Wallnuts shoot a little.
SE.
Sun, fine day, dark &
heavy clouds, showers
about.

Thursday 22.
29 5/10; 53; SW.   The heavy rains damage the flowers.
Vast rains with hail, sun
& clouds, vast showers
with hail, dark &
louring.

Friday 23.
29 4/10; 57½; SW.
Fog, sun, still & fine,
dark & still.

Cucumbers bear well.

Saturday 24.
29 2/10; 55; SW.
Dark & still, rain, rain.

Sunday 25.
29 3/10; 51; W, NW,
S, SW.
Bright sun, clouds, vast
showers with hail,
showers.

Monday 26.
29 5/10⅔; 58; NW,
N, S, E.
Bright sun, sun &
clouds, vast shower,
hail, thunder, fine
afternoon, vast clouds.

The grasshopper-lark whispers all night.
Cut 22 cucumbers.
The hail breaks-off the tulips.

Tuesday 27.
29 7/10; 60; W, NW.
Sun, sun & clouds,
summer's day.
Gryllus campestris.

Field-crickets begin their shrilling summer sound.
My horses begun to be turned-out a nights.

Wednesday 28.
29 8/10; 61¼; N, SE,
SW.
Grey, bright, sun,
summer, vast clouds,
red evening, soft.

Cut 24 fine cucumbers.
Clouds flie different ways.
Distant thunder.

Thursday 29.
29 8/10½; 62; NE,
NW.
Bright, grey, sweet
summer's day.

No chafers are seen.
Blue mist about.
Distant lightening.

Friday 30.
29 7/10; 59, 63; NE,

Clouds flie different ways.

E, N, S, SE, W.
Bright, sultry, dark
heavy clouds.

Saturday 31.
29 7/10; 69; E, S, SW.
Sun, sweet day.

The *apis longicornis* begins to bore holes in the walks for the
purpose of nidification.

JUNE 1777

Sunday 1.
29 6/10¾; 63; SW.
Fog, sun, clouds &
brisk air, dark clouds.

Monday 2.
29 8/10; 63, 66; W,
SW, W. Dark, hot &
still, sweet afternoon.

Began some alterations previous to the building my parlor.
Begun planting out annuals.

Tuesday 3.
29 9/10; 69; W, SW.
Grey, sweet summer's
day.

The foliage of the nectarines is much blotched & shriveled, so
that the trees look poorly.

Wednesday 4.
29 7/10; 70½; W,
SW, W.
Bright sun, vast dew,
sultry, sweet even.

Began tacking the wines.
Sheep begin to be shorn.

Thursday 5.
29 9/10½; 65; N.
Bright sun, cold wind,
bright & chilly.

The caterpillars of some *phalaenae* abound on the foliage of the
apricots, which they tye together with their webs, & gnaw &
deface in a bad manner. We wash the trees with the garden-
engine.

Friday 6.
30, 30; 56; NE, S, E.
Bright sun, brisk air,
sun, cloudless.

Began to build the walls of my parlor which is 23 feet & half by
18 feet; & 12 feet high & 3 inch:

Saturday 7.
29 7/10½; 56; NE, N.

The bees gather earnestly from the flowers of the buck-thorn.

Sun, hot sun & drying
air.

Sunday 8.
29 6/10; 61; NE, NE.
Sun & clouds, harsh
air, dark & louring,
harsh air.

Monday 9.
29 6/10; 54; NE.
Bright sun, harsh wind,
sun, cold air.

Tuesday 10.
29 5/10; 55; NE, NW,
W, E, W.
Sun, harsh air, sun,
dark clouds, showers
about, hail, dark &
chilly.

Wednesday 11.
29 4/10; 52; SE, S,
SW.
Vast rain, rain,
showers, sun sets red.
꙯ Ophrys nidus avis.

Thursday 12.
29 4/10¾; 51; W, N,
NW, W, NW.
Sun, fog, white frost,
sun & clouds, bright
afternoon.

Friday 13.
29 4/10¼; 54; W, S,
SW.
Sun, dark, showers,
showers, sun, dark &
cool.

Saturday 14.
29 5/10; 60½; W,

Tho' we are exempt from chafers this season round this district; yet between Winchester & Southampton they swarm so as to devour everything: the country stinks of them.

Cut 22 cucumbers.

The ground chops, & bakes very hard.

From the egg-shells flung-out it appears that young martins are hatched in a nest built last year. The circumstance of the ready-built nest makes the brood so much the forwarder.

SW.
Rain, wind, dark &
brisk wind, rain.

Sunday 15.
29 5/10⅓; 60; SW.
Rain all night, rain &
wind, rain, fog, rain &
wind.

The wheat looks badly being injured by continual rain.
The spring-corn looks poorly.

Monday 16.
29 4/10½; 59; SW
Rain, rain, rain, rain.

The S^t foin is much lodged by the rain.

Tuesday 17.
29 6/10⅓; 59; W.
Rain, showers about,
brisk wind, brisk wind,
sun.

My building is interrupted by the rain.
Wheat-ears begin to sprout.

Wednesday 18.
29 8/10; 62; W.
Sun, no dew, sun &
clouds, sweet day, dark
clouds to the W.

Thursday 19.
29 6/10¼; 55; SW,
W, NW.
Rain, rain, fog &
dripping rain with
wind.

Building interrupted.

Friday 20.
29 3/10¼; 60; SW.
Vast rains in the night,
great showers, showers,
heavy clouds.

Tremella nostoc¶ abounds in the field-walks; a sign that the earth is
drenched with water.

Saturday 21.
29 4/10½; 64; SW.
Grey, sun, sweet day,
heavy clouds in the
horison.

Wheat begins to come into ear.
A pair of martins began a nest this day over the garden-door.

The brick-burner has received great damage among his ware that
was drying by the continual rains.

Sunday 22.
29 4/10; 59; SW, NW.
Sun, great clouds, sun,
heavy clouds.

Swallows are hawking after food for their young 'til near nine o'
the clock. They take true pains to support their family.

Monday 23.
29 5/10¾; 60; W,
NW.
Grey, sun, shower, fine
day, vast bank in the
W.

Swallows have all broods, & are very earnest in pursuit of their
prey from three in the morning 'til nine at night.

Tuesday 24.
29 9/10; 56; NE, E,
NW, N.
Sun, cold wind, sun &
clouds, much thunder,
showers, sun set red.

Turned the white cucumbers out from under their hand glasses.
Kidney beans look miserably. A poor cold solstice for tender
plants.
My bees when swarming settle every year on the boughs of the
Balm of Gilead Fir.
Yesterday they settled at first in two swarms, which soon coalesced
into one. To a thinking mind few phenomena are more striking
than the clustering of bees on some bough, where they remain in
order, as it were. to be ready for hiving: . . . *arbore summâ
Confluere, & lentis uvam demittere ramis.*¶

Wednesday 25.
29 9/10¾; 56, 61; W,
S.
Sun, dark shower, grey
& still.

Wheat looks yellow.

Thursday 26.
29 5/10; 62; W, SW.
Sun, fog, dark, shower
& wind, broken clouds.

Began to cut my Sᵗ foin: large & much lodged, & full of wild
grasses. The tenth crop.

Friday 27.
29 4/10, 5½; 56; SW.
Sun, dark, showers,
showers, fine afternoon.
⚘ *Ophrys nidus avis.*

Boys bring me female
wasps, & hornets.

Birdsnest Orchid.
Selborne High Wood.
20 June.

Saturday 28.

29 6/10; 60; SW.
Grey, sun, fine day, air
chilly, dark in the
horizon.

Wheat begins to blow.
The weather is too cold for tender annuals.

Sunday 29.

29 4/10; 58; SW.
Grey, sun, dark, chilly,
shower, dark.

Snails engender.

Monday 30.

29 4/10½; 58½; SW.
Grey, sun, showers,
chilly, fine even:
rainbow.

The pair of martins that began their nest near the stair-case
window on June the 21: finished the shell this day.

About the beginning of July a species of Fly, (*Musca*) obtains,
which proves very tormenting to horses, trying still to enter their
nostrils, & ears, & actually laying their eggs in the latter & perhaps
in both of those organs. When these abound, horses in woodland-
districts become very impatient at their work, continually tossing
their heads, & rubbing their noses on each other, regardless of the
driver: so that accidents often ensue. In the heat of the day men are
often obliged to desist from plowing: saddle-horses also are very
troublesome at such seasons. Country-people call this insect the
nose-fly.

In the decline of the year, when the mornings & evenings
become chilly, many species of flies, (*muscae*) retire into houses, &
swarm in the windows. At first they are very brisk & alert: but as
they grow more torpid one cannot help observing that they move
with difficulty, & are scarce able to lift their legs, which seem as if
glued to the glass: & by degrees many do actually stick-on 'till they
die in the place. Now as flies have flat skinny palms or soles to their
feet, which enable them to walk on glass & other smooth bodies by
means of the pressure of the atmosphere; may not this pressure be
the means of their embarrassment as they grow more feeble: 'til at
last their powers become quite inadequate to the weight of the
incumbent air bearing hard on their more languid feet; & so at last
they stick to the walls & windows, where they remain, & are found
dead.

JULY 1777

Tuesday 1.

29 2/10; 58½; SE,
SW.
Bright, dark, rain,

Hay in a bad way.
Hops look well.
Some labourers digging for stone found in an hole in the rock a

rain, vast showers, sun, wind.

red-breast's nest containing one young cuckow half-fledged. The wonder was how the old cuckow could discover a nest in so secret, & sequestered a place.

Wednesday 2.
29 4/10; 58; SW, SW.
Grey, showers, grey, showers, dark & mild.

The first young swallows, perchers, appeared this day.
The *apes longicornes* do not bore many holes in the walks this cold wet season.

Thursday 3.
29 1/10; 59; SE, E.
Grey, sun, rain, rain, rain, rain.

If the weather was favourable the solstitial flowers would now make a gaudy show in the garden.

Friday 4.
29 2/10; 58¼; SW, S.
Vast rain in the night, sun, & showers, vast clouds. New moon.
🌱 *Vitis vinifera.*

Some white cucumbers seem to be set. The vines begin to blow: They blowed in 1774 June 26: & in 1775 June 7: & in 1776 June 25.

Saturday 5.
29 5/10¼; 57; SW.
Vast rain, showers with wind, dark & blowing, still & more light.

My building is interrupted.
Bad weather for the blowing of the wheat. Annuals suffer.

Birds are very voracious in their squab-state, as appears from the consequences of eating which they eject from their nests in marvelous quantities: as they arrive so rapidly at their full ἡλικια.¶ much nutrition must be wanted.

Sunday 6.
29 8/10; 57; W.
Dark & cold, small shower, dark & cold, gleam of sun in the W.

My St foin lies in a rotting state.

Monday 7.
29 5/10¼; 55; W.
Dark & cold, shower with strong wind, sun sets bright, cold.

Winter-like: we are obliged to keep fires.
The brood of martins hatched June 11th seem to be flown.

Tuesday 8.
29 7/10; 55; W.
Dark & cold, rain, rain, rain, gleams of sun, vast clouds.

Stopped down the vines.
Bees cluster round the mouth of one hive, but cannot swarm.
Bees must be starved soon, having no weather fit for gathering honey: no sun, or dry days.

A swarm of bees, which had waited many days for an opportunity, came-out in a short gleam of sunshine just before an heavy shower, between 9 & 4 in the afternoon, & settled on the balm of Gilead-fir. When an hive was fixed over them, they went up into it themselves.

Wednesday 9.
29 9/10; 55, 59; NW, N.
Dark, with strong cold wind, gleams of sunshine, still & mild, clouds high.

The young swallows that come-out are shivering & ready to starve.

Thursday 10.
30, 30; 63; N, NE, N.
Dark & still, dark, sun breaks out, sweet afternoon.

A swarm of bees has hung-out in a torpid state round the mouth of the hive for many days.
Cuckow cries: white throat whistles.
The rainy fit lasted just a month.

Friday 11.
30; 67; N, NW.
White mist, sun, sweet day, some heavy clouds.

Wheat much in bloom. Young swifts not out yet. Field-crickets crie: Bees swarm by heaps. 31 swifts appear: so that if near half of them are not strangers, the young broods are out.

Saturday 12.
29 9/10½; 67½; W, SW, W.
Fog, sun, heavy clouds, soft gloomy afternoon.

White throats sing.
Ricked the S^t foin; it lay 12 days washed with continual showers, & yet is not quite spoiled.
Began to cut my meadow-hay; a large crop.

Sunday 13.
30; 63; NW, N.
Sun, clouds, sweet summer's day.

The backward wheat is in beautiful bloom: the fields look quite white with the blossoms. The forward wheat is out of bloom, & therefore from the late weather not likely to be so good.

Monday 14.
30; 64, 73; N, W.
Sun, sweet day, brisk air, flisky clouds, hollow wind.

The bloom of the vines now smells delicately. Continue to cut my meadow. White cucumbers grow. Hops begin to be infested with honey-dews. Hay makes well.

Tuesday 15.
29 9/10½; 72; NW, N, NW.
Sun, sweet day, brisk

Rye, which blows early, in a bad state: no promise of a crop.

air, still.

Wednesday 16.
29 8/10; 66, 77; NW,
SE, S. Fog, sun, sultry,
sweet afternoon.

Wheat finely blown.
Hay in large cock.
Hay is made most delicately.

Thursday 17.
29 6/10; 77¼; SW, S,
SW.
Great dew, sun, sultry,
cloudless, sweet even,
heavy clouds to NW.

Ricked my meadow-hay in most delicate order without one drop
of rain. A large crop: 9 jobbs. Left some grass in each mead to
cut for the horses.

Friday 18.
29 5/10; 72; SW, W,
NW.
Fog, sun, sultry, distant
thunder, clouds, small
showers, red evening.

Grapes begin to grow into berry.
Cut the first white cucumber.
Swifts dash & frolick about, & seem to be teaching their young
the use of their wings.
Thatched my rick of meadow-hay with the damaged S᥀ foin
instead of straw.

Saturday 19.
29 4/10½; 65; SW.
Distant thunder, grey,
no dew, brisk wind,
clouds, showers, dark
& still, rain.

Bees begin gathering at three o' the clock in the morning: Swallows
are stirring at half hour after two.

Sunday 20.
29 3/10½; 65; N, SW.
Great rain in the night,
rain, grey & mild,
heavy clouds.

Much wheat & barley lodged.

Monday 21.
29 3/10¾; 63½; NE.
Great rain in the night,
rain, rain, rain, dark &
misty.

My building is interrupted by the rain.

Tuesday 22.
29 4/10½; 59; SE.
Dark & still, small
showers, shady, heavy
clouds, rain.

The lime-trees begin to blow.

Wednesday 23.
29 2/10½; 62; SE, S.
Dark, showers,
showers, heavy clouds.

Much hay damaged.

Thursday 24.
29 2/10; 61; SE, E, N.
Grey, shower, sun,
broken clouds, showers,
dark and hazy.

Friday 25.
29 5/10; 60; N.
Vast rains in the night,
dark, sun, showers,
great showers about.

Saturday 26.
29 6/10; 56; N, NW.
Sun, very cold, grey,
sun, sweet even.

Some hay housed in poor order.

Sunday 27.
29 5/10½; 56; NW,
N.
Shower, clouds,
showers about, dark &
still.

Notwithstanding the disadvantageous season for hatching, some considerable coveys of partridges have been seen.

Monday 28.
29 4/10½; 60; W, SE,
S.
Grey, showers, sun,
vast clouds.

A pair of martins, which began their nest June 21 have now young.
Lime-trees in full bloom: on these the bees gather much honey.

Lime trees in flower.
The Wakes, looking
towards the butcher's shop.
Selborne Street

Tuesday 29.

29 1/10; 58½.
Dark, rain, rain, vast
rain.

The bricklayers are much interrupted by the rains. Much hay quite rotten.

This morning more than 50 swifts sailed slowly over the village towards the S: there were almost double the number that belong to this place; & were probably actuated by some tendency towards their retreat, which is now near at hand.

On July 29: such vast rains fell about Iping, Bramshot, Haselmere, &c: that they tore vast holes in the turnpike roads, covered several meadows with sand, & silt, blowed-up the heads of several ponds, carryed away part of the county-bridge at Iping, & the garden-walls of the paper mill, & endangered the mill & house. A paper-mill near Haselmere was ruined, & many £100 damage sustained. Much hay was swept away down the rivers, & some lives were lost. A post-boy was drowned near Haselmere: & an other as he was passing from Alton to Farnham: the Gent: in the chaise saved himself by swimming. These torrents were local; for at Lewes, which lies about the middle of the county of Sussex, they had a very wet time, but experienced none of these devastations.

After ewes & lambs are shorn there is great confusion & bleating, neither the dams nor the young being able to distinguish each other as before. This embarrassment seems to arise not so much from the loss of the fleece, which may occasion an alteration in their appearance; as from the defect of that *notus odor*, discriminating each individual personally: which also is confounded by the strong scent of the pitch & tar wherewith they are newly marked. For the brute creation recognize each other more from the smell than the sight; & in matters of Identity & Diversity appeal much more to their noses than to their eyes.

Wednesday 30.

29; 58½; SW, SE.
Dark, rain, rain, heavy
rains.

Great flood at Gracious street. Several mills are damaged. Hay drowned. Pond-heads are blown-up; & roads torn up by torrents. Finished the walls of my new parlor.

Thursday 31.

20 2/10⅓; 60; W,
SW.
Rain & wind all night,
sun & showers, dark.

Garden much torn by the wind.¶
Only two or three swifts to be seen.

AUGUST 1777

Friday 1.

29 4/10; 58½; W,
SW.

Reared the roof of my new building.¶
Several swifts.

Dark, showers, hot sun,
showers about.

Saturday 2.
29 7/10; 59; NW.
Grey, clouds, mottled
sky, fine even.

Young swallows & martins abound.
Many swifts.

Sunday 3.
29 9/10; 60; NW.
Grey, sun, clouds, dark
& louring, bright stars.

The wheat hardly begins to turn colour.
Swifts still.

Monday 4.
29 7/10¼; 64; SW, S,
W.
Bright sun, sun &
clouds, sweet evening.

The missel-thrushes, that have got-out their young broods,
appear in flocks.

Tuesday 5.
29 6/10; 61; SW.
Dark, spitting rain,
showers.

Many swifts.

Wednesday 6.
29 6/10¾; 61; SW,
W.
Grey, showers, fine
even.

Young martins, & swallows abound.
Swifts still.

Thursday 7.
29 6/10; 61; SE, S.
Fog, sun, fine day.

Finished the chimney of my parlor: it measures 30 feet from the
hearth to the top.

Friday 8.
29 4/10; 64, 67; SE,
SW.
Fog, sun, dark, distant
thunder, dark & still.

Swifts many.
Flocks of lap-wings resort
to the downs & uplands.

Saturday 9.
29 3/10, 5/10½; 65;
SW.
Shower, dark, dark,
sweet even.

Swifts.
Vast dew.

Sunday 10.
29 7/10; 65; S.
Sun, rain-bow, clouds,
sun & brisk wind.

Monday 11.
29 6/10; 70; S.   Wheat-harvest begins.
Fog, sun, hot sun &   Some swifts.
brisk air, sweet even:

Tuesday 12.
29 6/10½; S. Fog,
dark, dark & spitting.

Wednesday 13.
29 8/10½; 68, 71;   No swifts.
SW, NW. Small rain,   One swift, the last.
sun, sultry, sweet even.

                                The swifts went away this year just as the beautiful weather began.

Thursday 14.
29 9/10½; 65, 74½;   Sweet harvest-weather.
NE, SW, W.   Wheat turns colour very fast.
Cloudless, sweet   Brisk gale.
summer's day.   One swift.

Friday 15.
29 9/10; 73; NW.   Male & female ants come forth, & migrate in vast troops: every
Fog, hot sun, sweet   ant-hill is in strange commotion, & hurry.
even: No swift.

                                The pair of martins which began to build on June 21 brought out
                                their brood this day in part: the rest remain in the nest Aug: 17.

Saturday 16.
29 8/10; 75; W, NW.   No swift.
Fog, sun, brisk air,   Some wheat in shock.
sweet even.

Sunday 17.
29 7/10¼; 70; N.   White butter-flies settle on wet mud in crouds.
Bright, hot sun, dark &   No swift.
sultry.

Monday 18.
29 7/10¼; 67; NE.   Pease are housed.
Thick fog, sun, dark &   No swifts.

still, sweet even.
Full moon.

Tuesday 19.
29 6/10¾; 69; NE, E,
S, SE.
Fog, sun, hot sun,
sweet even.

Pease are housed.
Wheat harvest is general.
No swifts: swifts seem to be gone.

Wednesday 20.
29 6/10½; 65, 70; SE.
Bright sun, gale of
wind, sun, sweet even:

No swifts.
Men begin to put their wheat in shock.

Thursday 21.
29 4/10½; 70; S, SW.
Dark, strong gales,
showers, sun & gales,
clouds.

Apricots ripen.

No swift was seen after Aug: 14: so punctual are they in their
migrations, or retreat! The latest swift I ever saw was only once on
Aug: 21. but they often withdraw by the 10.

Friday 22.
29 7/10¼; 65; W.
Clouds, & strong wind,
still even with a dark
bank.

Wheat begins to be housed in fine order.
Fern-owl chatters.

Saturday 23.
29 7/10½; 67; W,
SW.
Dark, brisk gale, sun,
fine even: brisk gale.

Much wheat housed.

Sunday 24.
29 6/10; 68½; SE,
SW.
Sun & brisk wind, sun,
clouds rise.

Grapes swell.
Wheat dries well.

Monday 25.
29 7/10½; 67; SW.
Spitting rain, dark,
sun, wet fog.

The hop-bloom begins to form into hops: several gardens
promise well.

Tuesday 26.
29 9/10½; 70; W,

Young swallows & martins swarm.

NW.
Grey, sun, dark &
sultry, sprinklings,
shower.

A spotted water-hen shot in the forest.¶

Wednesday 27.
30½, 30; 68; NE, SE,
E. Dark & moist, dark
& sultry, still & hot.

The large winged female-ants, after they have wandered from
their nests, lose their wings & settle new colonies: are in their
flying state food for birds, particularly hirundines.

Thursday 28.
29 7/10; 68; E, SE.
Bright sun, dark heavy
clouds, distant thunder,
spitting fog.

No wasps: & if there were, there is no fruit for them.
Young swallows cluster on chimneys.

Friday 29.
29 7/10; 68; W, NW.
Dark & fog, sun, vast
clouds, sweet even:

Some few wasps.
Much wheat housed.

Saturday 30.
29 1/10⅓; 61; SE,
SW.
Dark, rain, rain, rain.

Finished tiling the new parlor in good dry condition just before
the rain came. The walls & timbers will be in much better order
for this circumstance.
Wheat-harvest interrupted.

The pair of martins brought-out all their young. Aug: 26: they still
roost in their nest. The nest was begun June 21.
    Woolmer-forest produces young teals, & young large snipes: but
never, that we can find, any young jack-snipes.

Sunday 31.
29 6/10; 61; NW.
Strong wind all night,
sun, vast clouds &
showers, bright &
chill.

'Til now the whole month of Aug: has been dry & pleasant.
The evenings begin to feel chilly.

SEPTEMBER 1777

Monday 1.
29 8/10, 7/10; 54; W,
SW.
Cold white dew, sun,
brisk air, clouds about,

Destroyed a small wasps-nest: the combs were few, but full of
young. Hops come on very fast.
Much wheat housed: barley housed.

sun breaks-out.

Tuesday 2.
29 4/10½; 60; W, SW.
Shower, sun, brisk wind, dark, small showers, dark, & louring.

Swallows still bring out their young.
Much wheat ricked.

Wednesday 3.
29 7/10; 61; NW.
Hard shower, sun, brisk wind, sweet harvest weather.

The working-wasps are very small, perhaps half starved in their larva-state for want of pears, plums, &c.

Thursday 4.
29 7/10; 60½; SW.
Dark with spitting rain, spitting rain.

Friday 5.
NW.
Sun, dark & spitting, sultry & gloomy.

SHOPWICK near CHICHESTER
Wasps abound.

Saturday 6.
NW.
Sun, sweet harvest weather.

RINGMER
Wheatears (birds) continue to be taken: are esteemed an elegant dish.¶

Horse-ants travel home to their nests laden with flies, which they have caught; & the *aureliae* of small ants, which they seize by violence.

Sunday 7.
30; S, SW.
Cloudless, sweet weather.

Swallows & house-martins dip much in ponds.
Vast Northern *Aurora*.

Monday 8.
SW. Vast fog, grey, sweet afternoon, white creeping fog.

Tuesday 9.
NW, SW.

Fern-owls haunts Mrs Snooke's orchard in the autumn.

Fog, sun, sultry, dark
clouds.

Wednesday 10.
30; N, W.
Sun, vast dew, sweet
day.

One bank-martin among the other hirundines; dips frequently.
Fly-catcher still remains.

Thursday 11.
N, W.
Vast fog, sun, sweet
day.

Mrs Snooke's tortoise devours kidney-beans & cucumbers in a
most voracious manner: swallows it's food almost whole.

Friday 12.
30; NW.
Vast fog, sultry, sweet
afternoon.

The curious migration of cross-bills,¶ which comes often to the
pine-plantations round this house, still continues. These birds are
foreign, & not known to breed in the kingdom. They appear first
in July.

Saturday 13.
NE, E.
Fog, grey, cold brisk
wind, cloudless &
chilly.

Roads very dusty.

Timothy the tortoise weighed six pounds 3 quarters, 2 oun: & an
half: so is not at all encreased in weight since this time last Year.
The scales were not very exact.

Sunday 14.
NE, E.
Sharp wind, cloudless.

Black cluster-grapes begin to turn colour. A tremendous, &
awful earthquake at Manchester, & the district round. The
earthquake happened a little before eleven o' the clock in the
forenoon, when many of the inhabitants of that district were
assembled at their respective places of worship.

Monday 15.
30; E.
Wh: frost, ice, sun,
cloudless, sharp wind.

Young martins still in their nests.
Wagtails chase swallows.

Tuesday 16.
E, S.
Wh: frost, cloudless,
sweet autumnal.

Rooks frequent their nest-trees. Much Gossamer on the pastures
& stubbles.

Wednesday 17.
S, W.
Fog, sweet day.
Full moon.

The sky this evening being what they call a mackerel sky, was
most beautiful, & much admired in many parts of the country.
Italian skies! As the beautiful mackerel-sky was remarked &

admired at Ringmer near Lewes, London, & Selborne at the same time; it is a plain proof that those fleecy clouds were very high in ye atmosphere. These places lie in a triangle whose shortest base is more than 50 miles.

The creeping fogs in the pastures are very picturesque & amusing, & represent arms of the sea, rivers, & lakes.

Thursday 18.
S.
Deep wet fog, sweet day.

FINDON

Friday 19.
SW.
Sun, sweet day.

CHILGROVE
Ring-ousels on the downs on their autumnal visit. Lapwings about on the downs attended by starlings; few stone-curlews. Sweet Italian skies. The foliage of the beeches remarkably decayed & rusty.

Saturday 20.
29 7/10½; 63; W, NE.
Grey, brisk wind, hot sun, chill & bright.

SELBORNE
Some corn abroad: a vast burden of straw, & many ricks.

Sunday 21.
29 3/10½; 60; E, S.
Sun, soft day, clouds, small shower, dark.

Little corn abroad: hop-picking almost finished. Grapes turn apace.

Monday 22.
29 5/10½; 54, 58; W, NW.
Sun, bright, clear & chilly.

Peaches, & Nectarines now very fine.

Tuesday 23.
29 7/10; 52; W.
Cold air, sun, bright day, heavy clouds, stars.

Wednesday 24.
29 5/10; 53; S.
Sun, cold air, sun & clouds, dark bank to the W.

The walks begin to be strewed with leaves. Vivid Northern *Aurora*.

Thursday 25.
29 4/10½; 63; S, SE.
Sun, sultry, sweet day,
soft air.

Peaches & Nect: are still delicate.

Friday 26.
29 3/10½; 64¾; S,
SE.
Sun, sultry, broken
clouds, brisk hollow
wind, thunder, shower.

Mackerel-sky.

Saturday 27.
29 6/10; 63, 69; SE,
E, NE.
Grey, sun, sultry,
summer weather,
broken clouds, distant
lightening.

We had but little rain, only the skirts of the storm.

The dry weather, which was of infinite service to the country after
so wet a summer, might fairly be said to last eight weeks; three of
which had no rain at all, & much sun-shine.
    Some of the store-wethers on this down now prove fat, & weigh
15 pounds a quarter. This incident never befals but in long dry
seasons; & then the mutton has a delicate flavour.

Sunday 28.
29 6/10¼; 68; SE, E.
Dark & lowering,
showers, sultry &
gloomy with great
showers to the SW. W.
& NW.

Thunder in the night with an heavy shower.
Swallows about.

Monday 29.
29 7/10; 65; SW.
Sun, sultry & dark,
showers, showers, grey
& still, mild.

Distant thunder in the night.
House martins abound.

Tuesday 30.
29 6/10; 64; SE, E.
Thick fog, spitting,
sun, & sultry, grey &
mild.

Nectarines delicate to the last.

OCTOBER 1777

Wednesday 1.
29 2/10; 62; SE, SW.

This day Mr Richardson of Bramshot shot a wood-cock: it was

Showers, loud thunder, heavy showers, bright stars.

large & plump & a female: it lay in a moorish piece of ground. This bird was sent to London, where as the porter carryed it along the streets he was offered a guinea for it.

Thursday 2.
29 2/10½; 58; S, SW.
Sun, heavy clouds, hot, mild & still.

Friday 3.
29 4/10; 58; SW.
Vast dew, sun, hot & bright, vast broken rock-like clouds, clear delicate even:

What becomes of those mossy clouds that often incumber the atmosphere in the day, & yet disappear in the evening. Do they melt down into dew?

Saturday 4.
† 29 [?]; 57; SW.
Showers, sun, wind & showers.

Many swallows & house-martins still.

Sunday 5.
29 7/10; 56; SW, W.
Sun, strong wind, some clouds, still & bright.

Monday 6.
29 5/10; 60½; SE.
Sun, warm, grey & mild.

Gathered first grapes: ripe but not delicate.

Tuesday 7.
29 6/10; 61; S, SW, W.
Heavy shower, showers, showers, hollow rumbling wind.

Many swallows & martins.
Began to light fires in the parlor.

Wednesday 8.
SW.
Sun, fine autumnal weather.

BRAMSHOT PLACE
Mr Richardson's nectarines & peaches still in perfection.

---

† Entry in manuscript illegible.

Thursday 9.
29 8/10; E.
Fog, sweet day.

Beans & vetches are housed.

Friday 10.
56, 60; E, S.
Vast fog, sweet day.

SELBORNE
Gossamer abounds.
Several swallows.
Swallows left Fyndon.

Saturday 11.
29 6/10; 56, 60; SE,
W.
Vast fog, sun, sweet
day.

No swallows or martins.
Gossamer.
Insects abound on the ivy-bloom, & on the late blowing annuals,
& perennials.
A squirrel in my hedges.
Insects retreat into the roof of my new building.

Found the *Sphinx atropos*, or death's head-moth, a noble insect,
of a vast size: it lays it's eggs on the Jasmine. When handled it
makes a little stridulous noise.

Sunday 12.
29 5/10⅔; 57¼; NW.
Deep fog, dark & still,
grey.

No hirundines.

Monday 13.

WORTING
Redwings appear.

Tuesday 14.

WHITCHURCH
Vast shower.

Wednesday 15.

OXFORD

Thursday 16.

Friday 17.

Some swallows seen.

Saturday 18.

Sunday 19.

Cold.

Monday 20.
Frost, ice.

Sweet dry weather.

Tuesday 21.

Wednesday 22.

Cold & sharp.

Thursday 23.

READING

Friday 24.

LASSAM
Much wheat sown.

Saturday 25.
29 4/10½; 51½; SW.
Sun, gusty & cloudy.

SELBORNE
Hogs are put-up in their fatting pens.
Strong wind.
The hanging woods are beautifully tinged.

Sunday 26.
29 1/10; SW.
Stormy, some rain.

Great rain.

Monday 27.
29 4/10; 49; W.
Grey & mild.

Rain was wanting for the sowing of wheat.
Many swallows seen at Cambridge.

Tuesday 28.
44.
White frost, soft &
sunny, clouds, strong
wind & rain.

Grapes are now delicate: but the crop will be small & many
bunches will not ripen at all.

Wednesday 29.
28 8/10; 51.
Stormy wind.

Thursday 30.
28 3/10¾; 54.
Stormy wind,
gluts of rain, much
thunder.

The trees & hedges are much broken, & the thatch is torn. Much
damage done to the shipping: chimneys, & some houses blown
down in London.

Friday 31.
29 2/10½; 51;
W.
Sunny, soft &
still.

The foliage of the beeches much discoloured.
Grapes very fine.

NOVEMBER 1777

Saturday 1.
29 4/10; 44; W.
Frost, ice, sun, still &
pleasant.

Sunday 2.
29 3/10¾; 50
Sun, soft day.

Ring-ouzels still on the downs near Alresford. They have left these parts some time.

Monday 3.
29 4/10; 58½; S.
Driving rain & wind,
rain & wind, soft &
mild.

Sea-gulls, winter-mews, haunt the fallows.
Beetles flie.

Tuesday 4.
29 7/10⅓; 58½; SW.
Dark & soft air, wet,
grey, mild, bright.

21 house-martins appeared, playing about under the hanger.*
The air was full of Insects.
No martins have been observed since Oct: 7ᵗʰ 'til this day, when more than 20 were playing about & catching their food over my fields, & along the side of the hanger. It is remarkable that tho' this species of Hirundines usually withdraws pretty early in Oct: yet a flight has for many years been seen again for one day on or about the 4ᵗʰ of Novʳ Farther it is worthy of notice, that when the Thermʳ rises above 50, the bat awakens, & comes forth to feed of an evening in every winter-month. These circumstances favour the notion of a torpid state in birds; & are against the migration of swallows in this kingdom. *Others that saw the martins in an other part of the hanger say there were more than 150! This was a mistake.

Wednesday 5.
29 8/10½; 51; SW.
Vast dew, sun, soft &
pleasant.

No martins.

Thursday 6.
29 9/10; 50; W.
Sun, pleasant day.

No martins.

Friday 7.
29 8/10; 45; W, NW.
White frost, sun, &
pleasant weather.

Put the sashes into my new room.
No martins.

Saturday 8.
29 2/10½; 45; W.
Great rain, showers,
showers, wind.

Put the first coat of plaster on the battin-work & ceiling of my
new room.
No martins.

Sunday 9.
29 2/10; W, NW.
Sun, bright, sharp
air.

No martins.

Monday 10.
29 4/10; 40; SW.
White frost, dark,
shower, grey.

The hanger is almost naked.

Tuesday 11.
29 3/10; 50; SW.
Showers, showers.

Stone-curlews are still heard.

Wednesday 12.
29 2/10¾; 50;
S, SE.
Fog, grey, sun, mild.

Some ring-ousels still lingering about.

Thursday 13.
29 2/10; W.
Frost, sun, soft day,
rain.

Friday 14.
29 5/10, 7/10; 45;
NW, NE.
Frost, sun, mild.

Thatched roofs smoke in the sun: when this appearance happens
rain seldom ensues that day. This morning they send-up vast
volumes of reek.

Saturday 15.
29 8/10; 44.
Wh: frost, sun, bright
& still.
Full moon.

Sunday 16.
29 9/10; 39½; N.
Wh: frost, thick ice,
sun, hot sun, grey &
mild.

Flies come forth, & the air swarms with insects.
Hen-chaffinches flock; scarce any cocks.

Monday 17.
30¼, 30; 42; NW, W.
White frost, sun, sweet
day, mild, brisk air.

Large field-fares abound: vast clouds of them on the common.
Insects about.

Tuesday 18.
30; 48; NW.
Grey & mild, bright.

All the bunches of grapes are now ripe, & in good perfection.
The leaves fall much from the vines.

Wednesday 19.
29 8/10½; 47; W.
Grey, sun, strong wind.

Thursday 20.
29 9/10; 49; W, NW.
Grey & mild, sun,
soft autumnal grey
weather.

Grapes delicate.
Bees come-out much from their hives, & are very alert.

Friday 21.
29 8/10½; 51, 52; W.
Grey, brisk wind, mild
& grey.

Planted a numbers of small beeches in the tall hedges.
Worms lie-out on the grass-plots in vast quantities.

Saturday 22.
29 7/10½; 52; W.
Grey & mild, sun,
brisk gale, strong wind.

Beeches love to grow in crouded situations, & will insinuate
themselves thro' the thickest covert, so as to surmount it all. Are
therefore proper to mend thin places in tall old hedges.
Strong N: *aurora* extending to the W: & S:W: some streaks fiery
red.

Sunday 23.
29 7/10¾; 50; NW.
Grey, sun, sharp drying
wind.

Paths very dry.
Trees & hedges are become naked.

Monday 24.
29 9/10; 42, 42; N.
Wh: frost, sun & sharp
air, bright.

Gathered-in all the grapes for fear of the frost.
We have now enjoyed a dry, good season, with no more rain than
has been useful, ever since the first week in August.

Tuesday 25.
29 9/10½; 40; W.
Wh: frost, sun, soft,
dark sky.

Men stack their turneps, a new fashion that prevails all at once; &
sow the ground with wheat. They dung the fields in summer as
for wheat.

Wednesday 26.

29 8/10; 45; W.
No frost, no dew, dark
& still.

Began to trim & tack the vines. The dry & warm autumn has
furnished the vines with well-ripen'd bearing wood.

Thursday 27.

29 3/10¾; 46; S, S.
No frost, grey, sun,
dark & louring, wind.

Began planing the floor-battins for my new parlor: they are very
fine, & without knots; 500 feet.
Crocuss begin to peep.
Finished the vines.

Friday 28.

29 7/10; 42; NW, N,
NW.
Stormy with rain,
snow, a small flight,
sun, frost.

Strong N: Auroras towards the morning.

Saturday 29.

29 4/10; 39; W, S, SE.
Hard frost, sun, dark,
rain & wind.

Sunday 30.

28 8/10; 46; SW.
Wind & rain all night,
rain, vast rain,
blowing.

Phalaenae swarm in the hedges; they come forth fm the hedges all
the winter.

DECEMBER 1777

Monday 1.

29 5/10; 46; SW.
Sun, soft, & delicate.

The brick-layers began to lay on the second coat of plaster in my
new parlor.

Tuesday 2.

29 6/10; 42; SW.
Sun, fine day, bright.

There is now in this district a considerable flight of woodcocks.
Large flocks of wood-pigeons now appear: they are the latest
winter-birds of passage that come to us.

Wednesday 3.

29 4/10; W.
Grey, dark & cold,
much rain with wind.

NEWTON
Vast N. Auroras.

Thursday 4.
28 7/10½; 42; NW.
Rain, rain, cold wind,
rain with snow, bright
& windy.

SELBORNE
N. Auroras.

Friday 5.
29 2/10; 38; NW.
Hard frost, sun,
flight of snow, keen &
bright.

Saturday 6.
29 3/10½; 34; NW.
Hard frost, snow on the
ground, sharp wind,
bright.

Sunday 7.
29 5/10; 35; NW, N.
Hard frost, sun, shower
of sleety rain, bright.

Monday 8.
29 5/10¼; 36; N.
Dark with driving
snow, dark & raw.

Tuesday 9.
29 7/10½; 38; NW.
Grey, sunny & soft.

BP'S SUTTON

Wednesday 10.
30 2/10; 39; NW.
Dark & mild, bright.

Moths flie about in the hedges.

Thursday 11.
30 2/10¼; 38½; SW,
W.
Vast white frost, soft
sunshine, grey.

SELBORNE
The plasterer began the cornice of my new parlor.

Friday 12.
30 1/10¾; 46; W.
Grey, still & mild.

Saturday 13.
30; 46; SW, W.
Soft & grey, grey, sun,
bright.

Bees come out.
Phalaenae come forth.

Sunday 14.
29 6/10⅓; 46, E. Fog,
dull & dark, deep fog.

Monday 15.
29 7/10½; 38; NE, N.
Deep fog, deep fog.

Rime on the hanger.

Tuesday 16.
29 7/10½; 41; N.
Cold rain, & sleet,
strong harsh wind with
showers.

One black rat was killed at Shalden some months ago, &
esteemed a great curiosity. ¶ The Norway rats destroy all the
indigenous ones.

Wednesday 17.
29 8/10; 38; N.
Frost, clouds & wind,
harsh, sleet, dark.

Wrens whistle.

Thursday 18.
29 6/10½; 37; N.
Dark, grey, sun &
clouds, sleet.

Clouds of wood-pigeons.
Phalaenae flie.

Friday 19.
29 6/10¾; 36½; NE.
Black frost, snow, sun,
dark & snowy.

This week Wolmer-pond was fished; & out of it was taken, an
eye-witness tells me, a pike that weighed 30 pounds.

Saturday 20.
29 6/10; 37½; NE.
Black with small snow,
dark & foggy.

Finished plowing-up the Ewel-close, a wheat-stubble, to prepare
it for barley, & grass-seeds: it must be plowed thrice. The
ground is pretty dry, but tough, & heavy, requiring naturally
much meliorating.

Sunday 21.
29 4/10; 36, 36; N,
NW, W.
Dark & cold, bright &
still, dark, frost.

Some snow on the ground.

Monday 22.
29 2/10½; 34½; W,
S.
Black frost, dark &
still, dark, frost,
louring.

For want of rain the millers are much in want of water. Carried-out many loads of dung from the cucumber-beds on the great meadow.
Finished the cornice of the great parlor.

Tuesday 23.
29 ½/10; 36½; SE, S.
Deep fog, sun, dark &
spitting.

No rain since Dec: 4.

Wednesday 24.
28 7/10; 39; S, SW.
Much rain in the night,
much snow, rain, rain,
gleam of sun, clouds.

This day the plasterers put a finishing hand to the ceiling, cornice, & side-plasterwork of my great parlor. The latter is done on battin-work¶ standing-out 3 inches from the walls.

Thursday 25.
29 ½/10; 41; N, NW.
Dark & foggy, grey &
mild.

Friday 26.
28 9/10; 40¼; W.
Snow, & rain, dark, &
spitting rain, bright.

A fox ran up the street at noon-day. Wrens whistle: the only songsters at present.

Saturday 27.
29 2/10½; 39; NE.
Dark & fog, dark &
harsh.

No birds love to fly down the wind, which protrudes them too fast, & hurries them out of their poise: besides it blows-up their feathers, & exposes them to the cold. All birds love to perch as well as to fly with their heads to the windward.

Sunday 28.
29 3/10½; 38; N, NE.
Dark, sun, bright,
grey, mild.

Vast banks to the SW in the horizon like snow.

Monday 29.
29 1/10½; 38; N.
Dark with flakes of
snow, dark & spitting.

Tuesday 30.
29 2/10⅓; 37; NE.

Ground covered with snow.

Dark & harsh, snow,
snow, frost.

Wednesday 31.
29 5/10½; 35; NE.
Dark, with hard frost
& cutting wind.

Snow on the ground.

The christenings at Faringdon near Alton, Hants from the year
1760 to 1777 inclusive were 152: the burials at the same place in
the same period were 124. So that the births exceed the deaths by
28. I have buried many very old people there: yet of late several
young folks have dyed of a decline.

JANUARY

— 1778 —

Thursday 1.
29 5/10; 35; N.
Dark & still, moderate
frost.

SELBORNE
Fires are made every day in my new parlor: the walls sweat
much.

Friday 2.
29 7/10; 35, 23 abroad;
NE.
Hard frost, dark &
harsh, bright, severe
frost.

There is reason to fear that the plasterer has done mischief to the
last coat of my battin-plaster, that should carry the paper of my
room, by improvidently mixing wood-ashes with the morter:¶
because the alcaline salts of the wood will be very long before they
will be dry at all; & will be apt to relax, & turn moist again when
foggy damp weather returns. If any ashes at all, he should have
used sea-coal, & not vegetable ashes: but a mixture of loam &
horses dung would have been best.

Saturday 3.
29 5/10; 28; SE, S.
Dark, thaw, harsh
wind, storm of sleet,
hail & rain for some
hours.

Sunday 4.
29 4/10½; 38; SW,
SE. Hard frost, thaw,
deep fog.

Monday 5.
20 2/10½; E.
Dark & still, sleet, dark
& cold.

Tuesday 6.
29 9/10¾; 37; E.

Hard frost, dark &
still.

Wednesday 7.
29 9/10; NE.
Frost, dark & still.

Thursday 8.
30; 34; E.   Dry, clean, & pleasant.
Frost, dark & still.

Friday 9.
29 9/10; 34; N.
Dark & still, gleam of
sun, small snow.

Saturday 10.
29 7/10; 34; NE.   Roads dry, & dusty.
Frost, dark & still.

Sunday 11.
29 4/10½; 34; N, S,   Fine agreeable frost. Ground very dry.
SE. Dark & mild,
still, & dark, frost.

Monday 12.
29 2/10; 36; SE, E.
Snow in the night,
grey, thaw, dark.

Tuesday 13.
29; 38; SE.
Snow in the night,
thaw, deep fog.
Full moon.

Wednesday 14.
28 1/10½; 40; E.   The wind very still for so very low a barometer.
Rain, rain, rain, rain.

Thursday 15.
28 4/10½; 44½; S.   Red-breast, & hedge-sparrow sing.
Dark, moist & mild,
spring-like, showers
with wind.

Friday 16.
29 ¼/10; 46; S, SW.
Dark & moist,
showers, showers, star-
light.

Snow-drops, crocus's, winter-aconite sprout: polyanths blow.
Spring-like.

Saturday 17.
29 1/10; 45; SW, S.
Grey, sun, mild, rain
& wind.

Foxes abound in the neighbourhood, & are very mischievous
among the farm-yards, & hen-roosts. The fox-hounds have lately
harrassed Harteley-woods, & have driven them out of those
strong coverts, & thickets.

Sunday 18.
29; 34; S.
Bright sun, deep fog,
dark, rain & wind.

Monday 19.
29; 34; S, SW.
Showers of hail & rain,
much thunder & strong
wind.

Much rain.

Tuesday 20.
28 9/10¾; 35; S.
Sun, frequent showers,
rain, rain & wind.

Much rain.

Wednesday 21.
28 9/10; 33; SW.
Sun & strong wind,
hail & distant thunder.

Thursday 22.
28 5/10; 41; W, NW.
Sun, showers with
strong wind.

Song-thrush sings.
Titmouse chirps.

Friday 23.
29 2/10; SW.
Sun, dark, rain.

Saturday 24.
29 ½/10; 41; NE.
Rain all day with cold
wind.

The ground is full of water.

Sunday 25.
29 4/¾; 37½; N.
Driving snow with
fierce wind, frost with
strong wind.

Snow melts.
Rugged weather.
Freezing wind.

Monday 26.
29 9/¾; 34; N.
Hard frost, sun, bright
& freezing.

Snow on the ground, which is icy, & slippery.

Tuesday 27.
29 7/10½; 18 abroad;
N.
Hard frost, bright sun.

Wednesday 28.
29 8/10; N.
Severe frost, bright
sun.

Frost comes in a doors. Bottles of water freeze. Little shining
particles of ice appear on the ceiling, cornice, & walls of my great
parlor: the vapor condensed on the plaster is frozen in spite of
frequent fires in the chimney. I now set a chafing dish of clear-
burnt charcoal¶ in the room on the floor.

Thursday 29.
29 8/10; NW, W.
Moderate frost, thaw,
thaw, dark & still.

Friday 30.
29 8/10; 38; W, S.
Grey, thaw, mild &
spring-like.

Made the seedling cucumber-bed.
Snow almost gone.

Saturday 31.
29 7/10¾; 39; E, NE.
Deep fog.

Some frost still in the ground.

FEBRUARY 1778

Sunday 1.¶
29 8/10½; NE.
Fog, dark & still.

Monday 2.
29 9/10; 38; NE.
Dark & cold, wetting
fogs.

Tuesday 3.
29 9/10½; 38; E, SE.
Dark & cold, partial
fog.

Snow lies about on the hills.

Wednesday 4.
29 7/10; 38; E, NE.
Grey, deep fog, dark &
moist.

Snow lies on the hills.

Thursday 5.
29 5/10; 38; SE, E.
Fog, dark & moist,
grey, fog.

Many bulb-rooted flowers begin to sprout.
Ice melts.

Friday 6.
29 2/10½; 43; SE.
Grey, gleams of sun,
rain.

Ravens carry over materials & seem to be building.

Saturday 7.
29 5/10; 45; S, W.
Fog, grey & mild,
gleams of sun, rain,
bright.

Winter-aconite blows.

Sunday 8.
29 3/10; 43; SW.
Grey, shower, wind &
wet.

Monday 9.
29 7/10¼; 46½; E,
NE.
Sun, sweet day, partial
fogs.

Snow-drops blow. Bees come-forth; & flies & gnats appear.
Phalaenae flie; they flie all yᵉ winter in mild weather.

Tuesday 10.
20 8/10; 43; E, SE, E.
Deep fog, dark & mild.

Hepaticas begin to blow.

Wednesday 11.
29 9/10; 42; E.
Dark & still.
Full moon.

Thursday 12.
30; 39; E.
Dark & still.

Friday 13.
29 8/10½; 38; E, S.
Dark & still.

Foxes begin now to be very rank, & to smell so high that as one rides along of a morning it is easy to distinguish where they have been the night before. At this season the intercourse between the sexes commences; & the females intimate their wants to the males by three or four little sharp yelpings or barkings frequently repeated. This anecdote I learned by living formerly at an house opposite to a neighbour that kept a tame bitch-fox, which every spring about candlemass began her amorous serenade as soon as it grew dark, & continued it nightly thro' yᵉ months of Feb: & March.

Saturday 14.
29 1/10; 38; W, NW.
Shower, sun, gusts & snow, bright, snow.

Sunday 15.
29 1/10; 38; NW.
Hard frost, snow on the ground, sun & clouds, dark & harsh, snow gone.

A fox in Priory Lane.
Early morning

Monday 16.
28 9/10; 36; NW.
Some snow, small frost, sun & clouds, & harsh wind.

The sun at setting just shines into the E: corner of my great parlor.
Drying harsh wind.
The ground plows well.

Tuesday 17.
29 2/10; 35½; N.
Light snow, harsh wind, snow flights.

Wednesday 18.
29 3/10; 32½; N.

Flights of snow, frost,
sun, & clouds, harsh
wind, frost.

Thursday 19.
29 4/10; 31½; N,
NW.
Severe frost. Snow on yᵉ
ground, sun & clouds,
dark, bright.

Friday 20.
29 5/10; 35; W, NW,
N. Thaw, rain, fog,
dark & still.

Saturday 21.
29 8/10; 41; W, NW.   Bees come out.
Dark & mild, soft &   The wheat this year in general looks very weak & poor: last winter
sunny, dark.   it was proud & gay; & yet after a cold wet summer the crop was
                           very indifferent.

Sunday 22.
29 6/10½; 45; SW.   Missle-thrush sings.
Grey, spitting rain,
grey, mild.

Monday 23.
29 2/10½; 45; SW.   Chaffinch sings.
Rain, grey, blowing,
showers.

Tuesday 24.
29; 43; W, NW.   Crocuss begin to blow.
Frost, sun, sharp air,   The dry air crisps my plaster in the new parlor.
clouds & sun.

Wednesday 25.
29 2/10; 38; NW.
Flights of snow, harsh
& severe wind, bright,
frost.

Thursday 26.
29 5/10; 32; N.

Severe frost, sun,
clouds & cutting wind.

Friday 27.
28 9/10½; 34; S, S.   The fierce, driving snow from the S: drifted in between the tiles,
Severe frost, ponds   & did much injury to my cielings, & those of my neighbours.
bear, fierce cutting
wind with driving
snow, much snow, wind
& rain.
New moon.

Saturday 28.
28 9/10; 36; W, NW.   Farmer Lassam feeds his early lambs, & their ewes with oats &
Sun, snow on the   bran: the lambs are large & fat.
ground, snow melts,
bright, vast clouds in
the horison.

MARCH 1778

Sunday 1.
28 9/10; 36; E.
Hard frost, fog,
shower, sun, grey &
still, rain.

Monday 2.   FARNHAM
N.
Snow in the night, sun
& mild.

Tuesday 3.   SOUTH LAMBETH
29 3/10; E.   Turkey-cock struts & gobbles.
Dark & harsh.

Wednesday 4.
29 4/10; E.
Dark & harsh.

Thursday 5.
29 4/10; NW.
Dark & harsh, some
sleet.

Friday 6.
29 5/10; 34; NW.
Dark & still.

Saturday 7.
29 8/10; 36; NE.   The spring is very backward.
Rain, harsh & dark,
much London smoke.

Sunday 8.
29 7/10; 35; NE.
Small rain, dark &
harsh.

Monday 9.
N.
Dark & harsh.

Tuesday 10.
29 8/10; 37; NW.   Titlarks in cages essay to sing.
Dark, moist & still.   For want of sun hot-beds languish.
                         Every matter in field, & garden is very backward.

Wednesday 11.
29 8/10; 36; NE.   Frogs come out of their hybernacula.
Dark & moist, gleam of
sun, dark & mild.

Thursday 12.   LONDON
30 2/10; 36; E.
Dark & windy, bright.

Friday 13.   S: LAMBETH
30 4/10; 34; N.
Ice, bright sun.
Full moon.

Saturday 14.
30 4/10; 27; NE.   The green woodpecker laughs in the fields of Vauxhall.
Hard frost, fog, sun.   Owl hoots at Vauxhall.

Sunday 15.
30 3/10; 34; E.
Sleet, dark & harsh.

Monday 16.
30 2/10; 36; E.
Dark & still.

Tuesday 17.
30 2/10; 36; 45; SE, S.
Sun, sweet day, creamy
clouds.

Wednesday 18.
30 1/10, 30; 45, 55;   Beetles buzz.
SW.
Sun, sweet day.

Thursday 19.
40, 47; W, E.
Dark & dry.

Friday 20.
29 5/10; 40; NE.
Grey, small rain.

Saturday 21.
29 5/10; 46; SW.   Crocus's blow.
Sun, sweet morn, soft
rain.

Sunday 22.
29 2/10; 50; SW.   Frog-spawn in ditches.
Showers, blowing
weather.

Monday 23.
29 1/10; 45; SW.
Gentle rain, sun.

Tuesday 24.
29 3/10; 45; SW.   Mild & growing.
Showers, sun, showers,
showers.

Wednesday 25.
29 7/10; 37; NE.
Dark, windy & harsh,
sun.

Thursday 26.
30; 34; NE.
Frost, ice, sun, bright
& cold.

LONDON

Friday 27.
30 3/10; 49; W, SW.
Frost, ice, sun, cold
air.

S: LAMBETH
Apricot begins to blow.

Saturday 28.
30 1/10, 30 ½/10; 39;
SW.
Rain & sleet, rain, rain,
harsh & windy.

Very great fall, & wind, for so high a barometer!

Sunday 29.
30 1/20; 48; SW.
Grey, windy.
❀ Persian Iris, Violet.

Monday 30.
30; 48; SW.
Soft rain, mild, &
spitting, dark.
    Pile wort, *draba
verna*.

Tuesday 31.
29 9/10; 50; SW.
Dark & moist, grey
with brisk wind.
Bank martin.

Three or four bank-martins were seen over Oakhanger-pond.
Flies abound in the pastry-cooks shops.

APRIL 1778

Wednesday 1.
29 9/10; 48; SW.
Small showers, gleams
of sun.

Shell-snails begin to come-forth.

Thursday 2.
29 6/10½; 45; S.
Sun, soft air, creamy.

LONDON

Friday 3.
SW.
Sun & clouds, soft.

Saturday 4.   LONDON, SELBORNE
29 4/10; 52; SW.   A swallow was seen this morning near Ripley.
Showers, clouds, & hot   Young geese.
gleams.
Swallow appears.

Sunday 5.
29 5/10; 52; SW.   Crocus's being very late this year, are still in bloom.
Sun, & clouds, gleams   Polyanths begin to blow.
of sun, & brisk wind.

Monday 6.
29 5/10; 51½; S.   Black snails.
Rain, rain, rain.

Tuesday 7.
29 8/10; 55; NW, N,   The cucumber-plants are gross, & strong: fruit begins to set.
NE.
Sun, sun & clouds,
mild & still.
Cuckow, Nightingale.

Wednesday 8.
29 7/10½; 57; NE.   Growing weather.
Fog, rain, sweet   Peaches & nectarines blow.
afternoon.

Thursday 9.
29 7/10; 62; NE.   Things grow at a vast rate.
Thunder & hard rain,   Two swallows at the parsonage at Faringdon.
sun, sultry, sweet even.

Friday 10.
29 8/10¼; 63; NE.   Three bernacle-geese on a pond at Bramshot: one was shot & sent
Fog, sun, cloudless,   to me.
sweet summer weather.

Saturday 11.
29 8/10½; 63; NE.   The plaster of my great parlor now dries very fast.
Sun, cloudless, sweet   Bat appears.
summer weather.

Sunday 12.
29 8/10; 62; NE, N.
Sun, bright, sultry,
thunder clouds.

Like midsummer!

Monday 13.
29 4/10½; 61; W.
Sun, sun & clouds, &
strong wind.

One beech is in full leaf in the Lythe.

Tuesday 14.
29 4/10; 47; NW.
Strong harsh wind with
clouds.

The great parlor dries very fast.

Wednesday 15.
29 3/10; 44; NW.
Harsh wind, flakes of
snow, clouds & sun.

Peaches & nectarines in fine bloom.
No swallow yet at Selborne. The pair of swallows that were so
brisk at Faringdon last week have disappeared for some days
since the harsh weather commenced.

Thursday 16.
29 3/10½; 40; W.
Sharp ice, sun, &
flights of snow, bright
& cold.

Planted three beds of asparagus.
Planted potatoes.
No swallow.

Friday 17.
29 2/10½; 44; W,
SW.
Harsh air, cold
showers, showers,
showers.

Cut the first cucumber: many more swell away.
No swallows appear.

Saturday 18.
29 6/10½; 44; W.
Frost, sharp air, ice,
sun & clouds, fine
afternoon.

Thomas began to mow the walks.
Cut the second cucumber.
Swallows at Selborne.

Sunday 19.
29 5/10; 46; SW.
Bright sun, sun &
clouds, dark & chill,
rain.

Cucumbers swell.
Apricots set & swell.
The little laughing yellow wren whistles.

Monday 20.
NE.
Sun, showers of hail &
sleet.

LASSHAM

Tuesday 21.
NE.
Frost, snow storm.

CAVERSHAM

Wednesday 22.
NE.
Frost, ice, snow, snow.

OXFORD

Toothwort
Priory Lane
19 April

Thursday 23.
NE.
Thick ice, sun, sharp.

Friday 24.
NE.
Sun, sharp air.

The *Lathraea squammaria*, a rare plant, is just discovered in
bloom in the Litton-coppice at Selborne just below the church,
near the foot-bridge.

Saturday 25.
NW.
Frost, sun, cloudless,
sharp air.

ALTON
Cut three fine large cucumbers.

Sunday 26.
29 2/10; N, S.
Hard frost, sun,
creamy.

SELBORNE

Monday 27.
29 2/10; 47; NE.
Rain, dark, raw, &
moist, rain.

Missle-thrush sits.

Tuesday 28.
29 1/10½; 49; NE.
Shower, dark & moist,
fog, moist & warm.

Cut a brace of cucumbers.

Wednesday 29.
E.
Dark, rain, rain, sun.

Thursday 30.
29/10; 55; E.
Sun & showers, vast
clouds, soft & pleasant.

The earth is well moistened.

MAY 1778

Friday 1.
29 2/10; E, S.
Dark & misty, grey &
mild.

Redstart sings.

Saturday 2.
29 2/10; 53; SE, S.
Grey, rain, rain, mild.
House martin, Black
cap, Grass-hopper-lark.

A hen ring-ouzel still about.

A day or two before any house-martins had been observed, Thomas Hoar distinctly heard pretty late one evening the twittering notes of those birds from under the eaves of my brewhouse between the ceiling & the thatch. Now the quere is, whether those birds had harboured there the winter thro', & were just awakening from their slumbers; or whether they had only just taken possession of that place unnoticed, & were lately arrived from some distant district. If the former was the case, they went not far to seek for an Hybernaculum, since they nestle every year along the eaves of that building.

Mr Derham wrote word to the R: Society "that some time before any Swifts had been seen, (I think before the month of March was out,) he heard them squeaking behind the weather-tiles on the front of his parsonage-house."

It is pity that so curious a Naturalist did not proceed to the taking-down some of the tiles, that he might have satisfyed his eyes as well as his hearing.

There can be no doubt but that the Horn shown to me at Mr Lever's museum, vast as it was, belonged to the Genus of *Bos*: for it was *concavum, antrorsum versum, lunatum laeve*: where as had it related to the Genus of *Capra*, it would have been *concavum, sursum versum, erectum, scabrum*. Neither can it by any means belong to the genus of *Cervus*, for then it would have been *solidum, corio hirto tectum, apice crescens*: nor for as strong reasons to the Genus of *Ovis* for then it would have been *concavum, retrorsum versum, intortum, rugosum*. It must therefore of course have belonged to the Genus of *Bos*.¶

Sunday 3.
29 1/10½; SE.
Rain, rain, rain, mild.

Swifts appear.
House-martins appear.

All the birds of passage are late this year: the spring is backward. Seven swifts.

As a notion had prevailed that the hirundines at first coming were lean & emaciated, I procured an H: martin to be shot as soon as it appeared: but the bird, when it came to be opened, was fat & fleshy. It's stomach was full of the legs & wings of small *coleoptera*.

Monday 4.
29 2/10½; 56½; SW.
Grey, grey & mild.

The king & queen are this day at Portsmouth to see the fleet at Spithead. There were five general running firings, which shook my house, & made the windows jar. The firings were at ten, twelve, one, four.

Tuesday 5.
29 5/10; 55; SW.
Shower, grey, clouds & wind.

A chafer appears.

Wednesday 6.
29 6/10; SW.
Grey, rain & wind, rain & wind.

Swifts always withdraw in wet & windy weather.

Thursday 7.
29 6/10; 55; SW.
Rain, rain with wind, sun, bright.
White-throat,
Shivering uncrested wren.

Much rain.
Cucumbers abound.

Friday 8.
29 6/10; 54; SW.
Showers, sun & wind, clouds.

Sowed the Ewel-close, now barley with 12 pounds of white clover, two bushels of Rye-grass, & a quarter of meadow-grass-seeds from a farmer's hay-loft. The ground is too wet, & will not harrow well. Strong wheat-land.

Saturday 9.
29 6/10½; 59; SW.
Showers, clouds & sun.
Musca meridiana.

My Horses began to lie abroad.
A pair of shell-snails copulate: in common they do not hold such intercourse 'til about midsum!
Some chafers emerge out of the ground. Fern-owl appears.

Sunday 10.
29 8/10; 55; SW.
Wh: dew, sun, bright,

Wild cherry-trees are full of bloom.

clouds, & cold wind,
dark.

Monday 11.
29 5/10½; 59; SW, S,
SE.
Grey, dark & lowering,
sweet afternoon.
Full moon.

H: martins, & swallows begin to build,
Chafers abound.

Tuesday 12.
29 3/10; 57; SW.
Shower, clouds &
strong wind.

Cut three brace & an half of cucumbers.

Wednesday 13.
29 2/10; 59; SW.
Showers, showers,
showers.

Missle-thrush sings much.
Tulips begin to blow.
Hirundines abound.

Thursday 14.
29 5/10½; 61; SW.
Showers, sun & clouds,
vast clouds.

Apple-trees begin to blow.

Friday 15.
29 6/10½; SW.
Sun & brisk wind, dark
& spitting.

The hanger is pretty well in full leaf.

Saturday 16.
29 6/10; 57; S, S.
Shower, wind &
clouds, dark, fog, &
rain.

Cut nine brace of cucumbers.
Nightingale returns to my fields.

Nightingales visit my fields & sing awhile, but withdraw, & travel
on: some years they breed with me.

Sunday 17.
29 2/10; SW, SW.
Stormy & wet, stormy
& wet.

Blowing & wet all night & all day. Strong wind.

Monday 18.
29 5/10; 53; S. W.
Shower, showers, sun,
& wind.

The wind damages the flowers, & beats-off the blossoms from the
apple & pear-trees.

Tuesday 19.
29 8/10½; 50; W.
Blowing & cold,*
pleasant evening.

*In such weather as this the swifts seldom appear. Bees suffer, & get weak.

Wednesday 20.
29 8/¾; 54; SW.
Mild, still & dark.

Apple-trees blow well.
Swallow, & H: martins build.
More chafers than have been seen here for many years.

Thursday 21.
29 7/10; 58; W, S.
Sun, dark, soft & still.

The rooks bring their young out after the chafers.
The fern-owl chatters.

Friday 22.
29 6/10; 54; W, N,
NE. Shower, dark &
moist, dark & wet.

The wind seems to have damaged the pear-bloom. Tulips are in full bloom.

Saturday 23.
29 7/10½; 54½; NE,
N, NE.
Bright, white frost,
summer day, sweet
evening.

Few currans, & gooseberries.

Sunday 24.
29 6/10; SE, E.
White frost, summer
day.

Monday 25.
29 5/10; 54; SE, NE.
Bright, fog, sun &
clouds, chilly air.

Fern-owl chatters.

Tuesday 26.
29 5/10; 56; NE, NW.
Cold air, summer day,
sweet even.

Nightingale with me.
Chafers abound.

Wednesday 27.
29 5/10; 58; NW, W.
Black & cold, showers,
showers, red even:

The missel-thrush sings much: his song is loud, clear, but without any variety; consisting of only two or three wild notes.

Thursday 28.
29 8/10; 56; NW.
Dark & cold, sun,
summer like, dark.

Swallows, & house-martins are busy in building.

Friday 29.
29 7/10; 59; NW.
Dark & threatning,
shower, sun, sweet
afternoon.

Grass grows much.

Saturday 30.
29 6/10½; 60, 64; SE,
S.
Sun, much dew,
summer day.

The flycatcher appears at last.
Field-crickets begin to chirp.
Apis longicornis. Turtle-doves.

Barn-owls are out in the day, taking their prey in the sunshine about noon.

Sunday 31.
29 7/10; SW.
Wet mist, sun &
clouds, sweet afternoon.

The fly-catcher usually appears about the 21 of May: is the latest summer-bird of passage.

JUNE 1778

Monday 1.
29 7/10; SW, W.
Fog, sun & brisk air.

Tuesday 2.
29 6/10; 56; W, SW.
Sun, showers, some
hail, showers, bright.

Sheep begin to be shorn.

Wednesday 3.
29 4/10½; 52; SW, S.
Sun, & showers, some
hail, bright, & cool.

Tulips decay, & fade.

Thursday 4.
29 4/10; 53; SW.
Sun, showers, showers,
bright & chill.

Sᵗ foin begins to blow.

Friday 5.
29 5/10; 54; SW.

Somewhat like frosts still, every morning.

Sun, showers, showers,
bright, & chill.

Saturday 6.
29 3/10; 63; S, SE.
Sun, summer-weather,
dark in the horizon to
the SE.

Snake gorges a toad much larger than itself. When full it is very
sluggish, & helpless, & easily taken.

Sunday 7.
29 4/10; 56; SW.
Sun, summer-weather,
heavy clouds.

The cucumbers abate in their bearing; & always do at this time of
the year.

Monday 8.
29 6/10½; 58; SW, S.
Sun, showers, hot sun,
showers.

Bees go into their hives covered all over with a yellow farina, so
that they look like wasps.

Tuesday 9.
29 8/10; 57; W, SW.
Grey, showers, still &
mild.

The white cucumbers under the handglasses begin to blow.
Finished transplanting the annuals, a vast quantity.

Wednesday 10.
29 8/10; 56; W, SW.
Sun, sweet summer's
day.
Full moon.

The laburnums are in bloom, & high beauty.
Wheat begins to push a few ears.

Thursday 11.
29 8/10; 58; W, S.
Sun, dark, sweet
afternoon.

Cut my S^t foin, the 11th crop. Weeds obtain much & the crop
grows thinner every year.
By the shells thrown-out it appears that the martins over the stair-
case-window hatched this day. They could not have been so early

Friday 12.
29 8/10; 71; S.
Sun, summer, sultry,
sweet even.

had they not laid in a nest of last year. Several pairs now
beginning to build.

Saturday 13.
29 9/10; 65, 71; NW.
Hard rain, rain, hot
sun, sweet even:

A considerable shower came very unexpectedly.

Finished laying the floor of my great parlor.

Sunday 14.
29 9/10; 65; NW.
Sun, grey & warm,
heavy clouds.

White butter-flies innumerable: woe to the cabbages!

Monday 15.
29 8/10; 61; NW.
Sun, dark & chill,
small showers, vivid
rainbow.

Heavy clouds about.

Tuesday 16.
29 8/10; 60; NW.
Sun, hot day with brisk
air.

Wednesday 17.
29 7/10; NW.
Sun, grey & hot.

Thursday 18.
29 7/10; W.
Sun, grey, vast cloud,
showers.

Ricked my S^t foin in good order. There were three jobbs & an half.

Friday 19.
29 7/10½; 62; NE.
Sun, hot & cloudy.

My garden is much bound up, & chopped.
Annuals languish for want of moisture.

Saturday 20.
29 8/10½; 68; NE, N.
Sun, sultry day, red
evening.

The elders, water-elders, fox-gloves, & other solstitial plants begin to be in bloom. Blue dragon-flies appear.
Cucumbers, which had stopped for a time bear again.

My favourite old Galloway, who is touched in his wind, was allowed to taste no water for 21 days; by which means his infirmity grew much less troublesome. He was turned to grass every night & became fat & hearty, & moved with ease. During this abstinence he staled less than usual, & his dung was harder & dryer than what usually falls from grass-horses. After refraining awhile he shewed little propensity for drink. A good lesson this to people, who by perpetual guzzling create a perpetual thirst. When permitted to drink he shewed no eagerness for water.

Sunday 21.
29 8/10¾; 69; N, SW.

Wheat shoots into ear very fast.

Glorious summer weather, red evening.

Bees resort to the chimneys: they seem to gather somewhat from the soot.

Monday 22.
29 8/10; 72; NW.
Sun, glorious weather, red even:

Barley at Bramshot begins to shoot into ear.
Cuckow cries still.

Tuesday 23.
29 7/10½; 75; NE, SE. Cloudless day, sultry, sweet even.

Began to cut my meadow. A good crop, especially where the ground was dunged.

Wednesday 24.
29 6/10; 75; NE, SE, NE.
Hot sun with brisk wind, distant thunder.

Strawberries ripen.
Nothwithstanding the vast bloom there are no plums nor many pears; & a moderate share of apples: few currans, & gooseberries. Few cherries. Great crop of medlars.
A tempest to the S:W. Tempest at Farnham. Brisk air. Hay in small cock.

Thursday 25.
29 7/10; 72; NE, SE, SW.
Distant thunder all night, dark & hot, vast clouds in horizon.

Friday 26.
29 7/10½; 71; SW, S.
Fog, dark, sun, fine afternoon.

Ricked the meadow-hay, six jobbs & an half in most delicate order. The hay this year fine, & free from weeds. Did not mow the little mead.
The garden suffers for want of rain.
Some early wheat in bloom.

Saturday 27.
29 5/10; 70; SE.
Grey, hot sun, distant thunder, small showers.

Sunday 28.
29 5/10; 70; SW, SE.
Shower, sun & clouds, fine even:

Wheat blows.

Monday 29.
29 5/10; 72; SE.
Sun, sultry, showers about, small shower.

My vines begin to blow.
Ponds and tanks fail.
The gardens are much scorched.

Tuesday 30.

29 6/10; 70; SW, SE,
S, SW. Great fog, sun,
sultry, dark, brisk air.

Finished-off the great parlor, & hung the door. The ceiling, &
sides are perfectly dry.

JULY 1778

Wednesday 1.

29 4/10½; 6/10; 66;
SW, SE, SW.
Fog, rain, rain, sun,
fine even: brisk wind.

The meadow-rick sinks much.
Dust hardly laid.

Thursday 2.

29 7/10; SW.
Sun, sun & clouds,
sultry.

Young martins peep out of their nests.

Friday 3.

29 6/10; 63; SW, S.
Sun, clouds, small rain,
fog.

Thatched the hay-ricks: delicate hay.
Began to inhabit my new parlor.

Saturday 4.

29 6/10¾; 68; S, SE.
Sun, dark, still & hot,
red even:

The gardens suffer for want of rain.
Flowers stand but a small time in bloom.

A colony of black ants comes forth every midsummer from under
my stair-case, which stands in the middle of the house; & as soon
as the males & females (which fill all the windows & rooms) are
flown away, the workers retire under the stairs & are seen no more.
It does not appear how this nest can have any communication with
the garden or yard; & if not, how can these ants subsist in
perpetual darkness & confinement!

Sunday 5.

29 6/10¾; 66, 71; S,
SE, W.
Sun, sultry, dark &
dropping, dark &
sultry, thunder all
around.

We have had no thunder-shower all this summer, tho' many have
fallen in sight all around us. Much mischief by this thunder in
distant parts.

Monday 6.

29 6/10¾; 71; W, S.
Sun, brisk air, hot day,
sweet even:

The thunder-clouds sunk all away in the night; & we had no rain.
My well sinks very fast. Watered the garden, which is much
scorched.

View from the Zig-Zag,
Selborne.

Tuesday 7.
29 6/10¾; 69; W,
NW.
Sun, hot day, dark &
brisk air.

Large white cucumbers bear well: cut some. Stopped down the vines which are in bloom, & smell most fragrantly. Watered the wall-trees.

The young martins that were hatched June 11th began to come-out of their nest July 7th, so that they arrive at their ηλικια¶ in some what less than a month.

Wednesday 8.
29 9/10; 71; NW,
N:NW.
Sun, hot sun with brisk
air, red evening.

Rasps begin to turn, but are dryed-up.
Much hay ricked in a most delicate condition.

Thursday 9.
29 8/10¾; 70; N.
Hot, severe sun-shine,
dark & sultry.
Full moon.

Much fine hay. The ground much burnt.
Young martins begin to congregate on the tower.

Friday 10.
29 9/10½; 67; 78; NE,
W.
No dew, sun, hot sun,
sultry.
Sweet even.

Lime-trees are in bloom: on these the bees gather with great delight.
Young swallows come forth, & are perchers. Bees swarm.
Water the cucumbers, & fruit trees well.

Saturday 11.
29 8/10; 69, 75; W,
NW.
Sun, fierce sun with
brisk air, clouds about.

Finished cutting the hedges.
Watered the garden.
Many ponds are dry. Much hay ricked.
By their numbers, & manner of flying about, the swifts seem to have brought-out some of their young: 25 appear at once.

Sunday 12.
29 8/10¾; 69, 75½;
W.
Sun, sultry, dark &
sultry, red even:

Several large coveys of partridges.
Young pheasants.
Spring-corn, & gardens suffer much: fine wheat.

Monday 13.
29 8/10; 71, 79¾; SE,
S, SW.
Sun, cloudless, severe
heat, red even:

Cucumbers bear plentifully. Kidney-beans wither.
Flying-ants come forth.
Bestowed great waterings in the garden.

Tuesday 14.

29 7/10; 72, 79½; W,
NW. Sun, severe heat,
cloudless, sweet even:

Field-pease begin to ripen. Some wheat begins to turn color.
Much fine hay ricked. The little pond on our common has still
plenty of water! Ponds in bottoms are dry.

Wednesday 15.

29 2/10; 70½, 77½;
NE, E, S, SE.
Hot sun, severe heat,
dark clouds.

Field pease begin to be cut.
Bestowed much water in the garden.

Thursday 16.

29 6/10½; 69, 79½;
SE, S, W.
Sun, cloudless, brisk
air, sweet even:

Watered raspberry beds.

Friday 17.

29 8/10; 71½; NE.
Small shower, hot sun,
cloudless, brisk air.

A considerable shower near Basingstoke.
The grapes swell; & grow large.

Saturday 18.

29 7/10; 64, 70; NE,
E, S.
Sun, clouds & brisk
air, hot sun, dark &
cool.

We have never had rain enough to lay the dust since saturday
June 13: now five weeks. By watering the fruit-trees we have
procured much young wood.

The thermometer belonging to my brother Thomas White of South
Lambeth was in the most shady part of his garden on July 5th &
July 14: up at 88, a degree of heat not very common even at
Gibraltar!! July 5: Therm. at Lyndon in Rutland 85.

Sunday 19.

29 4/10; 64, 71½; SE,
NE.
Fog, sun, sultry, dark
& threat'ning, some
great drops.

Hops continue to look finely.
Hot ripening weather.
Hops begin to blow.

Monday 20.

29 2/10; 71; SE, W,
NE, S.
Heavy rain, showers,
showers, sun, sultry,
sweet even: dark
horizon.

Much thunder. Some people in the village were struck-down by
the storm, but not hurt. The stroke seemed to them like a violent
push or shove. The ground is well soaked. Wheat much lodged.
Frogs migrate from ponds.

Tuesday 21.
29 3/10; 67, 65; NE, W.
Sun, sultry, distant thunder, vast showers, rain, rain.

Planted-out more annuals & sowed endive.
The garden much refreshed. Ponds are filled.

Wednesday 22.
29 4/10½; 62; W, SW.
Grey, sun, dark & soft, shower.

Sowed first endive. Planted-out Savoys, choux de Milan, cabbages, &c. The ground works well, & falls very fine.
Sowed parsley, which has failed before.
Planted out more annuals.

Thursday 23.
29 4/10; 63; W, SW.
Rain, rain, rain, dark, soft & still.
New moon.

The ground is well soaked.

Friday 24.
29 2/10, 4/10; 64; SE, NW, S.
Rain, vast rain, sun, red even:

Grapes are grown to a good size.

Saturday 25.
29 2/10; 64; W, W.
Rain, vast rain, sun, vast clouds.

Wheat is much lodged.
The water shines in the fallows.

Much damage done about London by lightening on July 20.

Sunday 26.
29 5/10; 59; W, S.
Sun, flying showers, brisk wind with clouds.

Hirundines abound: the first brood of every species is out. Young martins congregate on sunny roofs.

Monday 27.
29 4/10; 61, 64; SW.
Sun & clouds, & brisk air. Dark & mild.

Grass grows very fast.
Few turnips are yet sown: they were prevented first by the dry weather, & then by the rain.

Tuesday 28.
29 4/10; 66; W.
Vast shower, showers, sun & brisk wind, chill air, clouds.

Wallnuts & hazel-nuts abound.
One bank-martin at Combwood-pond: the only one I ever saw so far from the forest.

Wednesday 29.
29 6/10; 60; SW.
Sun & clouds, strong
gale, heavy clouds.

Apricots begin to ripen. The fruit of the wild merry-trees, ¶
being now ripe, diverts the thrushes &c: from eating the currans,
goose-berries, &c. therefore useful in outlets.

Thursday 30.
29 4/10; 62; SW.
Sun & clouds, heavy
showers with thunder.

Friday 31.
29 6/10; 62; W, NW.
Showers, thunder with
showers.

Much thunder about.

AUGUST 1778

Saturday 1.
29 8; 67; N, NW, SW.
Dark, bright & warm.

Sunday 2.
29 8/10½; 69; SW.
Grey, sweet day.

Monday 3.
29 8/10½; 64; S.
Grey, soft & sweet
weather.

Wheat-harvest begins.

Tuesday 4.
29 6/10½; 65, 74; S.
Sun, sweet harvest
weather.

Wednesday 5.
29 6/10; 5/10; 66; SW.
Sun, grey & sultry,
strong gale with spitting
rain.

Sowed spinage, & trenched-out celeri.

Thursday 6.
29 5/10; 67; SW.
Dark & still, & sultry.

Have not seen any swifts for these two days. The time of their
departure is near. Saw three swifts.

Friday 7.
29 5/10½; 67½; W,
NW.
Small rain, sun, &
sultry, lovely weather.

Sweet harvest-weather.
Sweet moon-light.

Saturday 8.
29 7/10; 64; N.
Full moon.

Trimmed the vines for the last time, & took-off their side-shoots.
The grapes swell & are very forward.
The pair of martins which build by the stair-case window, where
their first brood came-out on July 7: are now hatching a second
brood, as appears by some egg-shells thrown-out.

Sunday 8[9].
29 7/10½; 61½; 71;
NW, SW. Dark with
brisk air, sun, sultry.

Much wheat in shock.
No swifts appear.

Monday 9[10].
29 7/⅓; 64, 73; W,
SW.
Grey, sun, sultry, brisk
air, dark horizon.

Wheat in this parish is said to be heavy. Hops swell, & make
some show.
Three swifts.
Wheat begins to be housed. Much straw.

These swifts were the last.

Tuesday 10[11].
29 6/10½; 65; SW.
Dark & spitting, sun,
spitting, red even.

Wheat housed.
No swifts appear.

**Wednesday
11[12].**
29 7/10; 68; SW.
Sun, sweet harvest
weather.

Thursday 12[13].
29 6/10; 65; SW.
Dark & louring, sun,
broken clouds, bright.

No swifts appear.
Oats begin to be housed.
My well sinks very much.

Friday 13[14].
29 3/10; 67; SW.
Dark, rain, sun, grey,
brisk wind, showers,
showers.

There is this year the greatest crop of wheat in the North-field
that ever was remembered.

Saturday 14[15].
29 7/10; 59; W.
Sun, heavy clouds.

Sunday 16.
29 9/10¾; 59, 67; W,   No swifts.
NE, E. Sun, sweet
ripening day.

Monday 17.
30; 61; E, SE.   Red-starts, & flycatchers still apear.
Great dew, sun, sweet
day, red even:

Tuesday 18.
29 8/10; 62; 70; SE.   Wheat housed.
Sun, brisk air, sweet
day, red even:

Wednesday 19.
29 8/10½; 75½; SE,   Much wheat housed.
S.   No swifts.
Sun, great dew, sultry,
cloudless.

Thursday 20.
29 8/10; 64, 75½; S,   Many people finish wheat-harvest.
SW, N.
Sun, cloudless, sultry,
cloudless.

Friday 21.
29 8/10½; 67; NE, E.   Wasps begin to encrease.
Sun, grey, sultry, rocky   Autumnal crocus blows.
clouds, sweet even:

Saturday 22.
29 7/10½; 64; E.   Grapes are full grown: some vine-leaves turn purple.
Sun, fog, sun, sultry,   Peaches, & nectarines swell, & tend towards ripening. Orleans
whisky clouds.   plums turn colour.

Sunday 23.
29 9/10; 65; 73; NW.   Flies torment the horses in a most unusual manner.
Sun, blue mist, sultry,
hot sun.

Monday 24.
30 1/10, 30 1/10; 64,
71; NW.
Sun, cloudless, sultry,
red even:

Hop-picking begins round Alton.

Tuesday 25.
30 1/10¼; 68, 79¾;
N.
Sun, cloudless, fierce
heat, red even:

Orleans-plums ripen.

Wednesday 26.
30 1/10, 30; 67; N.
Fog, dark & heavy,
cool wind, dark.

The failure of turnips this year is very great.

Thursday 27.
29 9/10¾; 60, 62;
NE.
Sun & clouds with cold
wind, red even:

Selborne people begin hop-picking.
The tops of beeches begin to turn yellow.

Friday 28.
30¼; 30 ½/10; 59, 63;
NE, N.
Sun & white frost-like
clouds, dew, cool air,
red even:

The common-fields are thrown open.
My well sinks. In many gardens the hops are fine & large.

Saturday 29.
29 9/10; 58, 66; NE,
NW.
Sun, white dew, sweet
day, cool even:

Hops are picked in fine order.
The first flight of martins are very numerous: they swarm on the
roofs, & on the tower.

Sunday 30.
29 6/10; 58; NW.
Sun, dark & chill,
small shower.

Monday 31.
29 8/10; 55, 61; N.
Sun, cold dew, dry &
harsh.

SEPTEMBER 1778

Tuesday 1.
29 7/10¾; 52; NW.
Frost, sun, grey, sun &
cold air, red even:

The frost shrivels the cucumber-leaves.
The young martins of the second flight peep out of their nests.

Wednesday 2.
29 6/10; 59, 61; NW.
Dark, shower, dark &
still.

No wasps at all: but the blackbirds devour the plums.
The peaches are not high-flavoured.

Thursday 3.
29 5/10; 64; NW.
Sun, sun, dark & mild.

The black cluster-grapes begin to turn colour.

Friday 4.
29 5/10½; 60, 63; E,
NW.
Dark & mild, sun,
dark & still.

Ladies-traces blow, & abound in the long Lithe. A rare plant.

Saturday 5.
29 7/10; 59; NE, NW.
Sun, sweet autumnal
weather.

Some showers in the night. The dust hardly laid. My well seems
to be sunk about 14 feet.

The young house-martins of the first flight are often very
troublesome by attempting to get into the nest among the second
callow broods; while their dams are as earnest to keep them out, &
drive them away.

Sunday 6.
29 6/10½; 56; NE.
Grey, blue mist, sun,
cold air. Full moon.

Autumnal Lady's Tresses.
Nore Hill.
28 August.

Monday 7.
29 5/10¼; 57½; N.
Dark clouds,
sprinklings.

Tuesday 8.
29 6/10½; 59; N.
Sun, showers, hot sun.

Wednesday 9.
29 7/10½; 58½; NE.
Sun, dark, sweet
autumnal day.

Thursday 10.
29 6/10; 57; E.
Sun, sweet weather,
shower.

Annuals are stunted, & spoiled for want of rain.
Peaches & nectarines drop-off.

Friday 11.
29 1/10¾; 58½; W.
Dark, rain, rain, rain,
bright, frost.

Martins congregate in vast flocks, & frequent trees, & seem to
roost in them.

Saturday 12.
29 3/10; 57; W.
Sun, clouds, shower,
sun.

My peaches, & nectarines are much commended.

The second brood of Martins near the stair-case window, which
were hatched Aug: 8: came-out Septemʳ 5ᵗʰ. So that the building a
nest, & rearing two broods take up much about four months, May,
June, July & August: during September they congregate, & retire
in October.

Sunday 13.
29 5/10; 54; W, N.
Sun, grey & mild,
bright even:

Monday 14.
29 8/10; 53½, 61;
NE.
Fog, sun, cloudless,
sweet day.

The honey-bees devour the peaches, & nectarines.
Fern-owls still appear.

Tuesday 15.
29 7/10¾; 53½; NE,
E, SE.
Fog, sun, sweet day.

Fly-catchers still remain. Several broods of martins are still in
their nests.
Just at the close of day several teams of ducks fly over
the common from the forest: they go probably to the streams
about Alresford.

Wednesday 16.
29 6/10⅓; 55; W.
Vast dew, sun, rain,
dark & still.

MEONSTOKE
Many ponds are almost dry a second time.
Young swallows come-out.
Some Mich: daisies begin to blow.

Thursday 17.
NW.
Sun, & clouds, sweet
day.

Friday 18.
SW.
Sun & clouds, sweet
weather.

Saturday 19.
30; 58; S.
Sun & clouds, sweet
autumnal weather.

SELBORNE
A lime-avenue in Rotherfield park has cast all it's leaves.
Many ponds are dry a second time.

Sunday 20.
30 ½/10; 54; S, SE.
Red morn: sun,
cloudless, sweet day,
red even:
New moon.

Grapes turn colour very fast.

Monday 21.
30; 62; SE, NE.
Wh: frost, cloudless,
glorious day.

Gathered-in the large white pippins.
There are now some wasps.
Great Northern *Aurora*.

Tuesday 22.
29 9/10; 67; E, NE.
Sun, fog, glorious
summer weather, red
even:

Bee stalls are very heavy this year: this hot dry summer has
proved advantageous to bees.
Vast N. *Aurora*, very red, & coping over in the zenith.

Wednesday 23.
29 9/10; 62; E, SW.
Deep fog, sun, sultry.

CHILGROVE
Ring-ouzels appear on their autumnal visit.

Thursday 24.
62; NW.
Deep fog, sun, sultry,
dark even:

SHOPWICK
Tho' very few hirundines appeared all the way; yet at Steyning
there were young martins in their nests.
No stone-curlews congregate this autumn at Chilgrove.

Friday 25.
30; NW.
Grey & mild, sun, dark
& lowring.

RINGMER
Fern-owl appears.

Saturday 26.
29 6/10; NW, W.
Distant thunder,

Some house-martins.
Mrs Snooke has gathered in all her apples, & pears: her fruit is

sprinkling, soft rain,
rain.

finely flavoured in such hot years.
Few swallows but many martins.
Mrs Snooke's black grapes begin to ripen. No wasps here.

The distress in this place for want of water is very great: they have few wells in this deep loam: & the little pits & ponds are all dry: so that the neighbours all come for water to Mrs Snooke's ponds.

Sunday 27.
29 5/10; W, NW.
Rain, hail, sun &
clouds, strong, cold
wind.

Rain in the night: the ground well moisten'd.
Many swallows, & house-martins.

Monday 28.
30; N, NW.
Frost, sun with cold
wind, sweet still even:

Mrs Snooke's black cluster-grapes are ripe & good. Many hirundines.

Tuesday 29.
S, SE, SW.
Frost, thick ice, sun,
sweet day, dark clouds.

Herrings come into season.
The after-grass in this grazing country is very short, & scanty.

Wednesday 30.
S, SW.
Sun & clouds, brisk
air.

The greatest part of the hirundines disappear: a few pairs of martins that have young still in their nests are very busy in feeding them.

OCTOBER 1778

Thursday 1.
W, W.
Sun, & showers,
showers, showers.

Some nestling-martins are out, & the dams feed them as they flie about. Some swallows.

Friday 2.
NW.
Frost, sun, sharp wind,
red even:

Heavy clouds in the horizon all day.
Several swallows & martins.
Some young martins still in their nests.
Timothy, the old tortoise, weighed six pounds, & eleven ounces averdupoise.

Saturday 3.
29 5/10; NW, SW.
Frost, sun, pleasant,
showers, red even:

Young martins still in nest.
White low fogs over the brooks.

Sunday 4.
NW.
Frost, sun, dark, red
even: bright moon.

Swallows.
Creeping fogs.

Monday 5.
N.
Frost, fog, sun, fine
even: creeping fogs.

Whitings in season still.
Many martins & some swallows hover about the cliffs near
Lewes.

Tuesday 6.
E, SE.
Dark, rain, rain, rain.
Full moon.

Some swallows.

Wednesday 7.
S, SE.
Dark & mild, shower,
grey, & soft.

Several martins.

Thursday 8.
Sun & showers, fine
afternoon.

FINDON
Not one wheatear to be seen on all the downs.
Swallows abound between Brighthelmstone & Beeding.
Not one ring-ouzel to be seen on the downs either coming or
going.

Friday 9.
Dark & lowering, still
& moist.

CHILGROVE
Many martins near Houghton-bridge.
Some swallows all the way.

Saturday 10.
29 3/10; 52; N.
Dark & moist, still &
dark.

SELBORNE
Some swallows.

My crop of apples is large: pears are but few: medlars in
abundance: wallnuts many, but not very good. One apple tree
produced ten bushels.

Sunday 11.
29 4¾; 49; N.
Frost, sun, pleasant
day.

Redwings begin to appear on their winter-visit. Some ring-ouzels
still about. When redwings come, woodcocks are near at hand.

Monday 12.
29 6/10; 43; NE.
White frost, sun,
pleasant day, grey.

My black grapes are large & good. The large bunches hardly
ripe.

Tuesday 13.
29 4/10¾; 44½; NE, E.
Deep fog, sun & clouds, fine afternoon.

I have not seen any swallows or house-martins since I came home. Near 40 ravens have been playing about¶ over the hanger all day.

Wednesday 14.
29 3/10; 44; NE.
Frost, sun & clouds, mild & still.

The hanger & my hedges are finely tinged with a variety of shades & colours.
Ravens play over the hanger.

Thursday 15.
29 4/10; 45; NE.
Frost, sun, pleasant day, sprinkling rain.

Leaves fall very fast.

Friday 16.
29 6/10½; 43; NE, N, NE.
Frost, sun, bright & sharp, red even:

The rooks carry off the wallnuts, & acorns from the trees.
One house-martin appears: by it's air & manner it seemed to be a young one: it scouted along as if pinched with the cold.

Rooks collecting acorns.
Church Meadow.
10 October.

Saturday 17.
29 6/10½; 40½; NE.
Wh: frost, thick ice, sun, cloudless, & sharp.

Gathered-in the berberries,¶ a great crop.

Sunday 18.

29 6/10½; 38; N.
Severe frost, thick ice,
ground hard, bright
sun & keen air, blue
mist, with a strong
scent.

The ashes are all stripped of their leaves. The vines are cut by the frost, so that the fruit will be exposed & damaged.

Monday 19.

29 3/10; 38; NE, E.
Severe frost, ground
hard, dark, sun, &
sharp air, grey.

The vines are naked, & the grapes exposed to the frost. The crop is very large.
The farmers complain that the ground is too dry for sowing.

Tuesday 20.

29 1/10; 44; E.
Grey, cold & chill,
rain, rain.

Planted long rows of tulips in the garden, & field. Leaves fall very fast.
Linnets flock.
Some wasps about.

Wednesday 21.

29 2/10; 44½; W.
Shower, sun, rain, sun.

The ivy is in full bloom: but the blossoms are nipped by the late frosts.

Thursday 22.

29 4/10; 51½; W.
Fog, sun, still & soft.

My well is so low that if much water is wanted it soon becomes foul & turbid. This inconvenience has never happened before since my Father sunk the well about 40 years ago. But then it must be remembered that we have had no rains to influence the springs since July twelvemonth.

Friday 23.

29 ½/10; 53, 56; SW.
Much rain, gusty wind,
dark & still.

The single oak in the meadow has born this year about 6 & ½ bushels of acorns.
Black snails come forth.

Saturday 24.

28 9/10; 56, 59; SW.
Much rain, strong
gusts, mild & windy.

Farmers put-up their fatting hogs.

Sunday 25.

29 1/10½; 50; N.
Dark & moist, black &
spitting.

Truly winter-weather.
Red-wings abound.

Monday 26.

29 5/10; 43; NW, NE.

Wood-cock seen.

Hard frost, sun,
pleasant.

Tuesday 27.
29 5/10; 43; E.
White frost, raw &
moist, rain, dark &
raw.

Wednesday 28.
29 3/10; 45; E.
Fog, mild, rain, rain.

Thursday 29.
29 5/10½; 53; SW.   The bat is out. Beetles hum.
Grey, mild & pleasant.

Friday 30.
29 7/10¾; 53; SW, S.   Flocks of great field-fares.
Sun, soft & agreeable.

Saturday 31.
29 3/10; 53; S.   Great field-fares abound.
Strong wind, rain &   My well rises.
storm, bright.

NOVEMBER 1778

Sunday 1.
29 8/10; 49½; SW.
Sun, mild & pleasant.

Monday 2.
29 8/10½; 51; SW, S.
Sun, soft day.

Tuesday 3.
29 4/10; 48; SE.
Grey, mild, small rain.

Wednesday 4.
29 3/10½; 53; S, NW.   Tit-mice creep into the martins nests & probably eat the *pupae* of
Great rain, sun, sun.   the *hippoboscae hirundines*.
Full moon.

Thursday 5.
28 9/10; 45; N.
Frost, fog, harsh wind,
rain, rain.

Friday 6.
28 8/10½; 48; SE.
Dark, rain, vast rain.

Planted six proliferous fiery lily-bulbs from Hambledon in the flower-borders.

Saturday 7.
43; SW, SW.
Rain, sun, sun,
showers.

My Chaumontelle-pears now come into eating, & are very delicate.

Sunday 8.
29 4/10; 43; SW, NW.
Grey, sun, mild, dark
& still.

Monday 9.
29; 43; S, SE.
Wet mist, grey, rain.

Tuesday 10.
29 1/10½; 44; W,
NW. Grey, pleasant,
dark & still.

Wednesday 11.
28 7/10; 44; W, NW.
Strong, heavy gales,
grey.

Planted in the borders some ferrugineous foxgloves.

Thursday 12.
29 3/10; 40; W.
Frost, ice, sun,
pleasant.

The vast yew-tree at Prior's-dean is a female: males in general grow to the largest bulk. The yewtree of East-Tisted is a female. The great yew-tree at Selborne, & two very large ones at Faringdon are all males.

Friday 13.
29 5/10; 38; W.
Frost, ice, sun,
pleasant.

Saturday 14.
29 2/10½; SE.

Dark, rain, rain, great
rain.

Sunday 15.
29 2/10; 50; S.
Rain, rain, showers,
hard rain.

Monday 16.
29 3/10; 52; S, SW, S.   Much rain.
Rain, rain, rain.

Tuesday 17.
29 3/10; 50; SW.   *Phalaenae* flie in abundance, about my hedges; these & some
Sun, soft & pleasant.   others, such as spiders, woodlice, slippery jacks,¶ & some gnats
                             & *tipulae* come forth all the winter in mild weather.

Wednesday 18.
29 3/10½; 47; SW.
Sun, soft & pleasant,
heavy clouds.

Thursday 19.
29 6/10½; 47;   Small field-shell-snails are still moving in the hedges.
NW.   Bat appears. The bat preys on *phalaenae*.
Sun, grey & mild.

Friday 20.
29 6/10¾; 46; S.
Rain, rain, gleam of
sun, spitting.

Saturday 21.
29 6/10½; 46; S.
Dark & mild, small
rain, soft & dark.

Sunday 22.
29 5/10; 52; S.
Wet & warm, rain,
driving rain, rain.

Monday 23.
29 3/10½; 54; SW.
Rain, driving rain, rain
& wind.

Tuesday 24.
29 3/10; 54½; SW.
Rain, rain, rain with
strong wind.

Wednesday 25.
29 7/10; 47; SW.
Storm with lightening,
sun & strong wind,
some showers, bright.

Thursday 26.
29 6/10½; 44; SW, S.
Sun, sun & mild, grey,
small rain.

Friday 27.
29; SW. Vast rain,
strong wind, sun, windy,
bright & still.

Saturday 28.
29 5/10½; SW.
Sun, still, mild &
pleasant.

Sunday 29.
29 3/10; 46; S.
Dark & mild, grey,
lowering, rain, rain.

Monday 30.
29 5/10; NW.
Sun, sun & mild.

DECEMBER 1778

Tuesday 1.
29 7/10; 40; NW, S.
Frost, ice, sun, sun,
dark, broken clouds.

Wednesday 2.
29; 39; SE. Sun, frost,
ice, dark, sleet, rain.

Finished trimming & tacking my vines; the wood is pretty well ripened for next year. Notwithstanding the vehemence of last summer, & the lasting heat, yet my grapes were not so early nor so well ripened as in some moderate years. In particular in 1775 my crops began to be gathered the first week in Septem[r]: & were in high perfection all the autumn: whereas this year we could not gather at all 'till Octob[r]: & then the flavour was not delicate; & many clusters never ripened at all. A proof this that some what more is requisite in the production of fine fruits than mere heat. My peaches & Nectarines also this summer were not in such perfection as in some former seasons.

Planted an old Newington-peach, & a Roman Nectarine.

Thursday 3.
28 8/10; 44; SE.
Grey, dark, rain, vast
rain.

My well is risen very much.

Friday 4.
28 2/10½; 44; SW.
Rain, dark & chill,
rain, rain.
Full moon.

Saturday 5.
28 6/10½; 41; S,
SW.
Grey, & mild, rain,
rain, dark & still.

Vast flocks of fieldfares.

Sunday 6.
29 1/10; SW.
Grey, sun, mild &
bright, dark & still,
rain.

Monday 7.
29 1/10; 47; SW.
Mild & grey, sun, dark
& still.
Moonshine.

Lightening.

Tuesday 8.
29 3/10; 48; SW.
Stormy wind with rain,
rain, rain, rain, rain,
wind.

Wednesday 9.
29 5/10; 52; SW.
Warm fog, small rain,
small rain.

Vast condensations: the trees on the down, & hanger run in
streams down their bodies. Walls sweat. The dew this morning
was on the outside of the windows: a token that the
air was colder within than without.

Thursday 10.
29 3/10; 51; SW.
Rain, still & warm,
rain, hail, vast rain.

Thunder.

Friday 11.
29 3/10; 51; SW.
Rain, driving rain,
rain.

Saturday 12.
29; 52; S.   Many flies appear, & some black snails.
Much rain, grey, sun,
dark, much rain.

Sunday 13.
28 9/10½; 48½; SW.   Peter Wells's well at Gracious street begins to run over. The
Vast rain, sun, rain, sun   lavants rise at Faringdon.
& stars.

Monday 14.
29 1/10; 45; S, SW.
Grey & mild, rain,
rain, rain.

Tuesday 15.
29 7/10; 40½; W,
NW. Sun, bright day,
stars, still.

Wednesday 16.
29 8/10¾; SW.
Frost, grey & still.

Thursday 17.
30; 43½; W.
Grey & mild.

Friday 18.
30; 47½; SW.
Grey & soft, moist,
showers.

Saturday 19.
29 9/10; 49; S, NW.
Grey & mild, small
rain, red even, soft.

Sunday 20.
29 9/10¾; 43; W.

Wh: frost, sun, fine day.

Monday 21.
30 1/10; 43; W.
Grey, still, & mild.

Vast flocks of fieldfares. Are these prognostic of hard weather?

Tuesday 22.
30; 45; W.
Grey, still & mild.

Wednesday 23.
30¼; 43½; W.
Grey, still, & moist.

Wheat grows much. Grass grows.

Thursday 24.
30 3/10; 44; SW, NE.
Fog, dark, still, &
warm.

Several little black ants appear about the kitchen hearth. These must be the same that are seen annually in hot weather on the stairs, with which some how they have a communication thro' a thick wall, or under the pavement, into the middle of the house.

Friday 25.
30 3/10¾; 46; NE, E.
Dark & mild, grey,
bright.

Saturday 26.
30 4/10½; 40; E.
Frost, bright, sun.

Sunday 27.
30 1/10; 36; E, SE.
Hard frost, rime, sun,
grey, deep fog, thaw.

Monday 28.
29 8/10; 40; SW, NW.
Sun, grey, small
showers, grey & mild.

Tuesday 29.
29 5/10; 46; W, NW.
Dark; small rain, &
strong wind, bright.

Wednesday 30.
29 5/10; 43½; SW.

Dark & mild, small
rain, dark & still.

Thursday 31.
29 2/10½; 46; SW.
Strong wind, showers,
storm with hail, bright,
& windy.

JANUARY

Friday 1.
29 7/10; 36; NW.
Storm all night, frost,
sun & sharp wind,
small snow.

SELBORNE
The may-pole is blown-down.
Thatch & tiles damaged.
Great damage is done both by sea & land.

Saturday 2.
30 1/10½; 33½; N.
Frost, sun & still, frost.
Full moon.

Sunday 3.
30 2/10; 33½; N.
Hard frost, rime, sun,
sun, fog.

Monday 4.
30 ½/10; 31; N.
Severe frost, sun, sunny
& still, frost.

Water froze in my chamber-window.

Tuesday 5.
29 9/10; 33; N.
Dark, small snow, still
& dark, thaw.

Wednesday 6.
29 9/10; 36; NE. Dark
with thaw, still & dark.

Thursday 7.
30 1/10; 36; E. Hard
frost, bright & pleasant.

Friday 8.
30 2/10; 32½; NE.
Hard frost, bright sun,
bright & sharp.

Saturday 9.
30 ½/10: NE.
Hard frost, rime, grey,
gentle thaw, dark,
mild.

Sunday 10.
30 ¼/10; NE.   My therm.ᵣ is broken.¶
Dark with thaw, dark
& harsh.

Monday 11.
30 ½/10; NE.
Hard frost, bright &
still.

Tuesday 12.
30 1/10; NE.
Hard frost, sun &
sharp wind, dark, frost.

Wednesday 13.
30 ½/10; N, E.
Grey & moist, small
rain, thaw, still.

Thursday 14.
30; NW, N.
Dark, small snow, sun,
warm, grey & still.

Friday 15.
29 9/10; N.
Hard frost, bright &
still.

Saturday 16.
29 9/10; NW.   Sowed the great mead in part, & all Berriman's field (laid down
Dark, small snow, dark   last year with grass seeds) with good peat-ashes.
& harsh.

Sunday 17.
29 9/10; NE.
Dark & still with some
thaw.

Ice on ponds is very thick.

Monday 18.
29 9/10; E.
Grey & still, sun,
pleasant, frost.

Tuesday 19.
30 1/10; S, W.
Dark & still, thaw,
small rain, deep fog.

Wednesday 20.
30 1/10¼; SW, SE.
Deep fog with thaw.

Thursday 21.
29 9/10; SE.
Dark & still, thaw, sun
& mild.

Friday 22.
29 9/10½; SE.
Sunny & mild.

Bees come out, & gather on the snow-drops.
Many gnats in the air.

Saturday 23.
30 ½/10; W.
Grey, soft & still.

Sunday 24.
29 8/10½; SE, S.
Fog, grey, bright.

Path clean, roads dry.

Monday 25.
29 6/10½; S, W.
Dark, rain, bright &
still.

Tuesday 26.
29 4/10; S.
Dark, sunny & soft,
showers.

Wednesday 27.
29 4/10; W, NW.
Dark & still, sharp.

Thursday 28.
29 7/10; NW.
Dark & still, sun, sweet
afternoon, grey.

Song-thrush, & Missle-thrush sing.
Paths are dry; & the weather spring-like.

Friday 29.
29 9/10; S.
Wh: frost, sun, & mild
frost.

Made the seedling-cucumber-bed with two cart-loads of my own
dung.
Out of the wind there is frost; but none where the S: wind blows.

Saturday 30.
30; SW.
Grey & mild, sun, dark
& still.

Tulips begin to peep.

Sunday 31.
30 1/10; SW.
Grey, sweet sun-shine,
grey & mild.
Full moon.

Spring-like.

FEBRUARY 1779

Monday 1.
30 1/10; 46; NW.
Grey & mild, sweet
weather.

Missle-thrush sings.

Tuesday 2.
30; W.
No frost, sun, grey,
fog, spitting rain.

Bees come out.

Wednesday 3.
29 8/10½; W.
Small rain, sun & brisk
air, small rain.

Flies come out in the windows. Earth-worms lie out during these
warm nights. Gnats come forth. Sowed cucumber-seeds.

Thursday 4.
29 8/10; W.

Green Hellebore emerges, & blows. Spring-like.

Dark & moist, small
rain.

Friday 5.
29 8/10; W.
Grey & mild, spitting.

Saturday 6.
29 8/10½; SW.   Hasel blows; male & female bloom are open.
Sun, brisk air, dark &   Some few crocus's blow.
mild.   Thrushes sing.

Sunday 7.
30 ½/10; W.   Lambs come very fast.
Wet fog, grey & mild,   Field-pease are sowing.
bright   Bats appear.

Monday 8.
30; 50½; W.   The sun is very strong.
Fog, sun, sweet
weather, grey & mild.

Tuesday 9.
29 8/10½; SE.   The garden works well: sowed pease, & planted beans. Crocus's
Grey, mild & still.   blow.

Wednesday 10.
29 8/10; SW.
Dark & moist, dark &
still.

Thursday 11.
29 7/10; S.   Cucumber-plants thrive.
Grey, sun, sweet day,
soft & still.

Friday 12.
29 5/10; SW.   The dry season lasted from Dec: 14: to Feb: 12. This whole time
Rain, rain, dark &   was very still; & even the frosty part of it very moderate: The
moist, bright.   baromʳ was up at 30 great part of the time. We have experienced
                     no such winter since the year 1750.

Saturday 13.
29 5/10; S.
Wet with strong wind,
wet & windy.

Sunday 14.
29 9/10; SW, NW.
Sun, bright sun,
shower, bright.

Great rain in the night with wind.
The hazels are finely illuminated with their male-bloom.

Monday 15.
30 1/10; S, SE.
Sun, soft & bright.

A vivid *Aurora*: a red belt from East to West.

Tuesday 16.
30 1/10; W.
Grey, sun, bright day.

Crocus's blow-out. When the vernal crocus blows, the autumnal
crocus peeps out of the ground. Bees gather on the crocuss.

Wednesday 17.
30 1/10½; SW, W.
Deep fog, fog, sun, red
even:

Winter-aconites go out of bloom.
The walls of my great parlor seem very dry.
Bees rob each other, & fight.

Thursday 18.
30 ½/10; S.
Vast dew, cloudless,
sweet day, cloudless.

Brimstone-coloured butterfly appears.
Large humble-bees.
Summer-weather.

Friday 19.
30 2/10; NW.
Sun, cold air, bright, &
gay.

Saturday 20.
30 1/10; NW.
Frost, deep fog, sun,
deep fog.

Field-crickets have opened their holes, & stand in the mouth of
them basking in the sun! They do not usually appear 'til March.

Sunday 21.
29 9/10; SW.
Dark & still, harsh.

Monday 22.
29 9/10; SW.
Dark & cold.

Tuesday 23.
SW.
Dark & mild, sun,
sweet day.

SOUTH LAMBETH
Drivers use the summer track. Roads dusty.

Wednesday 24.
30 1/10¼.
Dark & cold, small
shower, shower.

Almond-trees almost out of bloom.
Peaches, Nectarines, & Apricots begin to blow. Elms in full
bloom.

Thursday 25.
30 3/10.
Dark & still, sun, chill.

Friday 26.
30 3/10; 60½; SW.
Grey & soft.
❧ Pilewort.

Summer-like.

Saturday 27.
30 5/10; 62; W.
Sun.

The gardener begins to mow my Brother's grass-walks.
Sparrows begin to build.

Sunday 28.
30 5/10; 38; SE, NE.
Cold dew, sun,
cloudless.

Gossamer abounds.
Frogs swarm in the ditches. Spawn.

MARCH 1779

Monday 1.
30 2/10; 35, 45; NE,
W, SW.
Fog, cold, sun, the
wind whistles, red even:

Peaches & apricots in full bloom.

Tuesday 2.
30 3/10; 49; W.
Dark & mild, bright.
Full moon.

Wednesday 3.
30 3/10½; 33; SW.
Frost, very white, grey,
shower.

Thursday 4.
30 5/10½; 46; S.
Dark, dark, moonlight.

Friday 5.
30 6/10; 33; S, E, NE.　　　Ice.
Fog, frost, cloudless.

Saturday 6.
30 6/10; 37; NE.　　　Radishes pulled in the cold ground.
Fog.

Sunday 7.
30 5/10; 42; NE.
Dark & harsh.

Monday 8.
30 4/10½; 40; NE.
Bright.

Tuesday 9.
30 3/10½; 36; E.
Wh: frost, bright.

Wednesday 10.
30 2/10; 40; E.
Grey, harsh.

Thursday 11.
30 1/10; 37; E.
Dark & harsh,
cloudless.

Friday 12.
29 9/10½; 31; E, S.　　　Ice.
Bright, white frost,
cloudless.

Saturday 13.
30 1/10½; 35; W.　　　The roads in a most dusty, smothering condition.
Bright sun.

Sunday 14.
30 2/10; 44; W. Dark,　　　Quick-set hedges begin to leaf.
small rain, small rain.　　　Dust is laid.

Monday 15.
29 9/10; 46; NW.　　　Laurels blossom.
Dark & louring.

Tuesday 16.
30 1/10; 39; N.
Dark.

Wednesday 17.
30; 38; W, SW.
Dark, sprinkling.
☙ *Tussilago farfara,*
Stellaria holostia.

Thursday 18.
29 6/10½; 45; SE.
37 – louring.

Friday 19.
29 7/10; NW.
Bright, sun &
clouds.

Saturday 20.
29 4/10; SW.
Grey, sun, mild, small
rain.

Sunday 21.
29 8/10; W.
Hail, sun & showers,
strong wind, bright &
still.
☙ *Caltha palustris.*

Monday 22.
30; W.
Grey, cold, drying
wind.

Tuesday 23.
30; SW.
Grey, brisk wind, sweet
afternoon.

Wednesday 24.
29 9/10¼; S.
Sun, cloudless, sweet
day.

Rain in the
night.

SELBORNE

Stitchwort.
Short Lythe.
2 March.

The cucumber-plants show fruit, but are rather drawn by the late
sunny weather.

Apricots begin to set.
Cucumber, male blows.

Cucumber, female, blows.
The haulm of the cucumber-plants is weak; being drawn by hot
sunshine.

Thursday 25.
29 7/10½; E.
Wh: frost, sun,
cloudless, sweet day.

Picturesque, partial fogs, looking like seas, islands, rivers, harbours, &c!!
Vivid *Aurora*.

Friday 26.
29 7/10; 58; W.
Wh: frost, cloudless,
summer, sweet even:

Made an asparagus bed: that which was made last spring was spoiled for want of rain. Planted potatoes; sowed carrots.

Saturday 27.
29 9/10; 55; N.
Cold dew, sun &
clouds, cold wind.

Ponds in bottoms begin to fail.

Sunday 28.
30; 51; NE.
Dark, sun, harsh wind.

The springs are very low.

Monday 29.
29 9/10½; 46; E.
White frost, sun, sharp
wind, sun, bright, &
sharp.

Watered the fruit-trees early in the day.
Mowed my grass-plot, & some walks.

Tuesday 30.
29 9/10; 41; E.
Frost, ice, hot sun.

Bombylius medius: many appear down the long Lithe. Field-crickets bask at the mouths of their holes: they seem to be yet in their *pupa*-state; as yet they show no wings.

Wednesday 31.
29 9/10; E.
Wh: frost, ice, strong
sun, cloudless.

Some ponds fail. Barley begins to be sown.
Cucumbers set, & swell.
Bat appears.

APRIL 1779

Thursday 1.
30 1/10; E.
Dark & harsh, bright.

Apricots swell very fast.
Ash-trees blow.

Friday 2.
30 1/10; E. Wh: frost,
cloudless, hot sun.

Efts appear.

Saturday 3.
30; E.
Hard frost, ice,
cloudless, sultry in the
sun.

The small uncrested wren chirps: this is the first summer bird of
passage.
Watered the fruit-trees, & the new asparagus-bed.
Ring-ouzel appears.
The garden suffers for want of rain.
Elms & quick-sets begin to leaf: goose-berries, currans, & pears
blow.

Sunday 4.
29 8/10; SE.
Frost, ice, sun,
summer-like.
Mackerel-sky.

Monday 5.
29 7/10½; SE.
Dark & mild, sun,
summer-like.

WORTING

Tuesday 6.
W. Sun, hot, &
summer-like.
Hirundo domestica.

CAVERSHAM, READING
Two swallows at Selborne.

Wednesday 7.
SW.
Dark, small rain.

OXFORD
Cut the first cucumber.

Thursday 8.
SW.
Dark, showers, wind.

Two swallows seen at Selborne.

Friday 9.
SW.
Sun & clouds, strong
wind.

Saturday 10.
29 6/10½; 51; SW.
Dark, showers, dark &
mild.

SELBORNE
The beeches on the hanger begin to show leaves.

Sunday 11.
29 7/10; 51; W.

A swallow at Faringdon.

Clouds with brisk air.

Ivy berries are ripe: the birds eat them, & stain the walks with their dung.

Monday 12.
29 7/10¾; W.
Dark & mild, showers.

Gardens & fields suffer for want of rain.
Shell-snails come forth.

Tuesday 13.
29 7/10½; 56; SW.
Sun, summer-like,
sweet even:

Many beeches in leaf.
Cut a brace of cucumbers.

Wednesday 14.
29 6/10; 66; S.
Sun, bright & sultry,
sweet even:

Two cuckows appear in my outlet.
The mole-cricket jars.
The wry-neck appears, & pipes.

Thursday 15.
29 5/10; 66, 69; S,
SW.
Sun, bright, sultry,
sweet even:

Thunder-like clouds in the W; at break of day.
Nightingale sings in my outlet. Black-cap sings.
Dark clouds to the W; & N:W. Lightening.

Friday 16.
29 7/10; NW, NE.
Fog, dark & still.

Peaches & Nectarines swell.
Many ponds are dry. Hot-beds suffer by too much sunshine, & want of showers.

Saturday 17.
29 8/10; 57; E.
Sun, sharp wind, sun & clouds.

Apple-trees blossom. Swallows withdraw.
Rain greatly wanted: no spring-corn comes-up.
Sowed large white cucumbers.

The dry weather has now lasted four months; from the 15 of Decemr 1778. Apple-trees blow this year a full month sooner than last year. The hanger is pretty well in full leaf: last year not 'til May 15. *Musca meridiana*. The field-crickets in the short Lithe have cast their skins, are much encreased in bulk, & show their wings, being now arrived at their ἡλικια.¶ 'Til this alteration they are in their *pupa*-state, but are alert, & eat; yet cannot chirp, nor propagate their kind.

Sunday 18.
29 6/10½; 62; SE.
Sun, sun & clouds,
sultry, summer,
dark to the W: & NW.

Some young grass-hoppers appear: they are very minute.
Several swallows.
Some little rain.

Monday 19.
29 7/10½; 60; W,
SW.
Dark & mild, sun,
sweet afternoon.

A ring-ouzel still appears.
Just before dark a party of swallows, 8 or 9, came scouting along over the S: E: end of the hanger, & went towards the village.
Many places are in want of water.
Continue to water the garden, which suffers much.

Tuesday 20.
29 6/10½; 59; SW.
Grey, sun & brisk
wind, heavy clouds to
the W, dark & still.

Wednesday 21.
29 4/10½, 6/10½;
55½; W.
Good shower, showers,
cloudy with wind.

Lathraea squammaria, in the Church-litten coppice near the bridge among the hasel-stems, is out of bloom.

Thursday 22.
29 3/10¼; 55; SW.
Strong wind with
driving showers,
bright.

The hanger is in full leaf. Hazels in full leaf.
Swallows withdraw. No house-martin.
The ground is well moistened.

Friday 23.
29 4/10½; 49; SW.
Stormy with thunder &
rain, showers & strong
wind.

White large cucumbers come-up well.
The caterpillars of some *phalaenae* attack the foliage of the apricots again.

Saturday 24.
29 3/10; 48; W.
Hail, stormy, strong
wind with showers, cold
& blowing.

The wind broke-off the great elm in the church-yard short in two; the head of which injured the yew-tree. The garden is much damaged by the wind. Many tulips & other flowers are broken by the hail.

Sunday 25.
29 5/10, 3/10; SW.
Sun & clouds with
brisk gale.

The *Bombylius medius* is very brisk still on the short Lithe: in flying it frequently bobs with it's tail against some grass, or plant, & seems at that juncture to be laying it's eggs.
The lightening on friday morning shivered the masts of the *Terrible* man of war in Portsmouth harbour.

Monday 26.
29 1/10; 3/10; 48; W,
NW.
Rain in the night, sun

Opened the leaves of the Apricot-trees, & killed many hundreds of caterpillars which infest their foliage. These insects would lay the trees bare. They roll the leaves up in a kind of web.

with showers & brisk
wind.

Tuesday 27.
29 3/10; 45; SW.
Sun, hail storm,
showers, showers.

Wednesday 28.
29 3/10; 44; W.
Showers, & hail with
strong wind.

Thursday 29.
29 3/10; 46; W.
Showers, sun & clouds,
sweet even:

Friday 30.
29 3/10½; 48; NW.
Sun & clouds, soft,
distant showers, small
rain.
Full moon.

MAY 1779

Saturday 1.
29 3/10; 51; W; 49,
2.¶
Rain all night, sun &
clouds, hail, sun &
clouds.

N.B. By care & attention the leaves were saved this year.

Five long-legged plovers,¶ *Charadrius himantopus*, were shot at
Frensham-pond. There were three brace in all. These are the
most rare of all British birds. Their legs are marvellously long
for the bulk of their bodies. To be in proportion of weight for
inches the legs of the Flamingo should be more than 10 feet in
length.
Field-crickets begin to cry.

Two Swifts seen at Puttenham in Surrey.
Bank-martins on the heaths all the way to London.

House Martins appear at Selborne.
Swifts, two pairs, appear, dash along, at Selborne.
The ground is well moistened.

A pair of creepers (*Certhia*) build at one end of the parsonage-
house at Greatham behind some loose plaster. It is very amusing to
see them run creeping up the walls with the agility of a mouse.
They take great delight in climbing up steep surfaces; & support
themselves in their progress with their tails, which are long, & stiff
& inclined downwards.

Crickets
Wool Lane.
30 April.

Sunday 2.
29 5/10; N, E, S.
Hard frost, ice, sun &
clouds, showers about.

No swifts nor H: martins appear.
Hawthorn blows.

Monday 3.
29 3/10½; 48; N,
NW; 21.
Dark & louring, rain,
shower of snow, small
rain.

Cut two brace of cucumbers.
The snow lay but a small time.
Began to turn my horses into my field lain down last year with
rye-grass & dutch clover.

Tuesday 4.
29 3/10; 44; NW, W;
2.
Small snow, sun,
pleasant.

Wheat looks wretchedly.

Wednesday 5.
3/10¾, 29 5/10; 46;
NW; 29, 23.
Rain, dark & cold,
rain, rain, bright &
cold.

The swifts which dashed-by on saturday last have not appeared
since; & were therefore probably on their passage.

Thursday 6.
29 4/10; SW; 11.
Sun & clouds, dark,
rain, heavy clouds.

H: martins begin
to come to their nests.
No swifts to stay yet.
Several H: martins.

Friday 7.
29 4/10; 56; SW; 2.
Sun, showers, sun &
clouds.

One swift about.

Treecreeper, wakes Orchard
Early May

Saturday 8.
29 2/10; E, NE.
Dark & louring, soft
rain, rain.

Several swifts round the church.
Swallows abound.

A good crop of rye-grass in the field sown last year; but the white
clover takes only in patches. Sowed 4 pounds more of white clover,
& a willow-basket of hay-seeds. The white clover since is spread all
over the field.

Sunday 9.
29 4/10; S; 69.

Much rain in the night.

Sun & clouds, sweet
afternoon.

Ponds are full again.
Soft, growing weather.

Monday 10.
29 3/10; 56; SE, S.
Sun & clouds, sweet
afternoon.

Hot, growing weather.
Several swifts.
Vast rock-like clouds in ye horizon.

Tuesday 11.
29 5/10; SW.
Sun, cold dew, small
showers, sun, pleasant.

Planted-out large white cucumbers under the hand-glasses.
H: Martins frequent their nests.

Wednesday 12.
29 6/10; 58; NW.
Sun, sun & clouds, soft
& summer-like.

Tulips begin to fade.
Growing weather.
Wheat mends.

Thursday 13.
29 6/10; 54; NW, SW,
W.
Sun, sun & clouds,
summer weather.

Fern-owl chatters.

Friday 14.
29 6/10; 58; SW.
Vast dew, sun, grey &
mild.

White-throat appears.

Saturday 15.
6/10; SW.
Grey & mild, hot
gleams.

House-martins begin to build.

Sunday 16.
29 3/10; SW; 63.
Rain, rain, rain.

Monday 17.
29 5/10; SW.
Sun, & clouds, brisk
wind, dark & mild.

Tuesday 18.
29 5/10; SW.

Sun, small showers,
showers.

Wednesday 19.
NW.
Frost, ice, sun, sun &
wind.

Thursday 20.
29 5/10¾; NW.   Saint-foin begins to blow.
Sun & small showers,
fine.

Friday 21.
29 7/10; SW.
Dark, small showers,
sun & cool air.

Saturday 22.
29 8/10½; 56½; NW,   Bees begin to swarm.
SE.
Bright sun, sweet   Nightingales have eggs. They build a very inartificial nest with
summer weather, vast   dead leaves, & dry stalks. Their eggs are of a dull olive colour. A
dew.   boy took my nest with five eggs: but the cock continues to sing: so
                              probably they will build again.

Sunday 23.
29 7/10; 71; SE, E.   The sparrows take possession of my H: martins nests.
Sun, cloudless with   Grasshopper lark whispers.
brisk air, sweet
afternoon.

Monday 24.
29 8/10; 74; S, SW,   Fiery lily blows: orange-lily blows.¶
W.
Sun, sultry, sweet even:

Tuesday 25.
8/10½, 8/10; 74; NE,   Kidney-beans come up delicately.
E.   White cucumbers thrive.
Sun, sultry, sweet even: Fern-owl chatters.

Sheep with lambs
Galley Hill
February .

Wednesday 26.
29 7/10; 65½; NE,
SE.
Dark & louring,
dropping.

Elders, roses, lilies, & other solstitial shrubs, & flowers begin to
blossom already. The nightingale continues to sing; & therefore
probably is building again.

Thursday 27.
29 7/10; 70; NE.
Sun, brisk air, sultry,
sweet even:

Friday 28.
29 6/10; 65½; NE.
Fog, dark, sun, sweet
even:

Young pheasants!

Saturday 29.
29 8/10; 73½; E, S,
NW.
Sun, sultry, sweet
afternoon.

The ants on my stair-case appear again.

Sunday 30.
29 8/10½; 64; NE.
Dark with brisk air,
gleams of sunshine.
Full moon.

The Flycatcher appears.
Corn-flags blow. Foxgloves blow.

Monday 31.
29 8/10; 62; NE.
Sun, & clouds, hot sun,
& harsh air, sweet even:

Cut my Saint foin the 12.thcrop.
Began to tack my vines.
The smoke lies low over the fields.
Glow-worms begin to appear.

JUNE 1779

Tuesday 1.
29 7/10; NE.
Sun, hot sun & brisk
air.

BRAMSHOT-PLACE
The promise for grapes seems moderate. In Mr Richardson's
garden ripe scarlet strawberries every day; large artichokes,
pease, radishes, beans just at hand.
Bramshot soil is a warm, sandy loam.
Small cauliflowers.

Wednesday 2.
29 7/10; NE.
Sun & clouds, hot
gleams.

Wheat shoots into ears. Barley & pease are good on the sands.
The sands by liming, & turniping produce as good corn as the
clays.¶

Thursday 3.
29 7/10; NE.
Cold dew, sun,
thunder-clouds,
sprinkling,
cold air.

Friday 4.
29 6/10; NW, W.
White frost, ice, hot
sun, brisk air, sweet
even: distant clouds.

SELBORNE
The tops of the cucumbers were cut-off by the frost.
Ricked my saint-foin. three jobbs, in delicate order. Kidney-
beans damaged by the frost.

Saturday 5.
29 5/¾; 59, 64½; NE,
W.
Bright, hot sun, sweet
even:·

The borders in the garden chop for want of rain.¶ Flowers fade
very fast.
Large white cucumbers show male-bloom.

Many large edible chestnut-trees which grew on the turn-pike road
near Bramshot place were cut this spring for repairs: but they are
miserably shaky, & make wretched timber. They are not only
shaky, but what the workmen call cup-shaky, coming apart in
great plugs, & round pieces as big as a man's leg. The timber is
grained like oak, but much softer.

Sunday 6.
29 5/10½; 68; SE,
SW.
Deep fog, sun, sultry,
sweet even:

Sparrows take possession of the martins nests. When we shot the
cock, the hen soon found an other male; & when we killed the
hen, the cock soon procured an other mate; & so on for three or
four times.

Monday 7.
29 3/10; 61; S, SE.
Fog, dark & louring,
grey.

No shower of any consequence since May 16.
Glow-worms abound.

Tuesday 8.
29 1/10; S, SW; 39, 8.
Great showers, sun &
clouds, shower with
hail, chill air.

Portugal-laurels, & martagons blow.
Planted-out many annuals.

Wednesday 9.
29 3/10; 58; SW; 9.
Showers, wind &
showers.

Planted-out more annuals.

Thursday 10.
29 3/10½; 59; SW,
NW, W; 8.
Shower, gentle
showers, fine even:

Martins that began breeding in an old nest are now hatching.
Planted-out more annuals.

Friday 11.
29 2/10½; 58, 60;
NW, NW; 25.
Dark, rain, rain, rain.

Large white cucumbers shew female-bloom.
The kidney-beans begin to climb their sticks.
Cows yield much milk this summer.

Saturday 12.
29 2/10; 59; NE, NW.
S; 3.
Dark, soft shower, sun,
heavy clouds.

Planted-out annuals.
Growing weather.

Sunday 13.
29 2/10; 59; NE, SE,
NW, W; 23, 5.
Grey & soft, rain, rain,
rain.

Monday 14.
29 4/10; 60; NE, E, S,
NW.
Sun, vast showers
around, mild & soft,
shower.

Began to cut the tall hedges.
Growing weather.

Tuesday 15.
29 7/10; 64; NE, NW,
NE; 3.
Grey, sun & clouds,
fine afternoon.

Vines begin to blow.

Wednesday 16.
29 8/10; 58; NE, N.
White frost, sun, grey
& cool.

Wheat begins to blow.

Thursday 17.
29 7/10¾; 57½; N.
No dew, grey, sun,
sweet afternoon.

Friday 18.
29 6/10½; 60; W,
SW, N.
Little dew, sun, grey,
dark clouds, small
shower.

Saturday 19.
29 6/10; 58; NW, W,
N.
Cold dew, sun &
clouds, vast clouds,
brisk, cool gale, bright
& chill.

Farmer Turner cut my great meadow. He bought the crop.
Wood-strawberries begin to ripen.

Sunday 20.
29 8/10; 60; NW.
Cold dew, sun &
clouds, chilly air.

Monday 21.
29 8/10¼; 57; NW,
W, NW.
No dew, sun & clouds,
dark, small rain, soft
air.

Tuesday 22.
29 8/10½; 60; NW,
NE.
Grey, dark &
threatening, sweet even:

The large white cucumbers begin to set, & swell.
Farmer Turner housed his hay: it should, I think, have lain a day
longer.

Wednesday 23.
29 8/10¼; 57½, 61;
NW, N.
Dark, sun, small
showers, chill air.

Golden-crowned wrens, & creepers bring-out their broods.
Trimmed, & stopped the vines, which are in full bloom.
Wheat blows well.

Thursday 24.
29 7/10½; 56; NE, N;
16.
Sun, cold air, clouds,
wind, showers, clap of
thunder.

Things in the garden do not grow.
Vine bloom smells fragrantly.

Friday 25.
29 6/10; 58; N; 32.
Rain, rain, dark &
louring, shower, dark
& moist.

Saturday 26.
29 6/10½; 58; N; 17.   Cold black solstice.
Showers early, dark,
sun, chill air.

Sunday 27.
29 6/10¾; 58; N.
Dark & cold, sun, chill
air.

Monday 28.
29 7/10; 59, 64; E,   Swallows begin to bring-out their young broods. Wood-
NE, N.   strawberries fail, & are very scarce.
Sun, chill air, sun, cool
& bright.
Full moon.

Tuesday 29.
29 8/10; 59, 66; N.   The bees in my garden do not swarm.
Good dew, sun, with   Turned out the white cucumbers from under their glasses.
chill air, sweet
afternoon.

Wednesday 30.
29 8/10½; 60, 67;   Young swallows come out.
NE, E, S.
Cold dew, sun, sweet
day.

JULY 1779

Thursday 1.
29 6/10; 61, 70; N, N,   Rasps begin to ripen.
SW.
Sun, sultry, sweet even:

Friday 2.
29 4/10; 63, 71; NE,   Swallows feed their young on the wing.
SW, W.   Brisk gale.

Large dew, sun,
summer weather.

Saturday 3.
29 2/10; 66; SW, W;
61.
Rain, rain, rain, sun &
heavy clouds.

Lime trees blow.
Hops are remarkably bad, covered with aphides, & honey-dews.

Sunday 4.
29 ¼/10; 63; S, W;
101.
Rain, vast rain, rain,
sun & clouds.

Wheat is much lodged.

Monday 5.
29; 59; SW; 50.
Sun, showers, thunder
& hail.

Some barley lodged.
Much hay damaged.

Tuesday 6.
29 3/10; 60; W, NW;
16.
Showers with strong
wind.

Jasmine blows.
The flowers suffer.

Wednesday 7.
29 6/10½; 59; NW.
Small showers, sun &
clouds, sweet afternoon.

Vipers are big with young.

Thursday 8.
29 8/10; 60, 66; NW.
Vast dew, summer
weather.

Apricots begin to turn colour.

Friday 9.
29 9/10; 63, 70½;
NE, N.
Vast dew, cloudless,
blue mist, sweet even:

A surprizing humming of bees all over the common, tho' none
can be seen! This is frequently the case in hot weather.

Saturday 10.
29 9/10; 64, 74; NW,
NE.

Mushrooms appear.
Young house-martins leave their nests.

Vast dew, cloudless,
cloudy, sweet even:
cloudless.

Many martins & some swallows collect dirt to build, & repair their nests.
Began to cut large white cucumbers.

Sunday 11.
29 9/10; 66, 76¾; N,
SW, NW.
Vast dew, sultry,
cloudless, sweet even:

By the number of swifts round the church, which seem to be encreased to more than 30, their young ones must be come out.

Monday 12.
30½ 10, 30; 69, 71;
N, E.
Vast dew, sun, sultry,
sweet even:

Wheat turns colour. Apricots, the young tree, ripen.
Mossed the hills of the white cucumbers to keep them moist.

Tuesday 13.
29 8/10½; 68, 79!;
NW, W, NW.
Great dew, cloudless,
sultry.

The grass-mowers complain of the heat.

Wednesday 14.
29 9/10; 69, 77; NE,
S.
Dew, cloudless, sultry,
red even.

Dwarf-elder blows. Red martagons begin to blow: large kidney-beans bad for bloom. Grapes swell.

Thursday 15.
29 9/10½; 69, 77;
NE, S.
Vast dew, sun, sultry,
red even:

Young wasps come forth.
Low creeping white mist.

Friday 16.
29 9/10½; 66½; 77;
NE, SE.
Cloudless, sultry, cool
gale.

Bees eat the rasp-berries.

Saturday 17.
29 8/10; 66½, 76;
NE, E.
Cold fog, brisk air,
sun, sultry, sweet even:

Apricots ripen, the large sort.
Much hay delicately made.

Sunday 18.
29 7/10; 68, 78; E,
SW.
Fog, sun, sultry, brisk
gale, sweet even.

Very ripening weather: wheat turns very fast.

Monday 19.
29 5/10½; 68, 71½;
SW, W.
Fog, sun, sultry,
showers about, sweet
even:

Ferruginous fox-glove blows.

Tuesday 20.
29 4/10½; 67, 71;
SW, S.
Fog, sun, sun &
clouds, sweet even.

Wednesday 21.
29 2/10¼; 67; NW;
93.
Fog, rain, rain, rain.

Thursday 22.
29 1/10¾; 63; SE, S,
SW; 40.
Showers, showers,
showers.

No wind.

Friday 23.
29 2/10; 63; NW; 63,
79.
Vast showers, vast
showers, vast showers.

Distant thunder.

Saturday 24.
29 4/10; 62; W.
Grey, sun, hot, shower,
grey.

Puff-balls come-up in my grass-plot, & walks: they came from the
common in the turf. There are many fairy-rings in my walks, in
these the puff-balls thrive best.¶ The fairy-rings alter & vary in
their shape.

Sunday 25.
29 4/10; 64; W; 19.
Grey, sun, shower,
shower, thunder.

Monday 26.
29 3/10; 64; NW; 3.   Wheat harvest begins.
Shower, grey & mild.

Tuesday 27.
29 6/10; 62, 66; W, S,   Planted out in trenches four rows of celeri.
W.
Bright, clouds, small
shower, grey.

Wednesday 28.
29 3/10; 66; SW, S.   Planted-out endive.
Dark & mild, showers
about.
Full moon.

Thursday 29.
29 4/10; 67; SW, S,   Planted-out bore-cole, broccoli, savoy.
SE.
Moist & hot,
sprinkling rain, soft &
mild.

Friday 30.
29 4/10; 68; 70; SW;   Young martins congregate on trees.
11.
Shower, sun & clouds.

Saturday 31.
29 7/10; 65; NW.   Sowed a crop of spinage to stand the winter.
Sun & clouds, sweet
even: cool air.   For some days past only two swifts.

AUGUST 1779

Sunday 1.
29 7/10; 67; NW, SW.   Several swifts.
Cold dew, sun, sun,
sweet even:

Monday 2.
29 6/10½; 68; SE,   Young martins, the first brood, are very numerous.
W; 4.
Sun, brisk air, clouds,
soft rain.

Tuesday 3.
29 7/10; 68; W.
Sun, brisk gale, sweet
harvest weather.

One swift.
Wheat-harvest is general.
Fern-owl chatters.

Wednesday 4.
29 5/10; 62; W, E; 5.
Grey, dark, small rain.

Thursday 5.
29 4/10; SE, NE; 33.
Rain, rain, rain.

One swift.

Friday 6.
29 3/10½; 60, 60;
NE, NW; 10.
Dark & cool, rain,
rain.

Much wheat down.
Fell-wort begins to blow.

Saturday 7.
29 4/10; 60; NW,
NW.
Rain, rain, rain, dark.

Wheat under the hedges begins to grow.

Sunday 8.
29 4/10½; 62½; NW.
Dark & still, sun, small
rain, gloomy & hot.

Wheat lies in a bad way.
Many swifts.
Distant thunder.

Monday 9.
5/10, 29 7/10; 65;
NW, N.
Dark & warm, misty
rain.

These swifts proved to be the last that I saw.

Tuesday 10.
29 7/10¼; 65; N; 3.
Misty rain, warm, grey
& damp.

Wheat lies in a bad way. Peaches, & plums rot.
Wheat grows.
Flying ants swarm in millions.

Wednesday 11.
29 7/10; 65½, 67½;
N, W.
Grey & sultry, sweet
gleams.

Martins congregate.

Thursday 12.
29 7/10; 69; W, E, W.   Distant thunder.
Grey, sun, heavy
clouds, showers, dark
& warm.

Friday 13.
29 7/10½; 64; NE, E,   Peaches & Nect: rot on the walls.
SW.   Thunder all around. Some wheat housed.
Wet fog, sun, showers,
sultry, thunder, stars,
fog.

Saturday 14.
29 7/10; 69; S, SE.   Much wheat housed, in bad order.
Fog, sun, sweet day,
grey & soft.

Sunday 15.
29 7/10; 69; SW.
Sun, sultry, sweet even:

Monday 16.
29 7/10; 67; W, SW.   Much wheat housed.
Sun, sweet harvest
weather.

Tuesday 17.
29 7/10¼; 64½; 69;   Much wheat housed.
N, NE. Sun, sultry,   Drank tea at the hermitage.
blue mist, grey & still.

Wednesday 18.
29 2/10; 70; NE, E.
Sun, sultry, grey.

Thursday 19.
29 8/10½; 68; E.   Wheat standing yet.
Sun, brisk gale, grey &
still.

Friday 20.
29 9/10; 68; E.
Sun, clouds & brisk
gale, sweet even:

Saturday 21.
29 9/10; 68, 73; NE,
NE.
Sun, brisk air, sweet
even:

Many people have finished wheat-harvest.

Sunday 22.
29 7/10; 74; NE.
Sun, sultry with a brisk
gale, sweet even:

Monday 23.
29 6/10½; 70; NE,
NW; 90.
Sun, clouds, thunder
shower, red even:

Great blackness.

Tuesday 24.
29 7/10; 71; NE, NW.
Sun, sweet autumnal
weather.

Wednesday 25.
29 7/10¼; 64; NE,
SE.
Vast dew, sun, sweet
day.

Nect: & peaches improve in flavour, but are destroyed by wasps.
Grapes begin to turn colour.

Thursday 26.
29 7/10; 69; SE.
Sun, brisk gale, sweet
even:

Friday 27.
29 8/10; 73; SE.
Dark, shower, sun,
showers about, hot &
still.
Full moon.

My well is shallow & the water foul.

Saturday 28.
29 8/10½; 76; N, NE,
E, W.
Sun, sultry, sweet
even.

Some people have finished harvest.

Sunday 29.
29 8/10; 77½; NE, S,
SE.
Sun, sultry, sweet even:

House-crickets are heard about in all the gardens, & court-yards.
One came to my kitchen-hearth.

Monday 30.
29 6/10; 77½; SE, S.
Sun, sultry, fleacy
clouds, sultry.

FYFIELD
Gathered all the nectarines.
Harvest is nearly at an end on the downs.

Tuesday 31.
29 7/10; 77½; S, NW.
Sun, sultry, hot gleams,
dark clouds, red even:

The grass burns.

SEPTEMBER 1779

Wednesday 1.
29 6/10, 3/10; 77; NE,
E.
Dark, gleams, thunder
& rain.

Thursday 2.
29 5/10; 70; W.
Sun, brisk air, cool.

Partridges innumerable.
Barley-harvest finished here.

Friday 3.
29 7/10; 70; SW.
Sun, fine air, clouds.

Saturday 4.
29 6/10; SW.
Dark, rain, sun, chilly.

Sunday 5.
29 4/10; 65; NW, SE.
Dark, showers, bright.

Monday 6.
29 6/10, 8/10; 65; N.
Sun, clouds, cool air.

The trufle-hunter tries my brother's groves, but finds few trufles,
& those very small. They want moisture.

Tuesday 7.
29 7/10½; 67; W.

No mushrooms for want of more moisture.

Shower, sun, & strong
gale.

Wednesday 8.
29 7/10½; NW.
Strong gale, sun &
clouds.

Strong gales all night.

Thursday 9.
NW.
Bright, hot sun.

WORTING
The greens of the turneps in light shallow land are quite withered
away for want of moisture.

Friday 10.
N.
Gloomy, still, sultry,
soft showers, gloomy.

UFTON in Berks, WORTING

Saturday 11.
29 9/10½; 69; SE, S.
Sun, & clouds, strong
sun with air, bright.

SELBORNE
The rain that fell in my absence was . . . 73.¶
My grapes are brought so forward by the hot season, that they are
ripe, & well-flavoured.

Sunday 12.
29 6/10½; 66; N, NE,
SW. White frost, sun,
hot sun, dark & still.

Monday 13.
29 7/10; 67; W.
Grey, sun & clouds,
soft even:

Gathered the filberts, a large crop.

Tuesday 14.
29 6/10; 62; W, NE,
NW, SW; 43.
Dark, rain, rain, sun,
clouds.

Wednesday 15.
29 7/10; 63; W, NW.
Sun, sweet day, soft &
still.

Ivy begins to blow.

Thursday 16.
29 8/10¾; 66½; W.

Grapes are delicate.

Grey, sun, sweet day,
brisk air, soft & still.

Friday 17.
29 7/10; 63; W, NW.
Sun, brisk gale &
clouds, sweet even:

Saturday 18.
29 4/10; 63; S, W; 34.
Sun, no dew, dark &
ruffling, rain, showers,
red even:

Sunday 19.
29 5/10; 56; W, NW;
14.
Sun, rain, thunder,
hail, strong gale, bright
& still.

Monday 20.
29 6/10¾; 54; NW,
W. Sun, chill air,
sun, cool even:

Tuesday 21.
29 4/10; 62; SE, W.
Small rain, strong
gales, clouds & wind.

Wednesday 22.
29 4/10¾; W.
Sun, dark, wind, small
showers, grey & mild.

Thursday 23.
29 3/10; W; 17.
Rain, dark & moist,
rain, great rain.

Friday 24.
29 2/10½; W, S, SE;
70.
Sun, pleasant morn:,

Fungi.
Selborne High Wood.
September.

louring, shower,
clouds.

Saturday 25.
29 2/10; 64, 66; SE, S;
53.
Rain, rain, dark &
threatning.
Full moon.

Warm & moist.

No mushrooms have appeared all this month. I find that the best
crop is normally in Aug: & if they are not taken then, the season
for catchup is lost. Many other fungi.

Sunday 26.
29 4/10; 63½; SE; 4.
Showers, dark & mild.

Thunder about.

Monday 27.
29 6/10; 62¼; SW.
Sun, showers, soft &
bright.

Gathered-in the pears. The Cadillac-tree born five bushels.
Apples are few; & the crop of grapes small.

Tuesday 28.
29 6/10½; 61; SW;
14.
Sun, showers, sun, soft
& still.

Grapes are rich, & sweet.

Wednesday 29.
29 4/10½; 62; SE.
Grey, sun, soft & still,
showers about.

Thursday 30.
29 3/10; 62½; S, SW.
Grey, sun, shower,
sweet afternoon.

OCTOBER 1779

Friday 1.
29 5/10; 58; W, NW.
Fog, rain, sun, sweet
afternoon.

Saturday 2.
29 7/10; 53; N.

White frost, sun &
sharp air.

Sunday 3.
29 8/10; 49; N.   Began lighting fires in the parlor.
White frost, sun & dry
sharp air.

Monday 4.
30; 43; N, N.   Rooks carry away the wall-nuts from the trees.
White frost, ice, sun,   Mushrooms abound. Made catchup.
grey & still.

Tuesday 5.
29 9/10¾; 45; NE.   Martins feed their young on the wing: These birds are just come
White frost, sun, blue   out of their nests.
mist, red even:

Wednesday 6.
29 6/10¼; 53; NE, E.   Grapes are delicate.
Grey, sun, sweet day,   Many martins & swallows.
soft & still.

Thursday 7.
29 7/10; 53½; NE,
W, SW, W; 2.
Small showers, grey,
sun, sweet afternoon,
stars.

Friday 8.
29 8/10; 49; E, S.
White frost, sun, sweet
day.

Saturday 9.
29 6/10; 48; S, SW.   Many martins.
White frost, sun, dark
clouds.

Sunday 10.
29 7/10¾; W;
25, 2.
Rain, sun & showers,
bright.

Monday 11.
29 7/10; 50½; W,
SW.
Sun, bright & warm,
clouds, rain.

Multitudes of house-martins, but few swallows.

Tuesday 12.
29 6/10; 56; W; 10.
Dark & moist, hot sun.

FUNTINGTON
Bad fevers round Chichester.

Wednesday 13.
SW; 7.
Small showers, sun.

SHOPWICH

Thursday 14.
SE.
Sun & brisk wind,
rain, rain.

Saw no hirundines in all the road.

Friday 15.
SW; 24.
Heavy clouds, rain,
rain.

RINGMER
One martin at Lewes.

Saturday 16.
S; 203.
Rain, rain, rain, rain.

Vast rain with strong wind for near 24 hours.
Thomas Hoar kept the measure of the rain in my absence.¶

Sunday 17.
SW.
Sun, wind & showers.

Several swallows.

Monday 18.
SW.
Fog, rain, sun, brisk
wind.

Mrs Snooke's black grapes are very fine.
Ponds are very low. Several swallows.
Bat.

Tuesday 19.
SW; 17.
Sun & clouds, strong
wind, thunder.

Swallows.

Wednesday 20.
W.
Sun, soft, sweet day.

Many *libellulae* in copulation.
Rooks frequent their nest-trees much.

Thursday 21.
SW; 69.   Many martins.
White frost, rain, rain.

Friday 22.
N.   Much rain in the night.
Grey & pleasant.

Saturday 23.
N.   Whiting, & herrings.
Fog, grey, mild & still.

Timothy, the old tortoise at this house, weighs 6 pounds 9 ounces & an half averdupose. It weighed last year, Oct: 2, an ounce & an half more. But perhaps the abstemious life that it lives at this season may have reduced its bulk: for tortoises seem to eat nothing for some weeks before they lay-up. However this enquiry shows, that these reptiles do not, as some have imagined, continue to grow as long as they live. This poor being has been very torpid for some time; but it does not usually retire under ground 'til the middle of next month.

Sunday 24.
SE, S.   Many hornets about the vines.
Fog, dark & mild.

Monday 25.
SW.
Hot sun, grey & mild.
Full moon.

Tuesday 26.
W; 28.
Dark, fog, rain, sun,
red even.

Wednesday 27.
W.   Apples & pears rot very fast.
Rain, rain, wind, sun
& clouds.

Thursday 28.   ARUNDEL
SW: 16.   Sheep-ponds on the downs are all filled by the rains. A great
Dark, blowing & wet.   beast-market this day at Arundel.

Friday 29.   SELBORNE
29 8/10; W, NW.
Sun, & clouds.

Saturday 30.
29 9/10; 56; W.
Sun & strong wind,
sweet afternoon.

Wood-cock is seen.
Thrush sings.

Sunday 31.
30; 55; W.
Grey, mild & still.

NOVEMBER 1779

Monday 1.
29 8/10; 54½; SE, E.
Grey & mild.

Red-wings appear.

Tuesday 2.
29 8/10; 51; N, NW.
Grey & mild.

My well is risen many feet.

Wednesday 3.
29 8/10; 54; SE.
Grey & mild.

Wood-pigeons appear. The last winter-birds of passage.¶

Thursday 4.
29 8/10¼; 55; W.
Grey, sun, sweet day,
red even:

A delicate season for sowing of wheat.

Friday 5.
29 8/10¾; 52½; W,
NW.
Dark & sprinkling,
bright.

On this day many house-martins were seen playing along the side
of the hanger.
See Novemʳ 4: 1777.

Saturday 6.
29 8/10½; 51; W,
NW.
Sun, sweet summer
weather.

Great flocks of wood-pigeons.

Sunday 7.
29 8/10¾; 51; NW.
Sun & fleecy clouds,
sweet day.

Monday 8.
29 8/10¾; NW.
Grey & still, dark &
spitting.

Great field-fares appear.

Tuesday 9.
30; 50; NW.
Sun & cold air.

Wednesday 10.
29 9/10; 50, NW.
Dark, small shower,
dark & harsh.

Thursday 11.
29 7/10½; 47; NW.
Dark & harsh, small
showers, gleams
of sun.

Friday 12.
29 4/10; 48; W; 13.
Dark & harsh, driving
showers, rain.

Saturday 13.
29 ½/10; N, SE, SW;
10.
Dark & moist, small
rain.

Sunday 14.
28 4/10¾; 40; NW.
Frost, ice, sun, & sharp
air, bright.

Some flakes of snow.
Rocky clouds, & distant lightening.

Monday 15.
28 2/10; 32; W; 18.
Snow, sleet, cold rain,
rain, dark & harsh.

True winter weather.

Tuesday 16.
29 2/10; 40; NW.
Frost, ice, sun, clouds,
small shower, grey.

Wednesday 17.
29 3/10; 40; NW, N.
Frost, sun & sharp air,
bright.

Thursday 18.
Frost, ice, snow, snow,
grey, bright.

UFTON in Berks

Friday 19.
Frost, sun, sun, sun,
moonshine.

Saturday 20.
28 3/10½; 37½; NW.
Frost, ice, snow, snow,
rain, rain, grey.

SELBORNE

Sunday 21.
29; NW.
Frost, ice, dark &
harsh.

Monday 22.
29: NW.
Dark & harsh, sun.

Tuesday 23.
28 9/10, 29; 36; NW.
Hard frost, sunny &
still, hard frost.
Full moon.

Vast banks of clouds in the horizon.
An eclipse of the moon, total but not central.

Wednesday 24.
29 1/10¾; 35; W.
Thaw, sun, pleasant,
frost.

Thursday 25.
28 6/10; 36; W, SE;
64.
Rain, rain, dark, rain.

M[rs] Snooke's old tortoise retired under the ground.

Friday 26.
28 5/10; 39; W; 7.

Rain, strong wind, grey
& cold, sun.

Saturday 27.
28 6/10; 38; E, NE;
40.
Rain, rain, rain.

Sunday 28.
28 7/10½; 48; W,   The ground is glutted with water.
NW; 34.
Rain, rain, grey bright.

Monday 29.
29; 42; W, SW; 54.   Snow was half-shoe-deep on the hill.
Snow, snow, sun, dark,   Distant lightening.
rain.

Tuesday 30.
28 9/10¾; 41½; W,   Lightening.
SW; 26.
Sun, pleasant day,
bright.

DECEMBER 1779

Wednesday 1.
29 2/10; SW, S.
Dark & moist, small
rain, small rain.

Thursday 2.
29; SW; 120.   Vast condensations in the great parlor: the grate, the marble-
Stormy wind, & vast   jams, the tables, the chairs, the walls are covered with dew. This
rain, rain.   inconvenience may be prevented by keeping the window shutters,
                         & door close shut in such moist seasons.

Friday 3.
29 1/10; 51; SW; 20.
Sun, soft, & pleasant,
great rain.

Saturday 4.
29 6/10½; 41; W; 60.   Paths dry, & firm.
Sun with a brisk gale.

Sunday 5.
29 9/10; W.
Frost, ice, sun & sharp
wind.

Monday 6.
29 8/10; 37½; W, S.
Frost, dark & still,
rain.

Tuesday 7.
29 1/10¼; SW, S,
SW.
Grey, shower, sun,
rain, rain.

Wednesday 8.
29 7/10; NE, N; 24.
Sun, bright & still,
frost.

Thursday 9.
29 3/10½; S, SW; 33.
Rain, rain, rain.

Friday 10.
29 4/10; 51; W; 22.
Rain with wind, rain.

Saturday 11.
29 5/10; W.
Dark & wet, sun,
pleasant.

Sunday 12.
29; S; SW; 22.
Rain, rain, sun &
clouds.

Monday 13.
28 7/10; SW, S; 38,
51.
Rain, vast rains, star-
light.

Much thunder. Great hail at Faringdon.

Growing on the Bostal,
26 August.

Tuesday 14.
29 5/10; W.
Sun, brisk, drying
wind.

Wednesday 15.
29 4/10; 38; W, SE;
29.
Frost, dark, snow,
snow, rain.

Thursday 16.
29 2/10; SW.
Dark & mild, rain,
rain, rain.

Friday 17.
29 3/10½; 52; SW;   Vast condensations on walls, & wainscots.
48. Rain, rain, rain.

Saturday 18.
29 2/10½; 52; SW; 6.
Grey, sun, pleasant,
grey & still.

Sunday 19.
29; 52; SW; 5.
Grey & mild, rain,
rain.

Monday 20.
28 6/10½; 51; SW,
64, 43.
Rain, vast showers, vast
hail! thunder, showers,
grey.

Tuesday 21.
28 5/10; S, 10.
Grey & mild, rain,
rain.

Wednesday 22.
28 9/10½; 38, 37; SE;   Ground covered with snow.
33.

Snow in the night,
frost, sun, sun, frost.

Thursday 23.
29 3/10; 35; SW.
Hard frost, sunny &
still, bright.
Full moon.

Snow on the ground.

Friday 24.
29 3/10½; 30; W,
NW.
Hard frost, rime, sun,
cloudless, fog.

Saturday 25.
29 6/10½; 29, 29;
NW.
Vast rime, strong frost,
bright & still, fog.

The hanging woods when covered with a copious rime appear
most beautiful & grotesque.

Sunday 26.¶
29 7/10½; 28; NW.
Vast rime, frost, bright
& still, fog.

Most beautiful rimes!

Monday 27.
29 5/10; 32; NW.
Dark, thaw, snow,
snow, snow.

Tuesday 28.
29 6/10½; 35; N, NE.
Dark, thaw, fog, small
rain.

Snow melts very fast.

Wednesday 29.
29 9/10¼; 35; N, NE.
Dark & moist, melting
snow.

Thursday 30.
29 9/10; 37; E.
Dark & mild, sun,
hard frost.

Friday 31.
29 8/10½; E.
Frost, sun, fog.

JANUARY   — 1780 —

Saturday 1.   SELBORNE
29 8/10¾; 33; NW.   Ice is very thick.
Frost, heavy fog, thaw.

Sunday 2.
29 8/10; W, SW.   Vast condensations, & dripping from the trees.
Fog, thaw, grey, swift
thaw.

Monday 3.
29 8/10; 42; NW; 4.
Dark & moist, mild &
dark.

Tuesday 4.
30; 41; NW, N. Sun,
still, mild, sun, frost.

Wednesday 5.
29 7/10¼; 36; NW.
White frost, sun, grey
& still.

Thursday 6.
29 6/10½; 36; W.
Frost, thaw, grey &
still.

Friday 7.
29 8/10; 38; SE, NE.
Grey, sun, grey, frost.

Saturday 8.
29 7/10½; 35; NE, N.   Hard frost.
Frost, rime, sun,   On this day Sʳ George Rodney took a large Spanish convoy off
cloudless, frost.   cape Finister.

Sunday 9.
29 5/10; 30; N, NW.

Severe frost, sun,
cloudless & still, frost.

Monday 10.
29 3/10; 33; NW.
Dark & still, thaw,
deep fog.

Ivy berries are pretty near full grown, & begin to turn black: the
ivy blossoms in Octobᵣ & the fruit ripens in March, & April.

Tuesday 11.
29 3/10; 30; NW.
Strong frost, sun, grey,
fog, grey, frost.

Wednesday 12.
29 5/10; 32; NW.
Severe frost, sun,
cloudless, sharp wind,
severe frost.

For want of snow to cover, the garden things suffer; cabbages,
spinage, celeri, &c.

Thursday 13.
29 5/10¾; NW.
Severe frost, sun &
fleecy clouds, severe
frost.

Thermᵣ abroad 16, 19, 14½.
Water frozen in my chamber.
Water frozen in Do:

Friday 14.
29 4/10; NE, E, NE.
Severe frost, vast rime,
cloudless, hard frost.

[Thermᵣ abroad] 18, 16½.

Saturday 15.
28 6/10; E, SE.
Hard frost, dark, thaw,
rain, hard rain, wind.

[Thermᵣ abroad] 16½.

Sunday 16.
28 3/10½; 40; SW;
64.
Wind, & showers,
strong wind.

A precipitate thaw. The rain last night tore-up the N: field lane
very badly. Turnips seem to be damaged by the frost.

On this day Sᵣ George Rodney defeated the Spanish fleet off Cadiz.

Monday 17.
28 6/10; 42; SW; 19.
Grey, sun, soft, &
pleasant.

Tuesday 18.
28 7/10¾; 42½; SW,
S. Fog, mild, partial
fog, showers, showers.

The ground very dirty, & hollow from the frost.

Wednesday 19.
28 9/10½; 42; N.
Fog, wet fog, rain,
rain.

Thursday 20.
29 3/10; N; 81.
Snow, snow, snow,
grey.

Friday 21.
29 6/10½; 36; N; 12.
Frost, sun, sun, frost.
Full moon.

Some snow on the ground.

Saturday 22.
29 6/10¾; 32; NW.
Hard frost, cloudless,
& still, frost.

Sunday 23.
29 7/10; 31½; N, NE,
N.
Hard frost, fog &
rime, fog.

Vast rime on the trees all day.
The naked turnips suffer, especially where the fields incline to the
sun: they are frozen & then thawed, & so rot. Those farmers are
best off this winter, who pulled their turnips, & stacked them up
in buildings, & under hedges.

Monday 24.
29 6/10½; 31; N.
Hard frost, rime, sun,
sun, small snow.

Tuesday 25.
29 7/10½; 30½; N.
Hard frost, sun, snow,
snow, frost.

Lambs fall very fast.

Wednesday 26.
29 6/10; 31½; N.
Hard frost, dark,
flights of snow, frost.

Snow on the ground.

Thursday 27.
29 6/10½; 32½; NE.
Hard frost, grey &
still, sun, bright &
sharp.

Hares, driven by the severity of the weather, crop the pinks in the garden.

Friday 28.
29 6/10; 29; NE, E.
Fierce frost, vast rime,
sun, dark & louring.

Saturday 29.
29 4/10; 32; NE.
Gentle frost, still &
louring.

Ground very hard, & snow on the ground.

Sunday 30.
29 3/10½; 31; NE.
Hard frost, dark &
louring with a severe
wind.

Rugged, harsh weather.
Cabbages are much damaged.

Monday 31.
29 3/10¼; 34; E.
Dark & still, dark.

The cabbage-plants that were to have stood the winter seem to be killed: lettuces under the fruit-wall are damaged; but they all recovered. Ground hard, & dusty.

FEBRUARY 1780

Tuesday 1.
29 2/10½; 32; N.
Frost, dark & still.

Ground hard, & dusty.
Some small sleet.

Wednesday 2.
29 2/10; 32; N.
Grey & still, gleams of
sun, grey & still.

The uplands still covered with snow.

Thursday 3.
29 4/10¼; 33; NW,
SW, SW. Sun, grey
& mild, bright, frost.

Made the seedling-cucumber-bed with two loads of dung.
Foot-paths are dusty.
Snow-drops blow.

Friday 4.
29 3/10; 36; SW, S.

Wag-tails appear about the streams thro' all the severe weather.

Grey, sun, soft & still,
thaw.

Saturday 5.
29 1/10; 36; N, NE,
SW, W.
Frost, sun & mild, dry,
thaw.

Sunday 6.
28 8/10; 40; SE, W;   Lightening.
41. Thaw & rain,
sun & clouds, bright.

Monday 7.
29 5/10; 39; NW.
Sun, sun, dark, frost.

Tuesday 8.
29 5/10; 38; SE; 22.   The paths very miry.
Frost, thaw, soft rain,
rain.

Wednesday 9.
29 8/10½; 44; SW, S.   The dew is on the outsides of windows: therefore the warm
Fog, warm air, grey,   air is not got in a doors; but it is colder within than without. Vast
falling fog.   condensations on walls, &c.

Thursday 10.
30; 47½; SW, W,   Vast condensations on walls, & wainscot.
NW.   Flies & gnats come forth.
Warm fog, mild &   Earth-worms appear on the turf.
moist, wet fog.

Friday 11.
30 1/10; 45; NE.   Eruptive fevers, & sore throats lurk about the parish: some die of
Grey, sun & mild, fog.   this disorder.

Saturday 12.
30 1/10; 41; NE.   The farmers begin to plow after the frost.
Fog, dark & harsh.

Sunday 13.
30 1/10½; 39; N.   Turnips are all rotten. Cucumber-plants come-up.
Dark & harsh.   Paths begin to dry.

Monday 14.
30 1/10; 40; N.
Dark & harsh.

Tuesday 15.
29 9/10¾; 39; N.
Dark & harsh, still.

Some scattering flakes of snow.

Wednesday 16.
29 7/10; 37; NW, N.
Dark, gleams of sun,
small rain, bright.

Sowed a crop of spinage, the autumn-sown being much diminished by the frost. Ground works well. Planted broad beans.

Thursday 17.
29 8/10¾; 37; N,
NW, W.
White frost, sun, dark
& still.

Crocus's begin to blow.

Friday 18.
29 4/10; 35; W, SW:
10.
Black frost, sharp air,
dark, sleet, showers,
showers.

Saturday 19.
29 3/10; 38; W.
Sun, sun & clouds,
strong gale, sun, frost.

Sunday 20.
29 4/10; 33½, 34;
NW.
Severe frost, sun,
clouds, snow-shower,
bright, hard frost.

Very white frost.

Monday 21.
29 5/10; 31; NW.
Severe frost, sun,
cutting wind, frost.

Thick ice.
Green Hellebore emerges.¶

Tuesday 22.
29 7/10; 31; NW.

The ground is so hard that men cannot plow.

Severe frost, sun, sharp
wind, frost.

Wednesday 23.
29 9/10; 30; NW.   Ivy-berries, now near-ripe, are coddled with the frost.
Severe frost, cloudless,   Heath-fires.
still, grey, stars, frost.

Thursday 24.
29 9/10; 37, 40; S, W,   All the cabbages, planted in the autumn to stand the winter, are
NW.   killed.
Small rain, thaw, fog,
bright.

Friday 25.
29 2/10; 44; SW.
Grey & mild, showers,
rain & wind.

Saturday 26.
29 9/10; 31; NW.   The ground is covered with snow. People that were abroad early
Severe frost, snow, sun,   say the cold was very intense. The ground is hard as iron.
& strong cutting wind.

Sunday 27.
29 6/10; 42; SW, W.   The snow is melted-away in general.
Snow, snow, rain,
strong wind.

Monday 28.
29 6/10½; 46; W.
Grey & mild, sun.

Tuesday 29.   S. LAMBETH
Grey, sun, bright.   No turnips on all the road.
                          Remarkable vivid *Aurora borealis*.

MARCH 1780

Wednesday 1.

Thursday 2.   LONDON

Friday 3.
16½.

Saturday 4.   S. LAMBETH

                               Thomas¶ kept the quantity of rain in my absence.
Sunday 5.

Monday 6.   LONDON
Sun & brisk air.   Sky-larks mount, & sing.

Tuesday 7.

Wednesday 8.
                               Mrs Snooke dyed, aged 86.

Thursday 9.

Friday 10.

Saturday 11.   S. LAMBETH

Sunday 12.   RINGMER
† 22.   No turnips to be seen on the road.

Monday 13.
                               Rooks are busyed in building.
                               Crocuss in full bloom.

Tuesday 14.
                               Chaffinches sing but in a shorter way than in Hants.¶

Wednesday 15.
                               Mrs Snooke was buried.

Thursday 16.
                               Primroses blow.

Friday 17.   DORKING
                               Brought away Mrs Snooke's old tortoise, Timothy, which she
                               valued much, & had treated kindly for near 40 years. When dug
                               out of its hybernaculum, it resented the Insult by hissing.

Saturday 18.   SELBORNE
29 4/10; †54.   No turnips to be seen on the road.
Rain, rain, heavy   Green plovers on the common.
showers.

---

† Rainfall.

The uncrested wren, the smallest species, called in this place the Chif-chaf, is very loud in the Lythe. This is the earliest summer-bird of passage, & the harbinger of spring. It has only two piercing notes.

Sunday 19.
29 5/10; 46½; SW.
Sun, dark, rain, rain.

Some pease, & oats are sown.

Monday 20.
29 5/10¾; 50; SW;
17.
Dark, moist & mild.
Full moon.

My crocus's continue in high bloom. Turned-out the cucumber-plants into their hills. We took the tortoise out of it's box & buried it in the garden: but the weather being warm it heaved up the mould, & walked twice down to the bottom of the long walk to survey the premises.

Tuesday 21.
29 5/10; 50; SW.
Grey, mild & moist.

The tortoise is quite awake, & came-out all day long: towards the evening it buried itself in part.

Wednesday 22.
29 7/10½; 46; W,
NW.
Sun, showers, hail, sun.

The tortoise keeps under ground all day.

Thursday 23.
29 8/10½; 41; NW,
SW.
Hard frost, sun, still,
grey.

Bombylius medius, the hairy fly with a long proboscis, appears. My garden works finely.

Friday 24.
29 5/10; 48; NW, SE.
Frost, sun, fleecy,
strong gale.

The cucumber-plants are vigorous & stocky, & show rudiments of much fruit.
Tortoise keeps under ground, but has made himself a breathing hole.
Much gossamer.

Saturday 25.
29 6/10¾; 53½; W.
Sun, summer-like,
sweet even.

Birds eat the ivy-berries, which are now ripe.
Sowed carrots, parsneps; planted potatoes.
Ground works well. Tortoise sleeps.

Sunday 26.
29 6/10; 51½; SW.
Grey, dark & moist.

The apricot-trees begin to blossom.
The black-cap whistles.

Monday 27.
29 4/10½; 58; SW,
SE.
Dark & moist, sun,
sweet afternoon.

Tuesday 28.
29 3/10½; 54; SW;   Two cucumbers in blossom; female bloom.
23.   Peaches, & nectarines in bloom. The tortoise put-out his head in
Sun, rain, rain, sun.   the morning.

Wednesday 29.
29 4/10¾; 51; SW.   Cucumbers blossom in the male bloom.
Dark & mild, & moist,   Crocus's go-out, & hyacinths blow.
rain.

Thursday 30.
29 4/10; 56; SW; 15.   The tortoise keeps close.
Grey, heavy showers,   Growing weather.
sun, bright.

Friday 31.
29 4/10; 51½; SW;   Planted-out lettuce from the fruit-wall. A Shell-snail appears.
45.
Sun & heavy showers,
sun & showers.

APRIL 1780

Saturday 1.
29 4/¾; 47; NE, SE.   Bank-martin seen near the forest.
Dark & harsh, dark,
rain.

Sunday 2.
28 8/10; 46½; SW;
58.
Grey, & mild, rain,
much rain, with wind.

Monday 3.
28 5/10; 44; W, NW;
6.
Sun, clouds & showers,
harsh.

Tuesday 4.
29 2/10; 39½; NW;
10.
Frost, ice, sun, hail-
storms, snow, snow.

Much snow.

Wednesday 5.
29 2/10; 38; NW, W.
Severe frost, thick ice,
thunder, hail, & sleet.

The frost injured the bloom of the wall-trees: covered the bloom
with boughs of ivy.

Thursday 6.
29 6/10; 39; NW.
Frost, ice, sun, &
clouds, sleet, bright.

Cucumbers swell.

Friday 7.
29 4/10; 39; NE, SE.
Severe frost, thick ice,
sun & clouds,
dark clouds to the
N:W.

Tortoise keeps still in it's hole.

Saturday 8.
29 7/10; 41; NW, N.
Small frost, sun, &
clouds, snow, snow.

Rooks begin to have Young.
Sowed an hand-glass with large white cucumber-seed.

Sunday 9.
29 9/10; 38; N, E.
Severe frost, sun &
clouds, & harsh wind,
bright.

Ground frozen hard.
Bank-martins near Godalming.

Monday 10.
29 7/10½; 39½; NE,
SW.
Severe frost, grey &
harsh, heavy clouds.

Cucumbers swell.
Planted two more beds of asparagus.

Tuesday 11.
29 3/10; 44; NW.
Rain, rain, dark, hail,
heavy clouds.

Wednesday 12.
29 2/10; 44; NW, N;
48.
Grey, showers, hail,
vast showers.

Thursday 13.
29 4/10; 44; N, NW.   Large white cucumbers come-up.
Dark & harsh, hail.

Friday 14.
29 5/10; 43½; N,
NW, N.
Sun, dark & harsh,
grey & pleasant.

Saturday 15.
29 4/10; 43½; NW.   Swallow appears.
Louring, sun & brisk   Cucumbers swell.
air, showers, wind.   Tortoise sleeps on.
                           Radishes are drawn.

Sunday 16.
29 3/10¾; 46; W.   Cuckow cries in the hanger.
Sun & clouds, strong
wind.

Monday 17.
29 2/10¼; 45½; W;   Showers in the night.
20.   Cut the first cucumber.
Sun, stormy wind,   On this day Sir G: B: Rodney defeated the French fleet off
great showers, hail,   Martinique.
bright & cold.

Tuesday 18.
29 2/10; 41½; W.   Cucumbers swell.
Sun, strong wind, hail
& rain, bright & cold.
Full moon.

Wednesday 19.
29 6/10; 43; NW, W.   The tortoise enlarges his breatheing hole, & heaves up the earth.
Sun & clouds, showers,   Bat appears.
vast hail storm, bright.

Thursday 20.
29 6/10¾; 42; W,
SW; 20.
White frost, sun,
clouds, showers, grey
& still.

A swallow near the village.

Friday 21.
29 4/10½; 47, 50; S;
40.
Rain, rain, dark &
moist, rain.

The tortoise heaves up the earth, & puts out it's head.
Shell-snails come forth in plenty.

Saturday 22.
29 3/10; 48½; W, S.
Sun, sun & clouds,
heavy clouds.

Cucumbers swell.
Tortoise comes-forth, & walks round his coop: will not eat lettuce
yet: goes to sleep at four o'clock p:m:

In the hot weather last summer a flight of house-crickets¶ were
dispersed about the village: one got from the garden into my
kitchen-chimney, & continued there all the winter. There is now a
considerable encrease, & many young appear in the evening,
running about, & hunting for crumbs. From this circumstance it
should seem that the impregnated females migrate. This is the case
with ants.

Sunday 23.
29 2/10; 49; SW.
Grey, sun, vast shower,
hail, heavy clouds.

Swifts several.

Monday 24.
29 2/10; 49, 50; SW;
33.
Sun, sun & clouds,
showers, vast shower
with hail, heavy clouds.

Martin house. Tortoise moved.
Cut two brace of cucumbers.

Tuesday 25.
29 4/10; 47; S, SE.
Sun, clouds, showers,
rain, rain.

Walk-mowing begins.
Swallows, several.

Housecricket in a Sussex cottage.
12 June.

Wednesday 26.
29 4/10¾; 46; SW,
W; 45.
Sun, sun & brisk wind.

Cut a brace of cucumbers.

Thursday 27.
1/10½, 29 4/10; 56;
W; 58.
Rain, rain with wind,
sun, strong wind.

Tortoise moves.

Friday 28.
29 4/10½; 53½, 55;
SW; 19.
Grey, rain, rain, rain.

Tortoise moves.
Cut a brace of cucumbers.

Saturday 29.
29 3/10¾; 55, 59;
SW.
Grey, sun, sultry,
moist.

Cut a cucumber. The grass grows in the meadow.
Swifts. Many h: martins. Martins frequent their old nests.
Nightingale sings in my fields.

A sprig of *Antirrhinum cymbalaria*, the ivy-leaved Toadsflax,
which was planted last year on a shady water-table of the wall of
my house, grew at a vast rate & extended itself full nine feet; &
was in perpetual bloom 'til the hard frost came. In the severity of
the winter it seemed to die; but it now revives again with vigor, &
shows the rudiments of flowers. When in perfection it is a lovely
plant.

Sunday 30.
29 4/10½; 56½; SW.
Grey, moist, sun &
showers, grey.

Lathraea squammaria blows in the coppice below the church-litten
near the footbridge over the stream.
The ground is drenched with rain.

MAY 1780

Monday 1.
29 4/10; 56; S.
Grey, shower, grey,
rain, rain.

Here & there a beech on the hanger begins to leaf. Cut a brace of
cucumbers.

Tuesday 2.
29 8/10; 54; NW; 49.
Sun, showers & hot
gleams, fine even:

Very growing weather.
Tortoise marches about: eat part of a piece of a cucumber-paring.

Wednesday 3.
29 8/10¾; 56; E, NE,
NW, S.
Sun, fine day, dark &
moist.

4 pairs of swifts. Cherry-trees, plums & pears blow. Apricots
swell; peaches, & nectarines set.

Thursday 4.

29 7/10; 54; W, S.
Grey, sun, summer-
like, dark & mild.

Cucumbers bear.
Shell-snails copulate.

Friday 5.

29 6/10; 54½; S, SW.
Dark & moist, rain,
rain, fine afternoon.

Early tulips blow.
Nightingale in my fields.

Saturday 6.

29 6/10½; 52; W,
NW.
Grey, sun & dark
clouds, sweet even:

Made an hot-bed for the hand-glasses.
I opened a hen swift, which a cat had caught, & found she was in
high condition, very plump & fat: in her body were the
rudiments of several eggs, two of which were larger than the rest,
& would probably have been produced this season. Cats often
catch Swifts as they stoop to go up under the eaves of low houses.

The quantity of rain¶ that fell at Selborne between May 1st 1779,
& May 1st 1780.

					inch:	hund:
In May 1779	.	.	.		2:	71
June	.	.	.	.	2:	0
July	.	.	.	.	5:	35
August	.	.	.		2:	12
September	.	.	.		3:	22
October	.	.	.		4:	3
November	.	.	.		2:	66
December	.	.	.		6:	28
January 1780	.	.			1:	80
February	.	.	.		1:	3
March	.	.	.		1:	92
April	.	.	.	.	3.	57
					36.	69

Sunday 7.

29 6/10; W.
Dark & moist, grey &
mild.

Swallows & house-martin collect dirt for their nests.
Wild cherries in bloom make a fine show in my hedges.

Monday 8.

29 3/10; 54½; S, SW;
54.
Rain, rain, sun &
clouds.

The *Lathraea squammaria* grows also on the bank of Trimming's
orchard, just above the dry wall, opposite Grange yard.

Tuesday 9.
29 1/10; 53; S; 25.
Dark, rain, rain, heavy
rain.

Planted-out the large white cucumber-plants under the hand-glasses.

Wednesday 10.
29 2/10½; 53; SW;
48.
Vast showers in the
night, sun & clouds,
fine even: shower.

Stormy all night. Tortoise scarce moves during this wet time.
Fly-catcher, the latest summer bird, appears.
Tremella nostoc abounds on the grass-walks.

Thursday 11.
29 5/10; 53; SW: 8,
22.
Sun, sun & showers,
hail, showers, fine even:

The hanger is quite in leaf.
Tortoise moves about, but does not feed yet.
Grass grows very fast. Peaches & Nectarines set.

Friday 12.
29 5/10; S.
Sun, white frost, sun &
clouds, rain.

The missel-thrush drives the mag-pies, & Jays from the garden.
Lettuces that stood the winter come into use. Hops are poled, but make weak shoots.

Saturday 13.
29 4/10; 53½; S, SW;
22.
Sun & clouds, shower,
sun & clouds, rain &
wind.

Vines are backward in their shoots; but show rudiments of fruit.
The cones of the spruce-firs, produced last year, now fall.

The cock red-breast is a gallant bird, & feeds his hen as they hop about on the walks, who receives his bounty with great pleasure, shivering with her wings, & expressing much complacency.

Sunday 14.
29 2/10½; 52; S, NE.
Sun, dark & moist,
rain, rain, cold & raw.

Apple-trees show much bloom.
Much spring-corn
not sown.

Jay.
Long Lythe.
July.

Monday 15.
29 7/10; 56; NW; 28.
Sun, fine, dry.

The ground drenched
with water.

Tuesday 16.
29 8/10½; 54, 60; W.
Grey, still & mild.

Wheat looks somewhat
yellow.
Men sow barley: but the ground is cold,
& cloddy.

Timothy eating salad.
24 May.

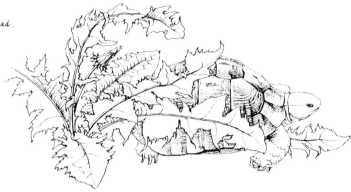

Wednesday 17.
29 8/10; 56, 59; W.
Grey, sun, summer
weather, sweet even:

The tortoise begins to feed voraciously.
Fern-owl chatters.

After a fast of 7, or 8 months the tortoise, which in Oct: 1779 weighed six pounds 9 oun: & ½ averdupoise, weighs now only six pounds 4 ounces. Timothy began to break his fast May 17 on the globe thistle, & American willow-herb: his favourite food is lettuce, & dandelion, cucumber, & kidney-beans.

Thursday 18.
29 7/10½; W.
Cold dew, sun &
clouds, grey & mild.
Full moon.

Field crickets in their pupa-state lie-out before their holes.
Magpies beat the missel-thrushes' nest to pieces, & swallow the eggs.

Friday 19.
29 8/10½; 56; W.
Dark with strong gale,
sun & clouds, strong
gale, shower.

Antirrhinum cymbalaria begins to blow.
Helleborus viridis sheds it's seeds in my garden, & produces many young plants.

Saturday 20.
29 8/10; 52; N, NW,
SW, W.
Cold dew, sun, summer
day.

Planted large white kidney beans.
Tulips in full bloom: hyacinths fade.

Sunday 21.
29 3/10; 53; S.
Grey & mild, sweet
afternoon.

Flesh flies appear.

Monday 22.
29 3/10½; 56; W.
Dark, no dew, shower,
sun, fine even.

The leaves of the Nectarines are much blistered. Apple trees are finely blown.

Tuesday 23.
29 5/10; 54; W.
Sun & showers, no
dew, showers, strong
gale, showers.

Apricots grow large.

Wednesday 24.
29 8/10; 53; W.
Cold air, dew, sun &
clouds, dark & louring.

Thursday 25.
†29 ?/10; 61; W.
Dark & moist, gleams
of sun, grey & mild.

Friday 26.
29 8/10½; 59; SW.
Gleams, sun & clouds,
brisk air, grey.

The shoots of the vines are very backward.

Saturday 27.
29 8/10½; 69; SW.
†[?], sun, cloudless,
sultry, sweet even:

Large blue flag-iris blows.
Hawthorn blows.
Apis longi-cornis appears. Flesh-flies abound.

Timothy the tortoise possesses a greater share of discernment than
I was aware of; & is much too wise to walk into a well, for when he
arrives at the haha, he distinguishes the fall of the ground, & retires
with caution or marches carefully along the edge: he delights in
crawling up the flower-bank, & walking along it's verge.

Sunday 28.
29 7/10; 64, 72; S,
SW.
Fog, dew, sun, sweet
summer weather.

Fern-owl chatters.

Monday 29.
29 6/10¼; 66, 76; S,
SE, W.
Dew, sun, cloudless,
still, sultry.

The tortoise shunned the heat, it was so intense.
Rock-like clouds in the horizon.

---

† Entry illegible.

Tuesday 30.

29 6/10½; 70; N.
Fog, sun, brisk air,
distant thunder, dark &
cool, thunder.

Columbines, a fine variegated sort, blow.
Orange lilies blow.

Wednesday 31.

29 7/10; 62, 63; NE;
43.
Grey, sun, cool air,
hazy, shower, distant
thunder.

Master Etty¶ went on board the *Vansittart* India-man at Spithead.
Thunderstorm in the night, with a fine shower. Bees come to the
flowers & set the cucumbers.
Crickets chirp.

JUNE 1780

Thursday 1.

29 6/10; 62, 75; E,
SE, NW; 6.
Sun, distant clouds,
sultry, thunder-clouds,
sweet even: small
shower.

Sulphurous smell in the air.
Strawberries blow well. Medlar skins much †[?]. Honey-suckles
blow.
Fern-owl chatters: †[?]
The tortoise shuns the intense heat by covering itself with dead
grass; & does not eat 'til the afternoon.
Terrible storms in Oxfordshire, & Wilts.

Friday 2.

29 5/10½; 64, 74½;
E, S, W.
Deep fog, sun, sultry,
sweet even:

St foin begins to bloom. Planted-out some annuals.
Kidney-beans thrive: cucumbers abound.
Finished papering my great parlor.

Saturday 3.

29 6/10½; 68, 71;
NE.
Shower, dark, sun,
sultry, sweet even:

Master Etty saild.
The *apis longicornis* bores holes in the walks for the purpose of
nidification.
The *phalaena*, called the swift night-hawk, appears.
Began tacking the vines, which shoot vigorously, & show much
fruit.

Sunday 4.

29 7/10; 63; NE.
Dark, cold air, rain,
rain, grey.

White cucumbers show male-bloom in their hand-glasses.
Haw-thorn still in full bloom.

---

† Entry illegible.

Monday 5.
29 6/10; 56; N; 42.
Dark, cold & wet.

Rain in the night. Cucumbers abound.
Tortoise does not move.
Tulips fade. Cinnamon-roses blow.

Tuesday 6.
29 6/10¼; 53; N.
Dark, cold, dry & still.

Red valerian blows.
Planted-out many rows of annuals.

Terrible riots in London:¶ & unpresidented burnings &
devastations by the mob!!

Wednesday 7.
29 7/10; 53, 57; N.
Dark & chilly, sun,
cool air.

The tortoise quite torpid.
Finished putting-out the annuals.

Thursday 8.
29 7/10; 52; N, NW.
White frost, sun & cool
air, cold even:

The limes show their bracteal leaves, & rudiments of blossoms.
Sweet Williams begin to blow.

Friday 9.
29 5/10; 57; SW.
Dark & still, moist,
fog.

Hoed the
quick-sets at the
bottom of the hanger.

Saturday 10.
29 5/10; 56; SW.
Dark & louring, dark
& mild.

Fraxinellas begin to blow.
Wheat-ears begin
to shoot-out.

Sunday 11.
29 6/10; 63½; W.
Sun, summer, grey &
mild.

Field-pease look well.
All the young rooks have not
left their nest-trees.
Glow-worms appear.

Sweet Williams by the fruit wall.
The Wakes.
Early July.

Monday 12.
29 7/10; 60½; NE, S,
NW. Sun, summer,
dark clouds, soft even:

Dragon-flies. Bees swarm.
Sheep are shorn.

Tuesday 13.
29 5/10; 61; W, SW.
Sun, sun, dark clouds,
shower.

Wednesday 14.
29 4/10½; 56; W; 11.
Sun, strong gales,
showers about, strong
wind.

Thursday 15.
29 6/10½; 52; W,   Vivid *Aurora* to the W.
NW.
Sun, strong gales,
flying showers, fine
even:

Friday 16.
29 6/10½; 54; W.   Wood-straw-berries begin to ripen.
Sun & clouds, dark,
cold & sprinkling.
Full moon.

Saturday 17.
29 5/10; 52; W.   The fruit of the white cucumber near blowing.
Grey, dark & cold,
rain, rain.

Sunday 18.
29 4/10½; 58; SW;   Elders begin to blow.
60. Rain, rain, rain.

Monday 19.   S. LAMBETH
29 8/10; SW.   Dust well-laid on the road.
Grey, warm, sun.   Barley in ear on the sands.
                        Much upland-hay moved near London.

Tuesday 20.
29 9/10; 54; SW.   Early pease abound. Straw-berries, & cherries ill-ripened, &
Sun, sun & clouds.   very small. Much wall fruit. Roses blow.
                        Showers about.

Wednesday 21.
30 1/10; 54; SW.
Sun & clouds, strong
gale, soft & still.

Thursday 22.
30 1/10; 58; SW; 41.   Sold my S^t foin the 13 th crop.

Gloomy & moist, rain, rain, rain.

Sold my S^t foin the 13th crop.
Lighted a fire in the dining-room.

Friday 23.
30 1/20; 55; SW, NW.
Sun, brisk air, sun, sweet even:

Rain at S: Lambeth – 32.
Swifts stay-out 'til a quarter before nine o' the clock.

Saturday 24.
30 1/10; SW.
Sun, brisk gale, dark.

Cistus ledon blows.

Thomas kept the rain account at Selborne.

Sunday 25.
30 1/10; 55; W.
Sun & clouds, strong, cold wind.

Strawberries are large, but not finely flavoured: cherries have no flavour.

Monday 26.
30 5/20; 54; W.
Sun & clouds, cold wind.

Tuesday 27.
30 3/10½; 50; NW.
Sun, summer weather, sweet even:

Swallows feed their young on the ground in Mr Curtis's botanic garden in George's fields.¶
Cut meadow-hay.

Wednesday 28.
30 3/10; 57; SW.
Dark & still, sun, sweet even:

Cut meadow-hay.

Thursday 29.
30 2/10½; 59, 66; E, SE.
Sun, sultry, sweet even:

SELBORNE
Jane White was married to Mr Clement.¶
Wood-straw-berries abound.

Friday 30.
29 6/10; 76; E, SE.
Sun, brisk air, cloudless, sultry, grey, sweet even:

The portugal-laurel blows in a beautiful manner.
Ricked my hay, seven jobbs, in most delicate order.
Vines begin to blow: the quantity of grapes will be large.
The white cucumber-plants are in bad plight; the early crop of green bears well.
The nectarine-trees are naked of leaves.

JULY 1780

Saturday 1.
29 6/10; 66; SW; 19.
Dark & moist, dark,
rain, rain.

The red valerians, roses, iris's, corn-flags, honey-suckles, lilies,
&c: make a gallant show.
Most of the pinks were destroyed in the winter by the hares.
Wheat in full bloom.

Sunday 2.
29 6/10½; 55½; SW.
Grey & soft, sun, sweet
even:

We put Timothy into a tub of water, & found that he sank
gradually, & walked on the bottom of the tub; he seemed quite out
of his element & was much dismayed. This species seems not at all
amphibious. Timothy seems to be the *Testudo Graeca* of Linnaeus.¶
    Dr Chandler,¶ who saw the operation, says there is a species of
tortoise in the Levant that at times frequents ponds & lakes; & my
Broᵗ John White affirms the same of a sort in Andalusia.

Monday 3.
29 6/10; 53; SW, S.
Grey & mild, dark,
wet.

Cut the first white cucumber.
The tortoise weighs six pounds & three quarters averdupoise, six
pds 12 oun.

Tuesday 4.
29 8/10; 53; SW.
Sun, summer-like, soft
& grey.

Stopped down the vines, which are now in full bloom.
Female ants, big with egg, come-out from under the stairs.

Wednesday 5.
29 7/10; 60½; W.
Grey, sun, dark in the
horizon.

Began to cut the tall hedges.
Put a bed of moss round the white cucumbers.
Young partridges run.

Thursday 6.
29 8/10; 60; W.
Sun, harsh gale, sun,
cool air.

Some young swallows out.

Friday 7.
29 6/10½; 58; W.
Sun, brisk air, sun &
clouds, cool even:

Earthed-out the late green cucumbers.
Wood-strawberries now delicate. Cherries are now ripe.

Saturday 8.
29 6/10½; 58; W.
Grey & cold, sun &
clouds, grey,

White cucumbers bear a little.
By their encreased number the swifts seem to have brought out
some of their Young.

bright & chill.

Field-crickets cry.

The excrement of the tortoise is hard & solid; but when that creature urines, as it often does plentifully, it voids after the water a soft white matter, much like the dung of birds of prey, which dries away into a sort of chalk like substance.

Sunday 9.
29 7/10½; 59; W.
Grey & mild, dark clouds, sultry, dark & warm.

Hops thrive, & throw-out side-branches.

Monday 10.
29 8/10; 61; N, NW; 34.
Great rain, grey, sun, sweet afternoon, vast dew.

Timothy eats voraciously; but picks-out the leaves & stems of Coss-lettuce, holding the outer leaves back with his feet.

Tuesday 11.
29 7/10; 60; NW.
Dark & mild, sun, sweet weather, great dew, mackerel sky.

The young of fly-catchers almost fledge.
Finished my great parlor,¶ by hanging curtains, & fixing the looking-glass.

Wednesday 12.
29 6/10; 63; NW; 34.
Dark, shower, great showers, sultry, loud thunder, grey & mild.

Young fly-catchers come-out.
Rasps begin to ripen.
The well sinks very fast.

Thursday 13.
29 7/10½; 62; N.
Dark & cold, grey, sun, soft & moist, heavy clouds in horizon.

Limes blow, & smell sweetly.
White lilies blow. Rasps ripens.
Swifts abound.

Friday 14.
29 8/10; 62; N, NW, W.
Bright, sun & clouds, sweet afternoon.

Seeds of *lathraea squammaria* ripen.
Fern-owls chatter.

Saturday 15.
29 6/10¼; 63; SW,

NW. Dark & wet,
with ruffling wind,
sun, bright, heavy
clouds in horizon.

Sunday 16.
29 6/10; 65, 73; NW.   Some fields of wheat begin to turn a little yellow.
Sun, strong sun, sultry,
sweet even:

Monday 17.
29 5/10; 67; 74; S.   White jasmine begins to blow.
Sun, bright, sultry,   The solstitial chafer now flies; this insect is the food of fern-owls
sweet even: dark   thro' this month.
horizon to the W.

Tuesday 18.
29 7/10; 69; SW; 32.   Sowed turnip-radishes.
Dark & moist, dark,   32 or 34 swifts.
heavy showers.

Wednesday 19.
29 7/10; 62; SW, W.   Puff-balls appear in my grass-plot.
Dark & damp,
showers, soft even.

Thursday 20.
29 7/10; 59; SW, W.
Bright, clouds, soft
showers, grey & mild.

Friday 21.
29 3/10¾; 62; SW;   The late orange, & the white lilies blowing together make a fine
35. Dark & wet, rain,   show.
rain.   Wood-straw-berries still.

Saturday 22.
29 2/10½; 62½; SW,   Vast rain in the night.
N: 73, 20.
Rain, rain, rain, rain.

Sunday 23.
29 8/10; 62; N, NW.   Young house-martins abound at yᵉ Bridge.
Dark, mild, & still,   Grasshopper-lark whispers.
gleam of sun.

Monday 24.
29 8/10; 59; SW, W.
Bright, hot sun, †[?]
sultry, heavy clouds.

Tortoise eats endive & poppies.
Wood straw-berries.

Tuesday 25.
29 8/10½; 65, 73;
NW, NW.
Sun, sweet summer
weather, sweet even:

Young martins & swallows begin to congregate on roofs.
Ferruginous foxglove blows.

Wednesday 26.
29 8/10; 67; W.
Wet fog, dark & warm,
sun, summer weather,
vast dew.

Much hay housed. Hollyhocks blow.
Cucumbers abound.
Vast fog out at sea, over the Sussex-downs.

Thursday 27.
29 8/10, 9/10; 67, 70;
NW, NW.
Dark, sun, with brisk
air, sweet afternoon.

Hops shew many side-shoots, & begin to blow.
Tortoise eats goose-berries.
Planted-out endive.
Tall kidney-beans blow.

Friday 28.
29 9/10; 62, 70; W.
Cold dew, sun & cool
breeze.
Vast Auroras.

Vast crops of cow-grass.
Late cucumbers begin to blow.
Much hay made.
Vast lights in the air from all quarters.
Crickets swarm in my kitchen-chimney, & have bored thro' into
the common parlor.

Saturday 29.
29 8/10; 62; E, NE.
Sun, sun & brisk air,
cool even:

Young partridges are become flyers.
Cucumbers abound.
Grapes swell.

The flies, called by our people Nose flies, torment the horses at
plow. They lay their eggs in the ears as well as noses of cattle. Some
of our farmers work their teams with little baskets tyed-on over the
horses noses. These flies seem to prevail only in July.
　　Round the eaves of the Priory farm-house are 40 martins-nests,
which have sent forth their first brood in swarms. At 4 young to a
nest only, the first brood will produce 160; & the second the same,
which together make 320; add to these the 40 pairs of old ones,

---

† One word illegible.

which make in all 400; a vast flight for one house!! The first, when congregating on the tiles, covers one side of the roof!

Sunday 30.
29 7/10½; 72¾; NE, E.
Dark skie, Sun, sultry, sweet even:

Pease begin to be hacked.
Much cow-grass made in fine order.
Young snipes were seen at the Bishop of Winchester's table at Farnham-castle on this day: they are bred on all the moory-heaths of this neighbourhood.

Monday 31.
29 8/10; 64; NE.
Dark & heavy, sun & brisk air, sweet even.

Dined at Bramshot.
Turnips flourish on the sands. Mr Richardson's garden at Branshot-place abounds with fruit.

AUGUST 1780

Tuesday 1.
29 8/10; 62½; NE.
Dark & louring, sun & strong gale, sweet, still even:

Much latter-grass made in delicate order.
Wheat turns very fast.
Old wheat rises in price.

Wednesday 2.
29 7/10; 64; NE.
Sun, brisk air, sweet afternoon.

Papilio Machaon¶ alis caudatis, concoloribus, flavis, limbo fusco, lunulis flavis, angulo ani fulvo,¶ appears in my garden, being the first specimen of that species that ever I saw in this district. In Essex & Sussex they are more common.

Thursday 3.
29 7/10; 66, 75; NE.
Sun, strong gale, sweet even:

A person brought me a young snipe from the forest.

Friday 4.
29 7/10; 69; NE.
Sun, strong gale, strong gale.

Wasps begin to come. Scarlet martagons blow.
Several broods of blackbirds & thrushes devour the currans, &c: 'til the wild cherries are eaten they do not annoy the garden.

Saturday 5.
29 7/10; 66; NW.
Sun, strong gale, strong gale.

Apricots begin to turn.
Swifts withdraw.

My pendent pantry, made of deal, & fine fly-wire, & suspended in the great wallnut-tree, proves an incomparable preservative for meat against flesh-flies. The flesh by hanging in a brisk current of air becomes dry on the surface, & keeps 'til it is tender without tainting.

Sunday 6.
29 7/10¼; 66; NE, N.
Dark & moist fog, sun
& brisk gale, sweet
even:

Sunflowers begin to blow.

Monday 7.
29 8/10; 66½; NE, N,
NE.
Dark & moist, sun,
brisk gale, large
clouds, sweet even;
cloudless.

Apricots begin to ripen.
No swifts.
Kidney-beans & cabbages are injured for want of rain. Walks (grass) burn.
Wheat-harvest begins.

Tuesday 8.
29 7/10; 65½; NE,
SW, SE.
Dark, gleams, showers,
thunder, showers,
bright, low creeping
mists.

Hops suffer.
Swifts not seen.
Pease are housed.
No swifts.
Much distant lightening to the S:E.

Wednesday 9.
29 6/10¾; 66½, 74;
NE, E; 23.
Thick wet fog,
shower, grey & warm,
sun, sultry, sweet
even:

Distant thunder to the S. The garden is refreshed.
No swifts.

Thursday 10.
29 6/10½; 67, 75½;
NE, E, NE.
Sun & brisk, sun,
sultry, brisk gale, calm,
sweet even: wet.

Sowed a crop of spinage for the winter; & spring: trod the seed well in.
Cucumbers abound. No swifts.

Friday 11.
29 6/10; 70½; NE.
Sun & brisk air, sun,
sultry, brisk gale, sweet
afternoon.

The *Papilio Machaon* never appeared but once in my garden.
Apricots abound.
Pease mostly housed: some wheat in shock.¶

The Zig ~ Zag.
12 June

Saturday 12.
69, 76; NE.
Sun, brisk gale, sun,
sweet even, cloudless.

Dust flies. Gardens suffer for want of rain.
Much wheat bound.
Swifts seem to have withdrawn themselves ever since the end of
last week.

Timothy, who in the beginning of May, after fasting all the winter,
weighed only six pounds & four ounces, averdupoise; is now
encreased to six pounds & 15 ounces averdupoise.

Sunday 13.
29 6/10; 66; NE, E.
Dark with strong gales,
sweet even:

Turnips suffer for want of rain.
Hops thrive, & promise for a large crop.
Ponds are very low.

Monday 14.
29 5/10½; 64; NE, E.
Dark & moist, shower,
shower, shower,
showers, dark & still.

Wheat-harvest becomes general.
Cucumbers abound.
Sope-wort blows.
Dwarf-elder continues in bloom.

Tuesday 15.
29 5/10; 62; NE, E;
122.
Rain, rain, vast
showers, dark & mild.
Full moon.

Wednesday 16.
29 6/10¾; 64; SE, S.
Sun, sun, heavy clouds
to the N., soft & still.

China-asters begin to open.
On this day Lord Cornwallis gained a signal victory over General
Gates in South Carolina, near Camden.

Thursday 17.
29 6/10; 67; S, SW.
Dark, soft showers,
showers, sun & clouds,
close & sultry, dark &
mild.

Fell-wort blows on the hanger.

Friday 18.
29 5/10; 67; E, SE; 56.
Rain, rain, rain, sun,
soft even:

Hot & moist. Wheat lies in danger of growing.
Vast rock-like clouds.

Saturday 19.
29 6/10¾; 67; N,

Much wheat reaped.

NW. Grey, sun, sun & clouds, sweet afternoon, hot & close.

Some wheat grows under hedges.

Sunday 20.

29 7/10¾; 65; SE. Grey, sun, dark & moist, still & mild.

Some wheat grown.
A pair of swifts appeared on to this day at Fyfield, but they seemed to bring out no young.

Monday 21.

29 7; 66, 70; S, W. Dark & moist, sun & air, dark & moist.

Mushrooms begin to appear.
Much wheat housed.

Tuesday 22.

29 6/10½; 65; W, NW, NE.
Sun, sun & clouds, showers about, shower.

Timothy is sluggish, & scarce moves.
Much wheat housed.
Trenched-out two rows of Celeri.

Wednesday 23.

29 8/10; 64½; NE. Sun, sweet harvest weather, soft & still.

Perennial Asters begin to blow.
Much wheat housed.

Thursday 24.

29 8/10; 66; NE. White dew, sun, delicate, bright.

Sweet autumnal weather.
Much wheat housed.
The tops of beeches begin to be tinged with yellow.

Friday 25.

29 7/10; 67, 72; E, N. Sun, hot sun with strong gale, cool air, bright.

Plums begin to ripen.
Wheat housed in fine order.

Saturday 26.

29 7/10¾; 73; NE. Dark, brisk gale, sun, blue mist, sun, sultry, fine even: chill air.

Timothy the tortoise is sluggish, & eats but little.
Wheat-harvest is pretty well finished in fine order.

The therm! which on the staircase stood at 67. in the wine-vault became 60¾: & again when it was at 66 on the stair-case, by being plunged into a bucket of water, fresh-drawn, it fell to 51.

Sunday 27.

29 7/10; 71½; NE, E.

The crop of grapes is very great.

Mist, sun & strong cold
gale, cloudless & chilly.

Monday 28.
29 8/10; 71; E.
Dark, hot sun, & brisk
gale, sultry in the sun,
chilly air.

WINTON, FYFIELD
There were at the King's house at Winton 1600 Spanish
prisoners; rather small men, & some very swarthy: here & there
a fairish lad.

Tuesday 29.
29 7/10½; 69; SE, S.
Dark, & cool, hot sun,
fine even: stars.

Barley-harvest is general.
My brother's vines abound with grapes.
Wasps abound.
On this day the people at Selborne were to begin picking of hops:
the crop of hops is prodigious.

Wednesday 30.
29 7/10¾; 76, 79; SE,
S.
Great dew, sun, sultry,
fleecy clouds, sultry.

Gardens are burnt-up.
Clear in the S:

Thursday 31.
29 7/10; 78½; SW,
W.
Dew, sun, sultry,
strong gale, soft even:

Barley & oats housed in fine order.
The season is so dry that no trufle hunter has yet tryed my
brother's grove.

SEPTEMBER 1780

Friday 1.
29 6/10½; 76; W.
Fog, sun, sultry, brisk
gale, soft even:

Many partridges.

Saturday 2.
29 6/10; 76; W, NW.
Dark, wettish air, sun
sultry, soft even:

Autumnal crocus blows.
Much barley housed. Distant lightening.

Sunday 3.
29 7/10; 68; NE.
Dark & moist, shady &
mild.

Monday 4.
29 8/10½; 68; NE, SE.
Cold dew, sun, bright, cool.

The trufle-man came & hunted my brother's grove for the first time; but found only half a pound of trufles, & those shrivelled & decayed, for want of moisture.

Tuesday 5.
29 8/10; SE, S.
Cold dew, sun, brisk gale, cloudless, & chill.

The evenings & mornings are cool.

Wednesday 6.
29 6/10½; 63; S, S.
Sun, & cool air, cloudless, brisk gale, strong gale, cloudless, cold air.

Much barley housed. The barley is delicate, & white.

Bergamotte d'Automne pear growing in the orchard at Wisley. 2 September.

Thursday 7.
29 4/10; 67; SE.
Grey, dark & louring, heavy showers.

Friday 8.
29 3/10; S; 38.
Sun, mild, & soft, rock-like clouds, bright & chill.

WINTON, SELBORNE
Barley harvest on the downs.

Saturday 9.
29 4/10; 62½; NW.
Vast dews, sun, sunny & soft.

My kidney-beans are much withered for want of rain: cucumbers bear: peaches begin to come: endives large, & tyed-up.
Gathered-in the Burgamot-pears; they easily part from their stems.
Hop-picking partly ended.
Myriads of flying ants, of the small pale, yellow sort, fly from their nests & fill the air.

The motions of Timothy the tortoise are much circumscribed: he has taken to the border under the fruit wall. & makes very short excursions: he sleeps under a Marvel of Peru.

Sunday 10.
29 4/10; 62; SE.
Dark, rain, rain, rain.

Lapwings frequent the upland fallows.
Peaches are not well-flavoured.
Grapes begin to turn.

Monday 11.
29 5/10; 64; W; 44.
Sun, showers, bright &
mild.

Fly-catchers withdrew early in this month.
Showers all around.

Tuesday 12.
29 7/10; 60; NW, SW.
Vast dew, sun, sweet
afternoon.

Timothy still feeds a little.
Ophrys spiralis, Ladies traces, blows plentifully in the long lithe
from the common near the beechen-grove adjoining to Mr
Yalden's† [?]

Wednesday 13.
29 6/10; 60; S, S.
Sun, grey, rain, rain.
Full moon.

Honey-bees devour the wall-fruit, & do more harm than the
wasps, which are not numerous.

Thursday 14.
29 5/10; 61½; SE, S;
84.
Rain, rain, sun &
clouds.

Rain all night.
Hop-picking ends: a vast crop, & in fine order.
Peaches & Nect: good, but not delicate.

Friday 15.
29 5/10; 61½; SE, S,
SE.
Fog, sun, soft &
pleasant.

Some buds of Ivy begin to blow.
Hirundines forsake the houses.

Saturday 16.
29 3/10½; 63; SE, S,
SE.
Dark & mild, rain,
rain, rain.

Timothy eats still.

The *Antirrhinum cymbalaria* is grown to an enormous size,
extending itself side-ways 15 or 16 feet, & 7 or 8 in height! it
grows on the water-table of a N:W: wall of my house, & runs up
among the shoots of a Jasmine.
    When we call loudly thro' the speaking trumpet to Timothy, he
does not seem to regard the noise.

Sunday 17.
29 1/10; 63; SE, SE;
81.
Vast showers, sun,
shower.

Thunder.
Lightening & thunder.

---

† Word illegible.

Monday 18.
29 2/10½; 64; S, SE;
17.
Sun, soft & delicate.

Grapes turn colour very fast.
Timothy eats heartily.

Tuesday 19.
29 3/10½; 59; W.
Fine morn, sun,
showers, bright.

Hornets settle on mellow fruit among the honey-bees & carry them off:
"Aut asper Crabro imparibus se immis armis."¶

Wednesday 20.
29 3/10; 56; E, NW.
Sun, dark, showers.

Endive well blanched.

Thursday 21.
29 5/10; 56; W.
Sun, sun, showers,
showers, rain-bow.

Friday 22.
29 7/10½; 55; NW, S;
29. Cold dew, sun,
sweet day, N. *Aurora*.

Gossamer abounds.

Saturday 23.
29 5/10¾; 55½; SE.
E.
Cold dew, sun, grey,
sun.

Fine day.

When people walk in a deep white fog by night with a lanthorn, If they will turn their backs to the light they will see their shades impressed on the fog in rude gigantic proportions. This phenomenon seems not to have been attended to; but implies the great density of the meteor at that juncture.

Sunday 24.
29 6/10; 59, 64; SW.
Shower, rainbow,
showers, sun.

SELEBURNE¶

Monday 25.
29 7/10; 60; SW
Sun, grey & soft, grey
& soft.

Tryed some grapes, but they are not good yet.

Tuesday 26.
29 5/10; 60; SW.

Moles live in the middle of the hanger.

Sun & clouds, dark,   Martins swarm under the hanger: some swallows still.
rain, dark.

Wednesday 27.
29 5/10½; 57; W; 32.   Finished a Bostal¶ or sloping path up the hanger from the foot of
Sun, grey, heavy sky.   the zigzag to the corner of the Wadden, in length 414 yards. In
                               digging along the hanger the labourers found many pyrites
                               perfectly round, lying in the clay; & in the chalk below several
                               large *cornua Ammonis*.¶ A fine romantic walk, shady & beautiful.

Thursday 28.
29 4/10; 60½; SW.   The China-hollyhocks in my strong soil grow too tall, & are but
Dark & moist, grey   just beginning to blow.
with brisk gale.   Martins abound.
                              Began to light fires in the parlor.

Friday 29.
29 2/10 59; SW; 28.   Martins.
Rain, rain, sun, bright.

Saturday 30.
28 8/10½; SW; 43.   Some martins.
Rain, rain, sun,
showers.

OCTOBER 1780

Sunday 1.
28 6/10½; 50; SW.   Some martins & swallows.
Grey, sun, rain, sun.   Gusts of wind.

Monday 2.
29 1/10½; 53; W,   Cleaned-out the zigzag. The spinage sown in Aug: now in
SW.   perfection.
Sun, sweet day, star-   Swallows & martins.
light.

Tuesday 3.
29 4/10; 54; SW, NW.   No ring-ouzels seen this autumn yet.
Sun, sun & pleasant,   Timothy very dull.
clouds, star-light.   Many swallows, & some martins.

Wednesday 4.
29 7/10; 50½; W, N.   Some swallows.
Showers, sun, showers,   Thunder.

showers, star-light.

Thursday 5.
29 8/10¼; 48½; NW,
SW.
White frost, sun,
clouds, sun, bright.

Gathered-in some apples & pears.

Friday 6.
50; SE, SW.
Grey, strong gales,
rain, rain with wind.

Swallows & martins.

Saturday 7.
29 3/10; 67.
Showers, sun, &
showers, sun, bright.

Swallows & martins.

Sunday 8.
28 8/10½; 51; S, SE.
Bright sun, grey, rain,
rain.

Swallows & martins.

Monday 9.
28 4/10, 5/10; 51; SW;
175.
Vast rain all night with
wind, showers,
showers, gusts of wind.

Many swallows, & Martins.
Black snails still appear.

Tuesday 10.
28 8/10; 53; SW, W;
55.
Grey, small showers,
grey & mild.

Rain in the night. Two ring-ouzels.
The grapes are very backward, & do not ripen well. Swallows, several.

A tremendous storm in the Leeward islands, which occasioned vast damage among the shipping, &c.

Wednesday 11.
29 2/10; 51; SW.
Sun, small showers,
grey & mild.

Some swallows.
Gathered the apples.
Vast halo round the moon.

Thursday 12.
29 6/10½; 49; W.
Sun, cold dew, fine

Spinage grown very large: a vast crop.
Several martins. No swallow.

autumnal weather,
bright moon.

Friday 13.
29 6/10; 51, 55; S,
SW.
Sun, sun & clouds, soft
even:, sweet moon-
light.
Full moon.

The tortoise scarcely moves.
No swallow. Several martins.
Bat appears.

Saturday 14.
29 3/10½; 55½, 58½;
SE, S.
Shower, grey & soft,
moist, shower.

Dug-up the carrots, & potatoes.
Many martins: a few swallows.

Octob.ʳ 13: 14. On these two days many house martins were
feeding & flying along the hanger as usual, 'til a quarter past five in
the afternoon, when they all scudded away in great haste towards
the S:E: & darted down among the low beechen leafy shrubs
above the cottages at the end of the hill. After making this
observation I waited 'til it was quite dusk, but saw them no more:
& returned home well pleased with the incident, hoping that at this
late season it might lead to some useful discovery, & point out their
winter retreat. Since that I have only seen two on Oct.ʳ 22 in the
morning. These circumstances put together make it look very
suspicious that this late flock at least will not withdraw into warmer
climes, but that they will lie dormant within 300 yards of this
village.

The cause, occasion, call it what you will, of fairy-rings,¶
subsists in the turf, & is conveyable with it: for the turf of my
garden-walks, brought from the down above, abounds with those
appearances, which vary their shape, & shift situation continually,
discovering themselves now in circles, now in segments, &
sometimes in irregular patches, & spots. Where-ever they obtain,
puff-balls abound; the seeds of which were doubtless also brought
in the turf.

Sunday 15.
29 2/10; 59½; 61; SE,
S.
Shower, grey & soft,
showers, bright.
Hunter's moon.

Two or three martins seen about the hanger: none in the evening.
Much lightening, & distant thunder.*
Glow-worms twinkle in the lanes.
*This storm did much damage at Hammersmith, Putney,
Wandsworth, &c, in the Isle of Wight & at Plymouth &c &c.

This storm did great damage in the Isle of Wight, Lancashire, at
Torbay where our fleet of observation lay, & over on the coast of
France near Brest: & was part of that hurricane which occasioned
such horrible devastations in the W: Indies.

Monday 16.
29 5/10; 57; SW; 30.
Sun, grey & soft, mild.

No swallow.
Many martins, in the morning.
Grapes improve.

Tuesday 17.
29 6/10½; 59, 60; S,
S.
Grey & moist, sun,
sweet & soft weather.

The hanger & my hedges are most beautifully tinged with
different shades of brown & yellow.
Some martins along the hanger in the morning.

Wednesday 18.
29 7/10; 57; E, N,
NE.
Deep fog, dark, still &
mild.

Leaves fall. No swallow.
Saw no martins.
Jet-ants still in motion.
A few large field-fares.

Thursday 19.
W.
Grey, strong gusts,
showers with strong
wind.

The China-hollyhocks blow, & make a fine appearance.
No Martins.

Friday 20.
29 1/10; 50; N; 20.
Clouds, sun & cold
wind.

Many leaves blown-down by the gusts last night.
No martins.

Saturday 21.
29 4/10½; 46½; NW.
Sun & clouds, & cold
wind, sharp wind.

Leaves fall very fast.
No martins.
Grapes are now very good.
No martins.

Sunday 22.
29 4/10; 49; S.
Dark & moist, rain,
rain.

A few martins over the village.

These proved to be the last martins that I saw.

Antirrhinum cymbalaria in full bloom.

Monday 23.
29 5/10; 49; S.
White frost, sun, grey,
small shower.

No martins. Redwings appear.
Grapes are fine.

Tuesday 24.
29 3/10½; 53; SW;
22.
Rain, rain, grey &
mild.

Ivy in full bloom: bees gather on the ivy.
No martins.
Bat appears.

Wednesday 25.
29 6/10; 49; W.
Wh: dew, sun, pleasant
day.

No beech-mast: many acorns. No martins.
Many wall-nuts. My great tree produced, when measured in
their husks, eight bushels.

Thursday 26.
29 9/10; 46½; NW.
Wh: frost, sun, bright
& pleasant.

Grapes are fine, & do not decay.
No martins.
Planted two rows of small lettuces under the fruit-wall to stand
the winter: the ground works very fine. The rows reach the whole
length of the wall.

Friday 27.
29 9/10; 43; N.
Dark, ice, deep fog,
great shower, rainbow.

China-hollyhocks make a great show.
Flies, bees & wasps, when the sun shines, gather from the ivy-
bloom.

Saturday 28.
29 6/10½; 48; NE.
Dark & moist, grey, &
mild, dark & moist.

Bees begin gathering honey on the bloom of crocus's, & finish
with the bloom of Ivy. Some forward ivy-berries are almost full
grown.
Bat appears.

Sunday 29.
29 5/10; 49; NW, W.
Dark & moist, rain,
dark & moist.

Men put their hogs up a fatting.

Timothy the tortoise, who in May last, after fasting all the winter,
weighed only 6 p^{ds} & four ounces; & in Aug: when full fed weighed
6 p^{ds} & 15 ounces; weighs now 6 p^{ds} 9 oun: & ½: & so he did last
Octr at Ringmer. Thus his weight fluctuates, according as he feasts
or abstains.

Monday 30.
29 5/10; 49½, NW.
Dark, rain, dark &
moist.

Tuesday 31.
29 6/10; 51; N; 20.
Dark & moist, rain,
dark & moist.

Woodcock appears.

NOVEMBER 1780

Wednesday 1.
29 7/10; 50; N.
Dark & moist.

Thursday 2.
29 7/10; 48; N.
Dark, dry & pleasant.

Leaves fall very fast. My hedges shew beautiful lights, & shades: the yellow of the tall maples makes a fine contrast against the green hazels.

Friday 3.
29 5:3/8; 48; N.
Wet fog, sun, sweet day.

The air abounds with insects & gossamer.
Dragon-flies, butter flies, & wasps appear.
Timothy, who is placed under a hen-coop near the fruit-wall, scarce moves at all.

Saturday 4.
29 7/10; 46; NW.
White dew, sun, cold dry air.

Planted-out some slips of red pinks: & set some rows of Tulips.

Sunday 5.
29 4/10¾; 46; W.
Grey, shower with strong wind, sun.

The leaves fall in showers.

Monday 6.
29 5/10; 44; NW.
Sun, strong, & sharp wind, snow, strong wind.

The tortoise begins to dig the mould for his winter-retreat: he has much moss in his coop, under which he conceals himself.

Tuesday 7.
29 5/10; 36; NW.
Snow, ice, strong wind, snow, hard frost.

Some snow on the ground.
Many trees were stripped last night: vine-leaves begin to fall.
Winter-weather.
Gathered the barberries, a vast crop.

Wednesday 8.
29 7/10; 36; N; 25.
Sleet, sun & clouds, bright, severe frost.

Gathered in a great many grapes, because the vines cast their leaves. The crop of grapes is prodigious: perhaps the greatest I ever had.

Thursday 9.
29 7/10½; 29 7/10;

The tortoise does not stir.

36½; SW.
Hard frost, dark &
moist, driving rain.

Friday 10.
29 7/10½; 47½; NW.
Grey, sun, pleasant day.

The China-Hollyhocks, that were in full bloom, much injured
by the frost. Grapes are very sweet.

Saturday 11.
29 8/10½; 46, 50;
NW.
Grey & mild.

Set more tulips.
Some grapes remaining on the vines.
The frost did not make all the leaves fall.
Several wood-cocks seen this day: stone-curlews are not yet gone.

Sunday 12.
29 8/10; 49; W.
Grey, still, & mild.
New moon.

SELEBURNE ¶
Wells, streams, & ponds are very low.

Monday 13.
29 3/10½; 50; W.
Dark & windy, rain &
wind.

Wheat-stubbles plow-up in fine order; green wheat comes-up
well.
Tortoise goes under ground: over him is thrown a coat of moss.

Tuesday 14.
29 5/10; 43; W.
Sun, grey & cold, small
showers, moonshine.

The border being very light & mellow, the tortoise has thrown
the mould entirely over his shell, leaving only a small breatheing
hole near his head. Timothy lies in the border under the fruit-
wall, in an aspect where he will enjoy the warmth of the sun, &
where no wet can annoy him: a hen-coop over his back protects
him from dogs, &c.

Wednesday 15.
29 7/10; 39; NW.
White frost, sun, sharp
wind, frost.

Thursday 16.
29 5/10; 31½; SE, E.
Fierce frost, sun, dark
& mild.

The ground carries horse & man.
Gathered-in all the grapes.

Friday 17.
29 3/10; 39; SE, S.
Grey & mild, thaw,
small rain.

Some what eats the pinks in the garden.

Saturday 18.
29 1/10½; 44; SW.

Crickets in the chimney cry but faintly, & do not appear much.

Grey & moist, dark & mild.

The cats kill all they can see.

The severity of the weather quickened Timothy's retreat: he used to stay above ground 'til about the 20th. At Ringmer he used to lay himself up in a wet swampy border: indeed he had no choice.

Sunday 19.
29; 43½; SW, E; 14.
Sun, sun, soft agreeable day.

Rain in the night.

Monday 20.
28 6/10; 44; SW, W; 77.
Rain, rain, rain, rain.

The ponds fill very fast.

Tuesday 21.
29 ½/10; 42; W; 85.
Dark & still, moist, dark.

Began to trim the vines: the bearing wood is rather small, & not very well-ripened, as usually happens when the crop is very great.

Wednesday 22.
29 3/10; 40; W. Grey & still, cold air, stars.

Some animal eats-off the pinks.

Thursday 23.
29 2/10; 36; NW.
Wh: frost, sun, sharp air, frost.

Multitudes of Starlings appear at Newton, & run feeding about in the grass-fields. No number is known to breed in these parts. This is therefore an emigration from some other district.

Friday 24.
29 2/10; 35; SW, SE; 33.
Frost, snow, rain, rain.

Saturday 25.
29 2/10½; 38; NW.
Grey, sun, pleasant, deep fog.

Haws abound, & aford a fine repast for the thrush-kind.

Sunday 26.
29 8/10¼; 42; NW.
Deep fog, grey & mild.

Monday 27.
30; 46; NW, N.
Grey, mild & still.

Phalaenae fly about under hedges.

Tuesday 28.
30 1/10; 45; E.
Grey, mild & still, red
even:

Timothy lies very snug, but does not get any deeper.

Wednesday 29.
30; 39; NE.
White frost, sun, grey
& still.

Antirrhinum cymbalaria still in fine bloom: this
plant extends over a vast space.
Rear Adm: Sʳ Samuel Hood sailed with 8 ships of the line.

Thursday 30.
29 9/10; 41½; NE.
Grey, still & mild.

Rooks frequent their nest-trees, & get into their nests.
Hares eat all the pinks.

DECEMBER 1780

Friday 1.
29 9/10; 40; NE.
Dark with brisk gale.

Paths very dry.

Saturday 2.
30; 42; NE.
Dark with brisk gale.

The well is risen two rounds.

Sunday 3.
30 1/10; 41; NE.
Dark with strong harsh
wind.

Planted about a doz: of the roots of the *Spiraea filipendula*, sent
me from London. Sʳ George Baker¶ directed Mʳˢ Barker to take
these roots powdered for the gravel. This plant does not grow with
us, but is common on Salisbury plain, & the downs about Winton,
& Andover, appearing among the bushes, & flowering about
midsummer.

Monday 4.
30 1/10; 41; NE.
Dark & sharp wind,
gleam of sun, dark &
still.

Tuesday 5.
30; 41; NE.
Dark & still.

Paths dry like spring.

Wednesday 6.
29 9/10; 41; NE.
Grey & still, sun, grey.

Planted out Sweet Williams, vine, & gooseberry cuttings, honey-
suckle cuttings; & several crab stocks grafted from a curious, &
valuable green apple growing at South Lambeth in Surrey.

Thursday 7.
29 9/10¼; 38½; NE.
Frost, wet fog, fog.

Friday 8.
30 ¼/10; 36¼; N.
Small snow, grey &
harsh.

Saturday 9.
30 1/10¼; 37½; N,
NW.
White frost, sun, grey
& still.

Sunday 10.
30; 37½; SW.
Grey & still, sharp air.

Monday 11.
30 ¼/10; 39½; NW.
Grey, sun, mild &
spring-like.
Full moon.

The air is full of gnats, & *tipulae*.
Gossamer about. The paths are dry like summer.

Tuesday 12.
30 1/10; 43; NW, W.
Grey, mild & still.

Bees play out from their hives. Spring-like.
The Barometer at S: Lambeth¶ was this day at 30 6/10: a sure
token that S: Lambeth is much lower than Selborne.

Wednesday 13.
30 ½/10; 43½; W.
Wet mist, grey
& still.

Spring-like.

Thursday 14.
30; 42; W.
Grey & mild.

Trimmed & tacked the wall-trees: the peaches & nectarines are
much decayed.
Spring-like.

Friday 15.
30 1/10; 42; NW, N.
Grey, sun & clouds,
grey.

Hen-chaffinches in vast flocks.
Summer-like.
Bees play before their hives.
Wren whistles.

Saturday 16.
30 1/10½; 42; E, SE,
E.
Fog, grey, sun & sweet
sunshine, dark.

The plant of missel-toe grows on a bough of the medlar: it
abounds in my hedges on the maple. Summer-like.
The air is full of Insects. Turkies strut & gobble. Many young
lambs at the Priory.

Sunday 17.
30 1/10; 42; NE, N.
Misty, grey & moist,
grey, stars.

My well has risen lately, notwithstanding the long dry season.

Monday 18.
30 1/10; 39; NE.
White frost, deep fog,
grey, dark.

Tuesday 19.
30; 37; NE.
Hard frost, sun, cutting
wind, frosty & dark.

At two o'clock in the shortest days the shades of my kitchen &
hall-chimnies fall just on the middle of the window of
J. Carpenter's work-shop; & the shade of the chimney of my
great parlor just in the midst of John Hale's side-front.
Hard frost all day. Covered the artichokes, & young asparagus
with litter.

Wednesday 20.
29 5/10½; 34½; NE.
Dark & frosty, small
snow, dark & sharp.

Thursday 21.
29 4/10; 33; NW, W;
Snow 3.
Snow, snow, snow,
bright & frosty.

Level snow; no
drifting.
Cutting wind.

Ivy - leaved toadflax
on the fruit wall.
The Wakes.

Friday 22.
29 6/10; 32; W, N.
Grey, sun, thaw, misty.

Antir: Cymbalaria still in bloom.
Two hares in the garden last night.
Snow-wastes: eaves drip. Cocks crow.

Saturday 23.
29 7/10½; 33½; NW,
SE, S, NW.
Frost, sun, snow melts,
grey.

No rain has fallen since the 24th of Novr the millers complain for
want of water.

Sunday 24.
29 8/10½; 35.

Deep fog, thaw, wet
fog.

Monday 25.
29 9/10; 35; NE.
Frost, sun, grey, thaw.

Tuesday 26.
29 9/10; 34½; NE.   Some snow still on the ground.
Frost, sun, bright,
frost.

Wednesday 27.
29 9/10¼; 33½; E, S.
Frost, grey, fog, thaw.

Thursday 28.
30; 35; SW. Frost,   Some snow lies still.
thaw, grey & still.

Friday 29.
29 6/10½; 41, 44; W.   Snow totally gone.
Swift thaw, grey &
mild.

Saturday 30.
29 7/10½; 43, 45; W.   No shower since the 24th of Novemr
Sun, soft & still, grey.   Earth-worms lie out, but do not copulate.

Sunday 31.
29 6/10¾; 46; W.   Foggy.
Moist, dark & mild.

JANUARY   — 1781 —

Monday 1.   SELBORNE
29 3/10; 46½; S.
Dark, rain, rain.

Tuesday 2.
29 2/10½; 40½; SW;
11.
White frost, sun, sun,
rain, snow.

Wednesday 3.
29 6/10¾; 38; NW;
33. Frost, sun, frost.

Some snow on the ground.
Vast halo round the moon.

Thursday 4.
29 8/10; 36; NW.
Frost, grey & mild.

Halo round the moon.

Friday 5.
29 9/10; 34; N.
Hard frost, rime, sun,
thaw, grey.

Saturday 6.
29 9/10; 38; SE, S.
Grey & mild.

In the church-yard at Faringdon are two <u>male</u> yew-trees, the
largest of which measures 30 feet in girth.

Sunday 7.
29 8/10½; 42; W.
Grey & mild, sun,
grey.

Monday 8.
30 1/10½; 42; NE.
Sun, brisk air, grey &
mild.

Tuesday 9.
30 2/10; 38; NE.
Sun, frost, harsh wind,
frost.

Wednesday 10.
30 1/10; 33½; NE.
Hard frost, sun &
clouds, sharp wind.
Full moon.

Thursday 11.
29 8/10½; 34; NE.
Hard frost, dark sky,
harsh & severe wind.

Friday 12.
29 9/10; 32; NE.

Hard frost, dark &
sharp.

Saturday 13.
29 7/10½; 34; NE.
Hard frost, dark &
harsh.

Sunday 14.
29 6/10; 33; NE.
Dark & hard frost,
sharp wind, sun.

The ground is as hard as a rock.
The roads & fallows are dusty.

Monday 15.
29 ¼/10; 34; NE.
Hard frost, dark, &
misty, sun, bright, hard
frost.

Millers complain for want of water.

Tuesday 16.
29 5/10; 33, 34; NE.
Hard frost, rime &
fog, dark & harsh.

Wednesday 17.
29 3/10¾; 35; E.
Rain, rain, deep fog.

The dew on the windows is on the outside of the glass.

Thursday 18.
29 2/10½; 38, 44; E,
W; 32.
Dark & mild, wet &
foggy.

Gnats come out from the laurels, & dance in the air.
Earth-worms lie out.

From Nov.ʳ 25 to Jan: 18: there fell only 69 of rain, & snow! less
than ¾ of an inch.

Friday 19.
29 7/10; 43; N; 19.
Sun, mild, frost.

The *Antyrrhinum Cym*: still in full bloom.
Snow-drops bud for bloom.

Saturday 20.
29 2/10½; 37½; S.
White frost, sun, rain,
rain.

At the end of the new parlor a box-tree is nearly killed by the
current of air; while a laurel in the same circumstances seems not
to be affected at all.
    At the corner of my great parlor there is such a current of air
that it has half killed a box-tree planted for a screen; while a laurel
planted in the same draught remains unhurt.¶
This laurel continues to flourish; Oct.ʳ 1782.

My Heliotrope,¶ which is J. Carpenter's workshop, shows plainly that the days are lengthened considerably: for on the shortest day the shades of my two old chimneys fall exactly in the middle of the great window of that edifice at ½ hour after two P:M: but now they are shifted into the quick-set hedge, many yards to the S:E:

Sunday 21.
29 3/10½; 44; SW,
NW.
Rain, rain rain.

The roads & paths very miry.

Monday 22.
29 3/10; 38; E; 30.
Snow, snow, snow,
bright.

Snow covers the ground.

Tuesday 23.
29; 32; E; snow 3½.
Snow, snow, snow.

Wednesday 24.
28 7/10¾; 36½; S.
Rain, rain, rain, rapid
thaw.

Flood at Gracious street.

Thursday 25.
29 2/10½; 36½; NW,
SW; 24.
Frost, small snow, sun,
frost.

Friday 26.
28 8/10; NW; 50.
Great rain, grey,
bright, frost.

Saturday 27.
29 7/10; 37; NW, SE.
Hard frost, bright,
grey.

Sunday 28.
29 6/10; 42; SW, S;
28.

Dark & moist, dark &
windy.

Monday 29.
29 6/10; 47; S.
Dark & moist, rain,
rain.

Vast condensations on the walls, &c.

Tuesday 30.
29 7/10; 47; W; 118.
Rain, sun, clouds &
strong wind.

Vast rain in the night.
Snow-drops, winter-aconite, & fetid-hellebore blow.

Wednesday 31.
29 8/10; 39; W, SW.
White frost, sun, grey
& mild.

Spring-like.
Vast halo round the moon.

FEBRUARY 1781

Thursday 1.
29 7/10; 43; SW, W;
30.
Rain, rain, grey &
mild.

Friday 2.
29 8/10½; 43; SW, S;
17.
Rain, rain, rain, dark
& moist.

Saturday 3.
29 9/10; 45; S, SW.
Dark, foggy & mild.

Marsh-titmouse chirps.

Sunday 4.
6/10½; 44½; SW.
Sun, soft & spring-like.

The nut-hatch brings his nuts almost every day to the alcove, &
fixing them in one corner of the pediment drills holes in their sides,
& after he has picked out the kernels, throws the shells to the
ground.

Monday 5.
29 4/10¾; 45; SW.
Rain, grey & mild.

Made a seedling cucumber-bed.
Wood-lark, thrush, & great titmouse sing.
Red-breast sings, & the wren.

Tuesday 6.
29 6/10; 46, 50; SW.
Grey, sun, spring-like.

Bees gather on the snow-drops. Flies come out in the windows. Bat appears; & moths flie under the hedges.

Wednesday 7.
29 6/10; 46; S.
Sun, grey, sunny &
mild.

Water-cresses come-in.
People begin to work in their gardens.

Thursday 8.
29 2/10½; 44½; S.
Grey, rain, rain.
Full moon.

Sowed cucumber-seeds.

Friday 9.
29 4/10; 47½; SW;
61.
Rain, sun & showers,
hail, showers.

Saturday 10.
29 6/10; 46½; SW.
Sun, sun & clouds.

Sunday 11.
29 2/10; 47½; S.
Grey, strong wind,
stormy, rain.

Cucumber plants appear.
Hasels blow.

Seagulls over the village.
2 June.

Monday 12.
29; 45; SW; 38.
Sun, dark, rain with
wind, stormy.

Thunder.
Sea-gulls appear: in stormy weather they leave the sea.

Tuesday 13.
28 8/10, 29 1/10; 47;
W; 116.
Stormy, sun, strong
wind, stiller.

Stormy all night. Much thatch blown-off, & some trees thrown-down.

Wednesday 14.
29 3/10; 43; S, W,
NW; 23.
Rain, strong gales,
bright, rain.

A pair of ravens build in the hanger.

Thursday 15.
29 4/10; 42; W; 24.
Sun, strong wind,
showers, bright.

Helleborus viridis emerges, & blows.
Strong N: *aurora*: very red in the N.E.

Friday 16.
29 8/10; 39; NW.
White frost, sun &
brisk gale, bright &
still.

A row of crocus's in the field in bloom.

Saturday 17.
29 6/10¾; 38; NW.
Frost, sun & sharp
wind.

The storms in the beginning of the week did great damage by sea,
& by land.

Sunday 18.
29 6/10; 37; W, SW.
Hard frost, sun, dark,
rain.

Monday 19.
29 5/10, 6/10; 39½;
NW; 20.
Sun, sharp air, sun &
clouds.

Tuesday 20.
29 9/10; 39½; N.
Dark & harsh, grey.

Wednesday 21.
29 7/10; 38;
N; 15.
Snow, snow, snow.

The snow melts as it falls, except on the hills.

Thursday 22.
29 8/10½; 35; N.
Hard frost, sun, sun,
bright.

Friday 23.
29 5/10½; 39; NW;
11.
Frost, sun, rain, rain.

Ivy-berries are full grown.

Saturday 24.
29 3/10½; 44; W,
SW; 21.
Grey, shower, rain.

Sunday 25.
28 9/10; 46; W.
Showers, hail, showers.

Monday 26.
29; 39; W, NW; 19.
Rain & snow, sun &
clouds.

Tuesday 27.   ALTON
28 6/10½; 40; S, W,   Had the duration of this storm been equal to it's strength,
NW.   nothing could have withstood it's fury. As it was, it did
Rain, wind, vast storm, prodigious damage. The tiles were blown from the roof of
calm & bright.   Newton church with such violence, that shivers from them broke
                       the windows of the great farm-house at near 30 yards distance.
                       This storm¶ blew the alcove back into the hedge, & threw down
                       the stone dial-post.

Wednesday 28.   SOUTH LAMBETH
W.
Sun, delicate day.

MARCH 1781

Thursday 1.
W.
Rain, dark & mild.

Friday 2.
SW.
Fog, mild, grey.

Saturday 3.
30 3/10; 50; SW.   Persian Iris blows.¶
Grey, mild.

Sunday 4.
30 2/10; SW.   Frogs begin to appear.
Dark, still, & moist.

Monday 5.
45; N.
Small rain, grey &
mild.

Wheat looks miserably in Battersea-field.
Frogs croak.

Tuesday 6.
30 3/10; 40; SW.
Sun, sweet day, red
even:

Elms blow.
Apricot-bloom begins to open.
Ants & flies appear.

Wednesday 7.
30 2/10; 40.
Fog, sun, sweet day.

Thursday 8.
40; SW.
Wet fog, dark & mild.

Friday 9.
30 2/10½; 47; SW, S.
Sun, sweet day, red
even.
❀ Pile-wort

Brimstone butterfly.

Saturday 10.
30 2/10½; 47.
Grey, sun, delicate.
Full moon.

Roads very dusty.
Rooks build. Insects abound.

Sunday 11.
38; W, NE.
Cold air, sun.

The tortoise came-forth, & continued to be alert 'til the 25th &
then eat some lettuce; when the weather turning very harsh he
retired under the straw in his coop.

Monday 12.
30 3/10; 36; NE.
Ice, grey.

About this time the shell-snails at this place began to move.

Tuesday 13.
30 3/10; 44; E.
Grey, sun, sweet day,
red even:

Apricot in full bloom: peaches & nectarines blowing.

Wednesday 14.
30 3/10; 35; E.
Frost, ice, deep fog, hot

sun, cloudless.

Thursday 15.
30 5/10; 30; E.
Frost, ice, fog, sun,
grey.

On this day Lord Cornwallis gained a considerable victory over
Gen: Greene at Guildford in N: Carolina.

Friday 16.
30 4/10½; 46; NE.
Dark & harsh, sun.

Humble bee.

Saturday 17.
30 2/10½; 40; E.
Dark, sun, pleasant.

Dust begins to be very troublesome.

Sunday 18.
30 1/10; 44, 55; E, W.
Deep fog, sun,
summer.

The chif-chaf, or small uncrested wren, was heard at Selborne.
The first summer-bird.

Monday 19.
44; W.
Wh: frost, fog, sun.

LONDON

Tuesday 20.
30 2/10; 60; W.
Sun, sweet day.

LONDON

Wednesday 21.
60; W.
Sun, summer, red
even:

S.L. [SOUTH LAMBETH]

Thursday 22.
60; W.
Fair, clouds, sultry,
small shower.

Friday 23.
30 3/10; 44; E.
Sun, cold air.

Saturday 24.
30 5/10; 35; E, W.
Cold fog, sun, summer.

The dust on the roads is become a terrible nuisance.
Apricots begin to set.

Sunday 25.
30 4/10; E, S.
Wh: frost, hot sun.

Plants languish for want of rain.
First radishes.

Monday 26.
29 9/10; W, N.
Sun, clouds, harsh
wind.

Tuesday 27.
30; 34; N.
Sun, & clouds, harsh.

Wednesday 28.
29 9/10; 34; NE.
Sun, ice, harsh, sleet.

Thursday 29.
NE.
Ice, sun & harsh wind.

ALTON
Young goslings.
Young thrushes.

Friday 30.
29 6/10½; NE.
Ice, sun & harsh wind.

SELBORNE
Apricots, peaches, & nectarines are well blown.

Saturday 31.
29 7/10; 43; NE.
Dark, sun, & harsh
wind, hail & rain.

Cucumber-plants show fruit; but are rather drawn, from the long
dry season, which never is favourable to hot-beds.

APRIL 1781

Sunday 1.
29 3/10¾; 49; E, SE;
19.
Sun, pleasant day.

The tortoise came-out for two hours.
Cucumber-fruit blows.

Monday 2.
29 6/10; 54; N.
Sun, hot, harsh wind.

Tortoise out.
Timothy weighs 6 pd 8¾ oz; the beginning of last May he
weighed only 6: 4.

Tuesday 3.
29 5/10½; 53; NE.

Timothy eats heartily.

Hard frost, sun,
cloudless, cold air.

The wry-neck appears & pipes.
Bombylius medius still: bobs his tail in flight against the grass, as if
in the act of laying eggs.

Wednesday 4.
29 2/10; 46; NE.
Dark, harsh wind.

Grass lamb.
Young ducks are hatched.
Swallow appears.

Thursday 5.
28 9/10¾; E, SE.
Dark & still, clouds,
small rain.

Searched the S:E. end of the hanger for house-martins, but
without any success, tho' many young men assisted. They
examined the beechen-shrubs, & holes in the steep hanger.

Friday 6.
29 2/10; SW, W; 15.
Dark, showers, hail,
bright & chill.

Swallow at Newton.
Wheat looks well on the strong land.

Saturday 7.
29 1/10; 47½; S; 15.
Dark & moist, rain,
rain.

Sunday 8.
29 3/10; 50; W, S; 46.
Sun, brisk air, rain,
rain. Full moon.

Ivy-berries are black & full ripe.

Monday 9.
29; 53; W, S; 41.
Rain, rain, dark.

Four swallows seen near the Priory.
Some cucumbers seem to set: the plants are weak.

Tuesday 10.
29 4/10½; 60½; S; 13.
Rain, sun, summer-like.

Shell-snails come-out in shoals.
Grass grows.

Wednesday 11.
29 1/10; 53; N, NE.
Dark & mild, rain,
rain.

Nightingale, Cuckow, House-martin, & Middle yellow wren,
appear.

While two labourers were examining the shrubs & cavities at the
S:E: end of the hanger, a house-martin came down the street &
flew into a nest under Benham's Eaves. This appearance is rather
early for that bird. Quae: whether it was disturbed by the two men
on the hill.

Thursday 12.
29 4/10; 50; NW; 43.
Sun, soft air, showers.

Planted four rows of potatoes.
Vines show shoots three inches long.

Friday 13.
29 6/10½; 48; NW,
W.
White frost, sun, soft
air, sweet afternoon.

Shell-snails copulate.
Apricots set, & swell.

Saturday 14.
29 4/10½; 47; W, S.
Frost, ice, sun, fine
day.

Sunday 15.
29 5/10; 47; W. Wh:
frost, sun, soft & grey.

Monday 16.
SE.
Sun, summer-like.

WORTING
Two house-martins in the village.

Tuesday 17.
62; S.
Sun, sultry, sweet even:

CAVERSHAM, READING

Wednesday 18.
Sun, clouds.

OXFORD
Some bank-martins at Wallingford-bridge.
Cut the first cucumber.

Thursday 19.
Shower, dark.

Friday 20.
NW.
Clouds, sun.

Saturday 21.
Sun, brisk air.

ALTON
White-throat on the road.

Sunday 22.
29 7/10; 59; W.
Sun, brisk air, showers
about.

SELBORNE
Few swallows & house-martins yet.

Monday 23.
29 7/10¾; 52½; NW,
N.
Sun, sun & clouds,
dark.

Cucumbers set, & swell.
Early tulips blow.
Sowed large white cucumbers.
Many beeches in the hanger are come into leaf; the wild cherries
blow, & make a beautiful appearance; pears blow well; & vines
show much promise of fruit; the crop of apricots is great; &
peaches & nectarines are set.
Apple-trees blow.

Tuesday 24.
29 8/10½; 52½; N.
No dew, dark, sun,
sweet even:

Laurels blow.

Wednesday 25.
29 9/10½; 55; N.
No dew, sun & clouds,
fine even:

Rain seems to be wanting.
Lathraea squammaria going out of bloom.

Thursday 26.
29 9/10; 50½; N.
Dark & harsh, sun,
dark & moist.

Antyrrhinum Cym: in beautiful bloom.
A pair of Nightingales haunt my fields: the cock sings nightly in
the Portugal-laurel, & balm of Gilead fir.

Friday 27.
29 8/10; N.
Dark & harsh.

Saturday 28.
29 6/10; 49; N.
Sun, hot sun, & cold
air, sweet even:

Flesh-flies appear.
Chafer comes out.

Sunday 29.
29 6/10; 52; N.
Sun, sun & clouds, red
even:

Hanger almost in full leaf.
Swallows now in plenty; few house-martins.

Monday 30.
29 5/10½; 51; N.
White frost, hot sun,
clouds, red even:

Men pole their hops.
Dragon-fly & *musca meridiana*.
Ponds begin to be dry.

The quantity of rain that fell at Selborne between May 1ˢᵗ 1780, &
May 1ˢᵗ 1781.

	inch:	hund:
In May 1780	2:	99
June	1:	60
July	2:	47
August	2:	1
Septemʳ	3:	67
October	3:	89
Novemʳ	2:	34
Decemʳ	0:	3
Jan: 1781	3:	48½
Feb:	3:	95
March	0:	0
April	1:	92
	28:	35½

MAY 1781

Tuesday 1.
29 6/10½; 52; N.
Cold & dark, hot sun,
red even:

Glow-worms shine.

Wednesday 2.
29 6/10¾; 53; N, E,
S, W, N.
Dew, cloudless, dark
clouds, sweet even:

Swift appears.
Field-crickets crink:¶ this note is very summer-like, & chearful.

Thursday 3.
29 5/10½; 52½; E,
SE, E.
Small shower, sun,
dark, small shower,
sweet even.

Three pairs of swifts. House-martins begin to come: they
frequent their nests.
Cucumber-beds are now in high order, & the plants are full of
fruit.

Friday 4.
29 6/10; 53; N, N.
Shower, dark & cold,
showers.

Cut some cucumbers, fine fruit.

Saturday 5.
48; N, N.
Dark & harsh, sun &
clouds, very cold air.

Not rain enough to measure.

Sunday 6.
29 7/10¾; 48; N, N.
Dark & cutting wind,
still.

Monday 7.
29 7/10; 48; NE.
White frost, dark &
sharp air, sun, sharp.
Full moon.

Vast bloom among the apples: the crop but small.
No rain to measure since April 12.

Tuesday 8.
29 4/10½; 48; NE.
Dark & harsh, sun,
cold wind, dark & still.

Timothy lies very close this cold weather.
No house-martins appear.

Wednesday 9.
29 3/10; 47; NE.
Very white frost, sun,
& cold air, mild even:

Many swifts: house-martins encrease & come to their respective
nests.
Large well-grown cucumbers.

Thursday 10.
29 2/10; 49; NE.
Very wh: frost, hot sun,
still, red at sun-set.

All sorts of hirundines now abound.
A small sort of caterpillar annoys the goose-berry trees.

Friday 11.
29 5/10½; 54½; 63;
NE, S, SW, S.
Misty rain, dark, hot
sun, red even:

Fern-owl chatters. When this bird is heard, summer is usually
established.

Saturday 12.
29 5/10; 59, 66; SE, S;
40.
Sun, sultry, strong
gale, dark, thunder, &
showers.

My well sinks very fast: indeed much water has been drawn lately
for watering. Mʳ Yalden's tank is almost dry.

Sunday 13.
29 6/10; 62, 68; NW,
NW.
Sun, sultry, dark,
showers.

The rain last night broke the stems of several of the tulips, which
are in full bloom.
The rain from the S.

Monday 14.
29 5/10½; 63, 69;
NE, S, SW; 32, 34.
Thunder showers, sun,
sultry, sweet
afternoon.

The hops wanted rain, & began to be annoyed by aphides. The
ground finely refreshed.
Vast rocklike, distant clouds.

Tuesday 15.
29 5/10½; 62; NE.
Dark & moist.

Killed some hundreds of shell-snails about the garden.
The boys every day kill some large wasps, that feed on the
sycamore-bloom on the Plestor.

Wednesday 16.
29 6/10½; 60; NE.
Dark & moist, &
warm.

Several small wasps appear, as well as large breeders.
Most growing weather.

Thursday 17.
29 7/10; 58; NE.
Dark & still.

Standard honey-suckles begin to blow.
Hawthorns blow.

Friday 18.
29 6/10; 56½; NE, N;
28.
Shower, dark & still,
grey.

Filled all the hand-glasses with white cucumber-plants.

Saturday 19.
29 5/10; 62; NE.
Fog, dark & warm,
wet.

Orange-lily begins to blow.
S! foin begins to blow. Growing weather.

Sunday 20.
29 6/10; 60½; NE; 33.
Showers, dark & moist,
gleams & clouds, red
even.

Wheat very gross in some fields.

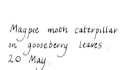

Magpie moth caterpillar
on gooseberry leaves.
20 May.

Monday 21.
29 8/10; 59½; NE, E;
5. Sun, clouds, &
showers, sweet even:

Tulips make a gaudy show.
Horse-chest-nut blows finely.
Grass & corn grow wonderfully.

Tuesday 22.
29 9/10; 57; NE.
No dew, strong, cold
wind.

The wind breaks-off the leaves of the beeches.

Wednesday 23.
29 9/10; 53; NE.
Cold wind, strong gale
all day, cloudless, red
even:

The wind injures the foliage.

Thursday 24.
29 9/10; 53; NE, E.
Cold air, cloudless,
strong gale, red even:
still.

Friday 25.
29 8/10; 52; E.
White frost, cloudless,
sharp wind, red even:

Tacked the vine-shoots: there is a promise for a good crop.

Saturday 26.
29 7/10½; 52; NE, E,
SE, NW.
Very white frost,
cloudless, red even:

Fiery lily begins to blow.
Finished the vines.

Sunday 27.
29 8/10; 55; 66; NE,
SE.
White frost, cloudless,
sweet even: red.

Monday 28.
29 8/10½; 59; E, SE,
NW.
White frost, cloudless,
fine, gale, sweet even:
red.

Tuesday 29.
29 7/10; 59, 70; E,
SE, S. Dew,
cloudless, sweet even:

The limes begin to show bracteal leaves.
S^t foin blows out.

Wednesday 30.
29 6/10; 63, 73½; SE,
S, SE.
Sun, sultry, grey, sweet
even:

Tulips begin to
go-off.

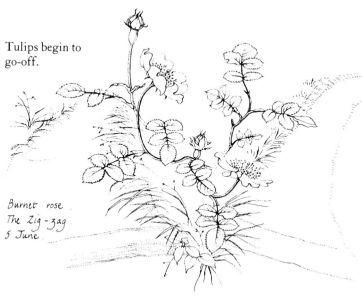

Burnet rose
The Zig-zag
5 June

Thursday 31.
29 6/10½; 63½, 72;
NE, SE.
Sun, cloudless, sweet
even:

JUNE 1781

Friday 1.
29 6/10½; 65, 79; SE,
S, SW.
Hot sun, sultry,
cloudless, red even:

Grass-walks burn very much.
Ground chops.
Roses begin to blow. Wheat spindles for ear.

Saturday 2.
29 5/10; 68½, 76; SE,
S, SW.
Sun, cloudless, sultry,
broken clouds, sweet
even: red.

Tulips are gone.
The heat injures the flowers in bloom.
S^t foin in full bloom. Fly catcher has five eggs.

Sunday 3.
29 4/10½; 66, 73;
SW, W.
Clouds, sprinklings,
sun & brisk gale, dark.

Wheat-ears begin to burst-out.
Boys bring hornets.¶

Monday 4.
29 5/10; 63, 65; W,
NW.
Clouds, strong gale,
sun, cool air, chill.

Tuesday 5.

29 3/10½; 60, 63; W,
S.
Grey, no dew, sun &
clouds, dark, rain, rain.

Wednesday 6.

29 2/10; 61, 63; W, S;
27.
Rain, sun & clouds,
sweet even:
Full moon.

The garden is somewhat refreshed.
Elders begin to blow.

Thursday 7.

29 2/10, 29 2/10;
60½, 63; W, NW,
SW.
Dark, moist, sun &
clouds, thunder,
showers, great showers
about.

Much distant thunder.
Great showers to the NE. & NW.

Friday 8.

29 2/10; 57; NW, SW,
SE.
Dark, showers,
showers, showers.

Began to put out the annuals.

Saturday 9.

29 4/10; 58; E, NE,
N.
Dark & moist,
showers, thunder,
showers.

Put-out more annuals: they were pricked out in a second bed, &
are stocky.
A pair of swallows hawk for flies 'til within a quarter of nine o'
clock: they probably have young hatched.

The planet Venus is just become an evening star: but being now in
the descending signs; that is, the end of Virgo, where it now is,
being a lower part of the Zodiac than the end of Leo, where the
sun is; Venus does not continue up an hour after the sun, &
therefore must be always in a strong twilight. It sets at present N:
of the west; but will be in the S:W: but not set an hour after the
sun 'til Oct! from which time it will make a good figure 'til March
in the S:W: W: & a little to the N: of the W.

Sunday 10.

29 4/10; 58; E, SE; 87.
Showers, showers, dark
& still.

Heavy showers about.
Wheat out in ear, & not lodged in this district.

Monday 11.
29 5/10; 58½; E, S,
West.
Sun & clouds, sweet
even:

Bees swarm much.
Sheep are shorn. Planted-out annuals.

Tuesday 12.
29 4/10; 60½; N, NE;
22, 87.
Dark, heavy showers.

Vines begin to blow: the bloom is early.
Thinned the apricots, peaches, & nectarines.

Wednesday 13.
29 3/10½; 61; S, SW.
Dark, sun & clouds,
sweet even:

The house-martins, which build in old nests begin to hatch, as
may be seen by their throwing-out the egg-shells.
Some wheat lodged. Wheat begins to blow.

Thursday 14.
29 4/10; 61; SE, SW;
22.
Rain, rain, dark, red
even:

We have planted-out a vast show of annuals, which will want no
watering.

Friday 15.
29 3/10; 60; S, SE.
Grey, cloudy, small
scuds.

Saturday 16.
29 4/10¼; 59½; S,
SE.
Sun & clouds, rain-
bow, showers about,
fine afternoon.

My garden in nice order, & full of flower in bloom. Lilies,
roses, fraxinellas, red valerians, Iris's, &c &c. now make a
gaudy show.

Sunday 17.
29 5/10; 61; S, SE.
Shower, sun & clouds.

Wheat blows finely, & promises for a great crop.

Monday 18.
29 5/10½; 62; S, SE;
22.
Early showers, clouds,
heavy showers,
thunder, vast showers
about.

The S^t foin is in a bad way about the neighbourhood.

Tuesday 19.
29 5/10; 64, 70; S, SE;
11.
Shower, sun, sultry,
soft hot even:

A strange swarm of bees came & settled on my balm of Gilead
Fir.
Much thunder, & heavy rains to the N:E.
Vast hail storm at Farnham.

Wednesday 20.
29 5/10; 67; SE, E.
Sun, sultry, clouds,
fog.

Much thunder, & vast showers to the westward.
Vast storm, & rain at Winton.
Young pheasants.

These storms were very terrible at Sarum, & in the vale of white-
horse; &c.

Thursday 21.
29 3/10¾; 66½; N,
NE. Fog, sun, sultry,
sweet even: red.

Finished cutting the S^t foin, which has stood full long. The 14th
crop. Sold it to John Hale. In some parts a good burden.

Friday 22.
29 3/10¾; 64; NE,
SE.
Grey, blue mist, sun,
brisk air, dark, wet.

Began to stop down the vines, which are in full bloom.

Saturday 23.
29 5/10; 62; NE, N;
24.
Rain, dark & moist.

We pick the catterpillars, which again annoy the goose-berry-
bushes.
The wheat is in full bloom, & is not lodged.
The large white cucumbers begin to set.
Finished the stopping down the vines: the grapes begin to set.

Sunday 24.
29 4/10; 60; NE.
Grey, & mild, dark &
still.

There are this summer about this church 11, or 12 pairs of
swifts.

Monday 25.
29 4/10, 5/10; 60; S,
SE. Dark & moist,
grey, fine even:

Our fields of pease are in a sad lousy state.
Took-off the frames from the cucumber-beds, which have not
born now for many weeks.

Tuesday 26.
29 6/10; 60; NE, N,
NW.
Grey, threatning, sun,
red even: vast dew.

My grapes are very forward, & out of bloom.
Fly-catchers have young.
Young redstarts come abroad.

Wednesday 27.
29 7/10; 60; NW, W.
Sun, sun, heavy clouds,
sweet even:

The honey-buzzard sits hard.
Young martins peep out of their nests.

Thursday 28.
29 9/10; 64; W, NW.
Sun, sun & clouds,
sweet even: red.

Began to cut my meadow-hay.
The early cucumbers, which have not born for many weeks, now
begin to show fruit.

Friday 29.
30/10; 63; W.
Vast dew, sun, brisk
gale, fine even:

Wheat begins to turn colour.
Jasmine blows. China hollyhock blows.
Rasps begin to ripen. Currans turn colour.

Saturday 30.
29 8/10; 65; SW, S.
Fog, sun, summer day,
mackarel sky, sweet
even: creeping mists.

Green cucumbers bear. White cucumbers swell.
Wheat is out of bloom, & the grain forming in the husk. Sweet
day.
Lime-trees begin to blow.
Some of the forwardest of those broods of young martins that
were hatched in old nests are out.
About nine in the evening a large shining meteor appeared falling
from the S; towards the E: in an inclination of about 45 degrees,
& parting in two before I lost sight of it. I was in Baker's hill in
the shrubbery, having a very bad horizon; & therefore could not
see how & where it fell.

Upon a tall slender beech near the middle of the Bostal a pair of
honey-buzzards¶ built them a large shallow nest composed of
twigs, & lined with dead beechen leaves. A boy climbed this tree,
tho' standing on so steep & dizzy a situation, & brought down one
egg, the only one in the nest, which had been sat-on for some time,
& contained the embrio of a young bird. This egg was smaller &
not so round as those of the common buzzard, was dotted with
small red spots at each end, & surrounded in the middle with a
broad red zone.
    The hen-bird was shot, & answered exactly to Mr Ray's
description of that species: had a black cere, short, thick legs, & a
long tail. When on the wing this species may be distinguished from
the common buzzard by it's hawk-like appearance, small head,
wings not so blunt, & longer tail. The specimen contained in it's
craw some limbs of frogs, & many grey snails without shells. The
Irides of the eyes of this species are of a beautiful yellow colour.
    The male honey-buzzard still haunts about the hanger; & on
sunny mornings soars above the hill to inhale the coolness of the
upper air.

JULY 1781

Sunday 1.
29 4/10; 64, 73; SE, S.
Dew, sun, sultry with
flisky clouds, dark
heavy horizon.

Wheel round the sun.
Some few young swallows are out.

Monday 2.
3/10½, 4/10; 69; SW,
W.
Sun, fog, dark &
threat'ning.

Made my rick of meadow-hay, which contains six jobbs, without
one drop of rain. Some part of it would have been better, I think,
had there been some sun on the day of making.

Tuesday 3.
4/10½, 29 5/10; 64½;
SW, SW.
Sun, strong gales, sun
& dark clouds.

Rasps ripen. All fruits are forward.
Cucumbers bear well.

Wednesday 4.
29 8/10½; 63; SW,
SW.
Sun, small showers,
sun, brisk gales, fine
even:

The bloom of the lime hangs in beautiful golden tassels.
The late orange, & white lily make a fine contrast.

Thursday 5.
29 7/10¾; 61; SW, E.
Sun, summer's day,
sweet even: red.
Full moon.

Men begin to mow their meadows.
Gardens suffer for want of rain.

Friday 6.
29 4/10¾; 64, 71; S,
S.
Sun, sun, dark clouds,
shower, showers.

Brisk gale.
The wheat, in large fields, undulates before the gale in a most
amusing manner.

Saturday 7.
29 3/10½; 64; SE, SE;
40.
Showers, strong gale,
showers, clouds &
wind.

Grapes swell, & are very forward.
Wind blows down the flowers.

Timothy the tortoise, who weighed April 2: after fasting all the
winter, only six pounds 8 oun: & ¾: weighs now seven pounds, &

one ounce: weighed last august six pounds, & 15 ounces.

From the encreased number of the Swifts, it seems as if they had brought-out many of their young. About eight in the evening they get together in a large party, & course round the environs of the church, as if teaching their broods the art of flying. As yet they do not retire 'til three quarters after 8 o' the clock; & before they withdraw the bats come forth: so that day & night-animals take each others places in a curious succession! All the swifts that play around the church do not seem to roost under it's eaves. Some pairs, I know, reside under some of the cottage-roofs.

Three or four pairs of lapwings hatched their broods this summer on the common: the young, which run long before they can flie, skulk among the fern. They usually affect low, moist situations.

A pair of house-martins, that built under the eaves of my stable, lost their nest in part by a drip, just as most of the young were flown. They are now repairing their habitation in order to rear a second brood.

A pair of sparrow-hawks bred in a crows nest in the hanger. A boy climbed the tree, & found the young so fledge that they all escaped: but he brought down a young blackbird, a young h: martin & jay, clean picked & half devoured, which the dams had carryed to their brood. The old ones have made havock for some days among the young swallows & martins, which being but just out have no powers or command of wing. They carried-off also from a farm-yard a young duck larger than themselves.

Sunday 8.
29 3/10; 5/10; 63; SW,
W; 115.
Showers, strong gales,
vast showers, thunder,
showers, clouds.

The cart-way runs.
H: martins feed their young on the wing.

Monday 9.
29 7/10; 62; W, W.
Gales, clouds, showers,
grey even:

Young swallows come out; & young fly-catchers.
The solstitial flowers begin to fade.
Trenched out celeri. Sowed endive.

Tuesday 10.
29 5/10¾; 61; SW,
W; 24.
Rain, rain, cloudy,
gales, grey.

The forward broods of the h: martins are out.
Much hay damaged.

Wednesday 11.
29 6/10¾; 67; W.
Dark & moist, grey,

Trenched-out some celeriac, & some of the new advertized large celeri. Planted out some endive.

brisk gale, sun, grey.

Jasmine now blows finely.
No swifts appear.

Thursday 12.
29 8/10; 64, 69½;
SW.
Dark, sun, gales, hot,
grey.

Only one swift.
The lapwings continue on the upland-fallows.
Several swifts came to roost in the evening.

Friday 13.
29 7/10½; 66; SW.
Grey, dark,
sprinklings,
sprinklings, grey &
mild.

Hay does not make. Two swifts about all day; they probably have
young not flown.
Men hoe their turnips.

Saturday 14.
29 6/10¾; 64½; SW,
NW; 23.
Dark & moist, soft
showers all day, grey.

The hay that is down is now entirely spoiled.
These soft rains sop & drench every thing.
Many swifts in the evening.
A young man brought me a live specimen of a *Papilio Machaon*,
taken below Temple. The first specimen that ever I saw of that
species in these parts was in my own garden last Aug! 2nd.

Sunday 15.
29 8/10½; 60½; N,
NW.
White dew, sun,
shower, bright.

The farmers complain of smut in their wheat.
Red martagons blow.
Many swifts.

Monday 16.
29 9/10; 60; N, NW.
Sun, cold dew, summer
weather, red even:

Wheat-harvest begins at Headley.
Wheat turns colour.
Martins frequent their nests for a second brood.
Numbers of swifts.

Tuesday 17.
29 8/10½; 60½; N,
NW.
Cold dew, sun, sweet
weather, red even:

Rasps, currans, & goose-berries all ripe: apricots turn colour.
The sparrow hawks continue their depredations.

Wednesday 18.
29 8/10½; 62; NE.
Vast dew, sun, sun,
sweet even: red.

BRAMSHOT PLACE
Lapwings haunt the uplands still.
Farmers complain their wheat is blited.
Swifts abound.

Thursday 19.
30; N.
Sun, air, dark horizon.

House martins abound at Lipock.
Barley large & fine; wheat mildewed.

Friday 20.
30; NE.
Dark, sun, glorious
day.

Pease are hacking.
Very ripening weather.

Saturday 21.
30; 65; NE.
Grey, sun, glorious
season, red.

SELBORNE
Wheat-harvest at Bramshot. Wheat much discoloured.

The planet Mars figures every evening, & makes a golden & splendid shew. This planet being in opposition to the sun, is now near us, & consequently bright.

At Bramshot place, the house of M[r] Richardson, in the wilderness near the stream grows wild, & in plenty, *Sorbus aucuparia*, the quicken tree, or mountain-ash; *Rhamnus frangula*, berry-bearing alder; & *Teucrium scorodonia*, wood sage & whortle-berries. The soil is sandy. In the garden at Dowland's, the seat, lately, of M[r] Kent, stands a large *Liriodendrum tulipifera*, or tulip-tree, which was in flower. The soil is poor sand; but produces beautiful pendulous Larches. Mr R'[s] garden, tho' a sand, abounds in fruit, & in all manner of good & forward kitchen-crops. Many China asters this spring seeded themselves there, & were very forward; some cucumber plants also grew-up of themselves from the seeds of a rejected cucumber thrown aside last autumn. The well at Dowland's is 130 feet deep; at Bramshot place†   . Mr R'[s] garden is at an average a fortnight before mine.

Late in an evening the swifts course round with their young high in the air. They are some times so numerous that one might suspect they are joined by parties from other villages.

The fly-catchers have quite forsaken my house & garden: they never breed twice.

All the first meadow-hay about us was spoiled: all the latter was ricked in delicate order.

Sunday 22.
29 8/10; 62, 71; NW.
Sun, sultry ripening
weather, broken clouds,
red.

Wheat turns very fast.
Vast flocks of young swallows & martins, the first broods: they begin to congregate on roofs.

Monday 23.
29 7/10½; 64, 71; E,

Of those China hollyhocks that stood the winter the tall ones are

† Space left in manuscript.

N, W.
Sun, sultry, sweet even:
red.

plain & single; the stunted ones are double & variegated.
Cucumbers in profusion.

Tuesday 24.
29 6/10; 66, 73; W,
SW, S.
Sun, sultry, mackerel
sky, grey, hot.

Gardens much burnt-up. Several begin wheat-harvest.
Ponds fail. My well is very low.

Wednesday 25.
29 5/10; 65; SW, W.
Sun, sultry, dark, small
shower.

The crop on my largest Apricot-tree is still prodigious, tho' in
May I pulled off 30, or 40 dozen.
Swifts still. Watered the annuals.

Thursday 26.
29 6/10½; 63; N, N.
Sun, sun & air, grey &
mild.

The blackbirds & thrushes, that have devoured all the wild
cherries in the meadow, now begin to plunder the garden.
Watered the garden.

Friday 27.
29 7/10; 63; W, SW,
W.
Grey, sun, dark
horizon.

Wheat-harvest begins to be
general.
Cran-berries ripen.
Some wheat housed.
Watered kidney-beans.

Thrush eating rowan
berries. Selborne.

Saturday 28.
29 6/10½; 63; SW.
Grey & mild, clouds,
moist, grey.

Gathered apricots.
Gleaners bring home bundles of corn.
Swifts.
The black-birds, & thrushes come from the woods in troops to
plunder my garden. The white throats are bold thieves: nor are
the red breasts at all honest with respect to currans. Birds are
guided by colour, & do not touch any white fruits 'til they have
cleared all the red: they eat the red rasps, currans, & goose
berries first.

We shot 30 black-birds, & thrushes.
    Timothy comes-out but little, while the weather is so hot: he
skulks among the carrots, & cabbages.

Sunday 29.
29 7/10½; 65, 69½;
W, NW. Small rain,
sun, sultry, grey,
distant sea fog, bright.

Hops blossom.
Red-breasts eat the berries of the honey-suckle.

Monday 30.

29 7/10½; 65, 75½;
SW, S.
Wet mist, sun,
cloudless, sultry, red
even:

Swifts.
The ants, male, female, & workers, come forth from under my
stairs by thousands.
Wheat housed.

Tuesday 31.

29 6/10½; 67, 76¾;
W, NW.
Vast dew, sun,
cloudless, dark to W,
red even:

Apricots ripen in vast profusion.
Grapes swell, & are very forward.
Sweet harvest weather. Swifts.

AUGUST 1781

Wednesday 1.

29 7/10; 70, 72½;
NW.
Shower, sun, brisk
gale, red even:

Wheat housed.
The honey-bees suck the goose-berries, where the birds have
broke the skin.

Thursday 2.

29 8/10; 63½; 66½;
NW.
Chill air, sun, sweet
moon-light, red even:

Delightful harvest weather.
Swallows, & h: martins congregate: the old ones sit on the second
eggs.

On this day the swifts at Fyfield withdrew.

Friday 3.

29 9/10; 60; NE, SE,
SW.
Chill air, sun, sultry,
red even:

One swift.
Now the ants under the staircase have sent-out their males, &
females, they no longer appear.
Much wheat in shock.

Saturday 4.

29 9/10½; 60½; NE,
SE, SW, W.
Sun, sultry, sweet even:
red. Full moon.

Pair of swifts. Several wheat-ricks made.
The house-martins begin to hatch, & to throw-out their egg-
shells.
Pair of swifts only.

Sunday 5.

29 8/10; 62, 67; NE.
Sun, dark clouds,
strong gust, red even:

Small scuds of rain.
No rain to measure since July 14.

Aug: 5th On this day a bloody & obstinate engagement happened between Admiral Hyde Parker, & a Dutch fleet off the Dogger-bank.

Every ant-hill is now in a strange hurry & confusion, & all the winged ants, agitated by some violent impulse, are leaving their homes; & bent upon emigration, swarm by myriads in the air, to the great emolument of the hirundines, who live luxuriously. Those that escape the swallows, return no more to their nests; but looking-out for new retreats, lay a foundation for future colonies. All the females at these times are pregnant.

The leaves of the vines begin to turn purple: the grapes are very forward.

Monday 6.
29 7/10; 64; NE; 9.
Shower, clouds, sun,
sweet even:

The fern-owl appears in the evening about the zigzag. Fly-catchers.
The first broods of swallows, & martins congregate in great flocks: the second broods are now hatching.

Tuesday 7.
29 6/10¾; 62, 67;
NE, SE, SW.
Cold white dew, sun,
sultry, dark & mild,
red even:

Much wheat housed.
Heavy showers to the N:E.
One swift only.

Wednesday 8.
29 7/10; 66; NE, SE.
Dark & moist, small
showers, dark & moist,
dark.

Some titlarks, as usual at this season, frequent the grass-plots.
Fly-catchers.
Much wheat housed.
We have shot 31 black-birds, & saved our goose-berries.

Thursday 9.
29 6/10; 66; SW, S.
Dew, sun, sun & brisk
gale, soft showers,
showers.

Watered the fruit-wall border.
One swift, perhaps a pair, going in & out at the eaves of the church. Why do these linger behind the rest, which have withdrawn some days? have they a backward brood delayed by some accident?
Swallows & h: martins hatch.

Friday 10.
29 6/10½; 69; SW, S.
Sun, sultry, sweet even:
red, lightening to the E.

Saturday 11.
67, 77; S.
Fog, sun, sultry,
cloudless, sweet even,

Ponds & streams fail.
Apricots become mellow.
Several have finished wheat-harvest.

lightening to the N.

People in many parts in great want of water.
A swift, or rather a pair, still frequent the church-eaves, with great assiduity; & have perhaps a brood of backward young. ¶

The reapers were never interrupted by rain one hour the harvest thro'.

Sunday 12.
29 6/10⅓; 70½, 76; W.
Wet fog, sun, sultry, brisk gale, dark clouds to NW, red.

One swift only still seen haunting the eaves of the church.
Barley & oats cut. Hops begin to be full formed.

Monday 13.
29 6/10; 70; W; 18.
Rain, dark, sun, brisk gale, showers about, red even:

The pond on Selborne down has still some good water in it; Newton pond is all mud.
Fly-catchers.
Many annuals are shriveled-up for want of moisture. The drought is very great. Hops are injured for want of rain.

Tuesday 14.
29 5/10½; 65; W; 30.
Grey, sun, strong gale, rain, rain, rain-bow, yellow even:

Apricots are over: the crop was prodigious. Tyed up endive.
China asters begin to blow. Peaches & nect: begin to blush, & swell.
Watered the fruit-wall border.
The bank-martins at the sand-pit on Short-heath are now busy about their second brood, & have thrown out their egg-shells from their holes. The dams & first broods make a large flight. When we approached their caverns they seemed anxious, & uttered a little wailing note.

Wednesday 15.
29 2/10½; 63; SW; 20.
Dark & windy, rain, rain, sun.

Missle-thrushes in small flocks.
White-throat.
China-asters begin to blow.

Thursday 16.
29 3/10; 63; S, W.
Sun, clouds & brisk gale, cool.

Sowed a plot of winter-spinage, & pressed the ground close with the garden-roller. The ground turned up very dry, & harsh.

Friday 17.
29 5/10; 62; SW, S; 22.
Sun, showers,

The small pond in Newton great farm field, near the verge of the common is full nearly of good clear water! while ponds in vales are empty.

showers, bright.

My well is low in water; but a constant spring bubbles up from the bottom. Some neighbouring wells are dry. My well is 63 feet deep.
One swift!

The crevice thro' which the swift goes up under the eaves of the church is so narrow as not to admit a person's hand.

Saturday 18.
29 5/10½; 61; NE, W;
10.
Sun, bright, showers,
still & mild.

Soft showers.
Fly-catchers.
Some wasps at the butcher's shop.
Planted out more endive.

Sunday 19.
29 4/10; 62; NE, NW.
Cool air, sun, pleasant,
dark horizon.

Mr Pink's turnips are infested with black caterpillars; he turned 80 ducks into the field, hoping they would have destroyed them; but they did not seem much to relish the sort of food. I have known whole broods of ducks destroyed by their eating too freely of hairy caterpillars.

Monday 20.
29 6/10; 61; NW.
Grey, cool, sun, sweet
autumnal day.

The young swallows & h: martins cluster on roofs in the sun, now the mornings are chilly.
Autumnal crocus's blow.

Tuesday 21.
29 8/10½; 59½; NE,
SW.
Sun, cool, sweet
autumnal day, red even:

No wasps, but several hornets, which devour the nectarines. The wasps are probably kept down by the numbers of breeders that the boys destroyed for me in the spring.
Gathered the first plate of peaches & Nectarines.
Vivid N: *Aurora.*¶

Wednesday 22.
29 7/10¾; 60; NW,
SW.
Sun, sweet autumnal
day.

Hop-picking begins in the neighbourhood.
One swift still!
Grapes just begin to turn colour.
The chilly feel that occasions the young martins to cluster on sunny roofs, probably induces the swifts to withdraw.
Many bunches of grapes quite black!

Thursday 23.
29 5/10; 64, 69; S, S.
Vast dew, sun, sultry,
sweet even: red, clear in
the S.

Second broods of swallows begin to come forth.
Caught 8 hornets with a twig tipped with birdlime. No wasps in my garden, nor at the grocer's, or butcher's shop.
Five or 6 hornets will carry off a whole nectarine in the space of a day.

Tho' white butterflies abound, & lay many eggs on the cabbages; yet thro' over-heat & want of moisture they do not hatch, & turn to palmers; but dry & shrivel to nothing.

Friday 24.

29 2/10½; 64½, 71; SE, S, SE.
Grey, sun, sun, sultry, dark & threat'ning, still & close, rain.

Hop-picking. The hops are small, & injured by the heat.
No wasps.
One swift still frequents the eaves of the church & moreover has, I discover, two young nearly fledged, which show their white chins at the mouth of the crevice. This incident of so late a brood of swifts is an exception to the whole of my observations ever since I have bestowed any attention on that species of hirundines!

Saturday 25.

29 4/10½; 65; W, W; 50.
Great showers in the night, sun, showers, gales, dark & warm.

The two young swifts put-out their heads, & look very brisk.
Fly-catchers.
No wasps.

Sunday 26.

29 5/10½; 65; SW; 12.
Sun, warm, small rain, dark & close.

Young swifts as before.
Young martins, second brood, put-out their heads.

Monday 27.

29 4/10; 65, 73; SW.
Sun, sultry, grey & mild.

Young swifts as before.
Harvest is over. No wasp. Fly-catchers.
Hop-picking becomes general.

Tuesday 28.

29 2/10⅓; 68½; SW; 30, 12.
Showers, showers, showers, thunder.

Young swifts could not be seen all day.
Peaches & nectarines come very fast, & are well flavoured.

Wednesday 29.

29 5/10¾; 63; SW, W.
Strong wind, sun & clouds, still & mild.

Young swifts not seen.
The hornets, tho' few in number, make havock among the nectarines.
Peaches & Nect: very finely flavoured.

Thursday 30.

29 5/10; 63½; SE; 12.
Grey, sun, dark & moist, soft even:

No young swifts to be seen.
Not one wasp. We have destroyed the greatest part of the hornets.
Thunder much.

Sowed a plot with brown Dutch lettuce, for plants to stand the winter.

Between nine & ten at night a thunder-storm with much vivid lightening began to grow up from the N:W. & W: but it took a circuit round to the S: & E. & so missed us. We had only the skirts of the tempest, & a little heavy rain for a short time. Ten miles off to the southward there were vast rains.

Friday 31.

29 5/10¼; 66½; SW, S.

Grey, sun, sun, sweet day, cool & pleasant.

Much distant thunder again to the S.

Began to use endive, which is large & well-blanched.

No swifts. We searched the eaves to no purpose. In searching the eaves for the young swifts, we found in a nest two callow dead swifts, on which had been formed a second nest. These nests were full of the black shining cases of the *hippoboscae hirundinis*.

SEPTEMBER 1781

Saturday 1.

29 6/10½; 65, 70½; SW.

Grey, sun, sweet day, yellow even: shower.

Peaches & Nect: now delicate.

No wasps. Some hornets.

Grapes grow black.

We have caught about 20 hornets with a twig tipped with bird-lime.

Sunday 2.

29 5/½; 65½, 70; NE, S.

Dark, sun & clouds, hot, showers about.

Full moon.

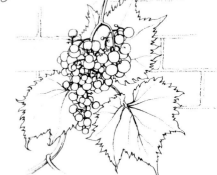

Grapes ripening on the garden wall.
The Wakes.
Early September.

Monday 3.

29 6/10; 66½, 70½; SW, S, SW.

Grey, sun, sweet day, soft even:

Wall-fruit dead-ripe.

Fallows in delicate order.

Turnips grow.

Tuesday 4.

29 4/10½; 66; SW, NW, W.

Sun, sun, dark & moist, rain all night.

Second broods of swallows, & h: martins come out very fast. Vast flocks of hirundines.

Some hornets. No wasps.

Gathered one bunch of black grapes, which was ripe & well-flavoured. It grew close to the wall, pressed down by a bough.

Wall-fruit is over.

Wednesday 5.

29 4/10; 63; W; 82, 22.

Rain, rain, rain, dark
& blowing.

Thursday 6.
29 5/10; 59; NW.
Sun, sun & air, sweet
even:

Fallows are in delicate order.

Friday 7.
29 7/10; 58; W, S.
Sun, hot & bright,
sweet even:

Dined at Bramshot-place.

Saturday 8.
29 7/10½; 63½; SW.
Dark & mild, shower,
sun, dark & hot.

Hop-picking ends: a poor crop at Selborne.

Sunday 9.
29 8/¾; 65, 71; E, SE.
Deep fog, sun, sultry,
sweet even:

Red-breasts whistle agreeably on the tops of hop-poles, &c: but
are prognostic of autumn.
Young fern-owl.

Monday 10.
29 9/10; 65, 68; NE.
Deep fog, sun, dark &
louring.

Red-breasts feed on elder-berries, enter rooms, & spoil the
furniture.
Broᵣ T: & M: come to Selborne.
Timothy, whose appetite is now on the decline, weighs
only 7 pounds & ¾ of an ounce: at Midsumᵣ he weighed
7 pd: 1 oun:

Tuesday 11.
29 8/10; 65; NE.
Dark, still, warm &
louring.

Bean-harvest, & vetch-harvest.
Grapes fine flavoured.

Wednesday 12.
29 7/10; NE, NW; 12.
Dark & still, rain, dark
& still.

Endives are large & finely blanched.
Distant thunder.
Fine crop of spinage.

Thursday 13.
29 7/10½; 65; NW,
W.
Dark, moist & mild.

Beans heavy.

Friday 14.
29 7/10; 63; SW, S.
Sun, grey, sun, sweet
even, bright & chill.

Bean, & vetch-harvest ends.
Timothy the tortoise dull & torpid.

Saturday 15.
29 2/10¾; 62; E, SE.
Grey & hot, dark to the
SE, thunder & some
rain, rain.

Grapes delicate.
Thunder & lightening in all quarters round.

The spring called Well-head sends forth now, after a severe hot dry summer, & dry spring & winter preceding, nine gallons of water in a minute; which is 540 in a hour; & 12960, or 216 hogsh: in 24 hours, or one natural day. At this time the wells are very low, & all the ponds in the vales dry.

Sunday 16.
29 1/10½; 65; S, S;
77.
Dark, showers,
showers, dark & mild.

The boys destroyed a hornets nest: it was but small.
Ophrys spiralis, ladies traces, seed.

Monday 17.
29 4/10; 63; SW, W.
Grey, sun, brisk gale,
bright, chill.

My well is very low.
Grapes delicate.
Endives of vast size.

Tuesday 18.
29 7/10; 55; W, NW;
10.
Rain & wind, grey,
sun, clear & chill.

Celeri very large.
Fly-catchers seem to be gone: they breed but once.
Ivy begins to bloom. Vast dew on windows.

Wednesday 19.
29 6/10¾; 54; SW.
Grey & cold, grey &
chilly.

Many hirundines.

Thursday 20.
29 6/10¼; 60; NW;
42. Rain, sun, mild,
bright even.

MEONSTOKE
† The Well is now so low, that Thomas found some difficulty in getting water sufficient to Brew with.

Friday 21.
29 5/10; 58; NW.
Bright, showers, fair,

† Hooker's hill mended by Tom Prior the ditch below which was

---

† Entry in Thomas White's handwriting.

chill even:

made about fifty years ago, is now open'd and cleaned.

Saturday 22.
29 4/10; SW, W.
Bright, grey & still,
moist & dark.

SELBORNE
The well at Filmer-hill is 60 yards deep: at Privet, on the top of
the hill, they have no wells, & have been greatly distressed for
water the summer thro'.
The Warnford, & Meon-stoke stream as full, & bright, as if
there had been no drought. Swallows, & martins.

Sunday 23.
29 2/10½; 56; NW.
Sun, & clouds, harsh
wind, showers about,
sharp air.

Few hirundines.
Began to light fires in the parlor.
Aurora.

Monday 24.
29 3/10; 51; NW.
Sun & clouds, strong
gales, showers & hail,
bright & cold.

Hirundines haunt sheltered vales.
The wind blows down apples & pears.
Vivid *Aurora.*

Tuesday 25.
29 4/10½; 48½; N.
Wh: frost, sharp wind,
sun, vast lights.

Wild honey-suckles blow.
Gathered swan's egg pears, a large crop.
Surprising Auroras, very red in the W!!!

The young swarms of bees of this summer are light; the old stocks
are heavy.

Wednesday 26.
29 3/10¼; 47; NW.
Frost, sun, sharp air,
dark & harsh, rain.

Few hirundines. Dug up potatoes: Earthed up celeri.
Swallows seem distressed by the cold.
Gathered knobbed-russetings,¶ a large crop.

Our building-sand from Wolmer forest seems pure from dirt: but
examined thro' a microscope proves not to be sharp, & angular,
but smooth as from collision. It is of a yellow colour.

Thursday 27.
29 4/10; 50; NW.
Grey & windy, sun,
bright & cold.

Many swallows at Oakhanger.
Gathered Cadilliac-pears,
dearlings, & royal russets.¶

Catillac pear.
~ grown at Wisley.
Early September.

Friday 28.
29 7/10¼; 51; NW.
Grey, sun, pleasant,
cool.

Dug-up potatoes, & carrots.
Swallows, & martins.
Vast halo round the moon.

Saturday 29.
29 8/10½; 51; SW.
Grey, pleasant & still.

Swallows, & martins.
Grapes delicate.

My well has now only three feet in water: it has never been so low, since my father sunk it, more than forty years ago.

"The amazing number of swallows* that at this time are flying in London, is a very uncommon appearance. They seem greatly affected by the severe cold weather we have experienced for some days past, since the wind has been northerly: they fly in at windows, & are so tamed or numbed, that boys beat them down, as they fly in the streets."

The Gazetteer.

* Probably house-martins, & swallows.

Sunday 30.
29 7/10½; 55; SW.
Shower, dark, driving
rain.

Many hirundines.
Men put-up their hogs to fat.

House-flies, *muscae domesticae*, now croud about the fire-place, run on hearths, & sport in the chimney-corners.

OCTOBER 1781

Monday 1.
29 8/10; 61; SW.
Fog, sun, hot, sweet
day, moonshine.

† Good riding round Woolmere-pond within it's banks, on the sand.
Many swallows.

Cleaned my well by drawing out about 100 buckets of muddy water: there was little rubbish at the bottom. There were two good springs, one at the bottom, & one about three feet above. Nothing had been done to this well for about 40 years. The man at bottom in the cleaning brought up several marbles & taws that we had thrown down when children.

Tuesday 2.
29 6/10¾; 59; W,
NW; 17.
Sun, grey, shower.
Full moon.

Gathered-in the wall-nuts.

---

† Entry in an unknown hand.

Wednesday 3.
29 8/10½; 56; N.
Sun, grey & pleasant.

Bought a bay-Welch Galloway mare. Out of the horses that were offered me to try, there were ten mares to one gelding.

Thursday 4.
29 8/10; 55; E, S.
White frost, sun, soft grey weather.

The frost killed the cucumber-plants.
No h: martins, nor swallows in the village, nor sand-martins about the forest.
L.ᵈ Stawel was fishing Wolmer-pond with a long net drawn by ten men.

Friday 5.
29 8/10½; 58; NW, W; 10.
Grey, sun, sweet weather, red even, shower.

No hirundines.
My celeri very large & forward: endive in vast abundance.
Grapes delicate. Spinage, fine crop.
No h: martins, nor swallows about the villages, nor sand-martins at the pit on Short-heath.
The white sand in the pit above, observed thro' a microscope, appears more sharp, & angular than the yellow sand of the forest.
Gathered in the nonparels, & royal russets.
Much gossamer flying.

Saturday 6.
29 9/10¼; 53½; N, NW.
Cold dew, sun, grey, red even:

The beeches on the hanger are beautifully tinged.
The ponds begin again to be almost dry.
No hirundines of any sort. Several herons at Wolmer-pond, & a *tringa ochrophus*, or white-rumped sand-piper.¶ Crammer-pond in Wolmer-forest is quite dry.
Ring-doves flock. Pheasants abound.

The swallow-kind seemed all to leave us about the 4th: many withdrew before.

Sunday 7.
30; 53; W, N.
Cold dew, sun, sweet weather.

Not one *hirundo* to be seen.
Fleecy clouds, & beautiful gleams of sunshine.
Rooks carry off the wallnuts from my trees.

Monday 8.
31; 53; W, S.
Grey, sun, sweet weather.

Much gossamer. One cock ring-ouzel appears still: few have been seen this autumn.
Grapes delicate.

Several women & children have eruptions on their hands, &c: is this owing to the lowness of the water in wells, &c? It seems this often befalls after they have been employed in hop-picking.

Tuesday 9.
30; 51; E.
Deep fog, sun,
pleasant, red even:

The grass was covered with cob-webs, which being loaded with dew, looked like white frost.

A grey hen¶ was lately killed on that part of Hind-head, which is called the Devil's punch-bowl. This solitary bird has haunted these parts for some time.

Wednesday 10.
29 9/10; 49; S, S.
Cold dew, sun, fog,
sweet autumnal
weather, grey.

My well rises. My hedges are beautifully tinged.
Wood-larks sing sweetly thro' this soft weather. No swallows.

All hirundines were gone in appearance ever since Octob.r 4th.

Thursday 11.
29 8/10; 48; E, W.
Fog, sun, bright &
chill, dark.

A brood of swallows over Oakhanger-pond!
Dragon-flies copulate.

Friday 12.
29 8/10; 56; NW, N.
Grey, grey & mild.

Farmer Parsons fetches a waggon-load of water from Dorton for brewing! Wells fail.
No swallows about the village.

Saturday 13.
29 9/10; 53; W.
Grey, sun, sweet
weather.

No swallows.
On frequented roads the dust is very troublesome.

The distress in these parts for want of water is very uncommon. The well at the Grange farm is dry; & so are many in the villages round: & even the well at Old-place in the parish of E: Tisted, tho' 270 feet, or 45 fathoms deep, will not afford water for a brewing. All the while the little pond on Selborne down has still some water, tho' it is very low: & the little pond just over the hedge in Newton great farm abates but little. The ponds in the vales are now dry a third time. Most of the wells in Selborne-street are empty; & mine has only three feet of water. The people at Medsted, Bentworth, & those upland parts are in great want. Well head sends out a considerable stream still, not apparently abated since we measured it last.
    The last wet month was Decem.r 1779; during which fell 6 inch 28 hund: of rain: since which the quantity of water has been very little.

Sunday 14.
29 9/10; 56; SW.
Grey, still & mild.

The greens of turnips wither, & look rusty.
Leaves fall.

Monday 15.
29 8/10½; 58; SW,
NW.
Grey & still, & mild.

No swallows.
Bright *Aurora*.

Tuesday 16.
30; 53; N, NW.
Grey, sun, bright &
pleasant.

My celeri is unusually large; & well blanched.
The mill at Hawkley cannot work one tenth of the time for want
of water.

Wednesday 17.
30; 46; NW.
White frost, sun, bright
& pleasant.

Greatham-mill can work but 3 hours in the day.

Thursday 18.
29 9/10; 49; NW.
Grey, still & mild.

The beechen-woods grow very brown.

Friday 19.
29 8/10½; 51½; NW.
Grey, sun & cold air.

On this ill fated day Lord Cornwallis, & all his army
surrendered themselves prisoners of war to the united forces of
France & America at York-town in Virginia.

Saturday 20.
29 8/10; 50½; NW.
Grey, sun, dark, &
harsh, bright.

Leaves fall very fast.
Endive very fine.
Grapes delicate.

Sunday 21.
29 8/10; 51; W.
Sun, bright & warm.

The distress for water in many places is great.
Redwings appear.

Monday 22.
29 9/10; 51½; N.
Sun, bright & cold.

Great fieldfare appears.
Men continue to fetch peat from the forest.

Tuesday 23.
29 8/10¼; 41; N.
Frost, ice, bright &
cold.

Farmer Eames of Oldplace fetches his water from well-head!
Jupiter is now very low in the SW; at sun set.

Swallows above the Plestor.
August.

Wednesday 24.
29 7/10; 47;
SW, W.
Frost, ice, dark &
windy.

Many trees are naked.
The tortoise is very torpid, but does not bury itself.
Grapes are delicate.

Thursday 25.
29 9/10; 50; NW.
Sun, dark & cold.

The upland villages are in great distress for want of water.
Acorns abound, & help poor men's hogs. Grass becomes very
scanty.

Friday 26.
30; 49; N.
Sun, bright & chill.

Men sow their wheat in absolute dust.
My vines cast their leaves.
Broʳ T: & M:¶ went away.

Saturday 27.
29 7/10½; 47; NW,
W.
Dark & mild, moist, &
foggy.

My well sinks, & is very low.
The tortoise begins to dig into the ground.
Mʳ Yalden fetches water from Well-head.
The bat is out this warm evening.

A notion has always obtained, that in England hot summers are
productive of fine crops of wheat: yet in the years 1780, & 1781,
tho' the heat was intense, the wheat was much mill-dewed, & the
crop light. *Quaere*, does not severe neat, while the straw is milky,
occasion it's juices to exsude, which, being extravasated, occasion
spots, discolour the stems & blades, & injure the health of the
plants?
    The heat of the two last summers has scalded & scorched the
stems of the wall-fruit trees, & has fetched-off the bark.
    "There has lately been felt in diverse parts of Hungary so
extraordinary a heat, that the husband-men could only work in the
night. All the snow that has covered the Carpathian mountains for
more than a century is entirely melted." *St James's Chronicle*.
    The planet Venus, which became an evening star in June, but
was not visible 'til lately, now makes a resplendent appearance.
    On Selborne down are many oblong tumuli, some what
resembling graves but larger, supposed by the country people to be
the earth of saw-pits. But as they mostly lie one way from S:E: to
N:W: & are many of them very near to each other, it is most
probable they were occasioned by some purpose of a different
kind. My Bro: Tho: ordered two to be dug across; one of which
produced nothing extraordinary; while in the other was found a
blackish substance: but how, & in what quantity it lay, & whether
it consisted of ashes & cinders, or of *humus animalis*, we had no
opportunity to examine from the precipitancy of the labourer, who

filled up the trench he had opened without giving proper notice of the occurrence.

No drought, equal to the present, has been known since autumn 1740, which being preceeded by a dry summer & spring, & the terrible long frost of winter 1739, exhausted most of the wells & ponds, & distressed the country greatly.

Sunday 28.
29 3/10; 51; W.
Grey, sun, soft air, heavy clouds, showers about, bright.

Turnips suffer much for want of rain.
Woodcocks are come.

Monday 29.
29 ½/10; 47;
W, NW.
Grey & still, heavy clouds, small rain, bright.

From the scantiness of grass I have given for some time 9: p^r p^d for butter; a price here not known before.
Heavy clouds to the NE.

Tuesday 30.
29 ¾/10; 39; N.
Frost, ice, grey & cold, clouds, cold showers.

Leaves fall very fast.
The tortoise retires under ground, within his coop.

Wednesday 31.
29 4/10; 38; W, SW;
6.
Frost, ice, grey & cold, bright & frosty.

The water is so scanty in the streams, that the millers cannot grind barley sufficient for mens hogs. Dairy-farms cannot fill the butter-pots of their customers.

NOVEMBER 1781

Thursday 1.
29 4/10½; 44½; SW.
Grey, sun, bright & mild, small showers, bright, mackarel sky. Full moon.

Much wheat-land not sown yet; because men are afraid to sow their corn in the dust.
Some water still in the pond on Selborne down: & the pond on Newton-farm, over the hedge, is more than half full.

Friday 2.
29 3/10; 50; SW; 34;
22.
Showers, showers, showers, grey & still.

The Hanger beyond
the Wakes herb garden.
Early September.

Saturday 3.
29 5/10; 45; W.
White frost, cloudless,
sweet sunshine, red
even:

The air abounds with insects.
Flies come-out in the windows.

Hogs, in eating acorns, chew them very small, & reject the husks.
The plenty of acorns this year avails the hogs of poor men, &
brings them forward without corn.

Sunday 4.
29 7/10; 43½; NW,
NE.
White frost, sun, sweet
day.

Monday 5.
29 2/10; 52, 55½;
SW; 78.
Rain, rain, rain.

The air is very warm, & the dew all day on the outside of
the windows.
Grapes delicate still.

Tuesday 6.
28 8/10; 54; SW; 58,
63.
Rain, rain, rain.

The walls of the hall & entry are all in a float with condensation.
Soft air.

Wednesday 7.
29 4/10; 45; W, NW.
Grey, cold & dark, &
blowing.

John Hale has cleansed the pond on the down, & carried out a
large quantity of mud.
Men sow wheat: the ground works very fine.

Thursday 8.
29 8/10½; 44; NW.
Sun, mild & pleasant.

The tortoise came out of his coop, & has buried himself in the
laurel-hedge.
When my great parlor is kept close shut-up, it is not at all
affected by condensations on the wainscot or paper tho' the hall &
entry are all in a float.

Friday 9.
29 8/10; 45; S.
Wh: frost, sun, mild,
still, grey, rain.

Saturday 10.
29 6/10; 50; SW: 18.
Dark & wet, & warm,
fog, dark & wet.

The dew is on the outside of the windows.
Planted two rows of lettuces close under the fruit-wall to stand the
winter.
Hares eat down the pinks, & cloves in the garden: & yet
sportsmen complain that the breed this year is very small;
alledging that dry summers, tho' kindly for partridges, are
detrimental to hares.

The wintry & huge constellation, Orion, begins now to make his

appearance in the evening, exhibiting his enormous figure
in the E.

Tho' my grapes ripen in the most disadvantageous years: yet
from the concurring circumstances of a hot summer, a dry
autumn, & a failure of wasps, I think my crop was never so
delicate before, nor ever supplyed my table so long.

Husbandry seems to be much improved at Selborne within these
20 years, & their crops of wheat are generally better: not that they
plough oftener, or perhaps manure more than they did formerly;
but from the more frequent harrowings & draggings now in use,
which pulverize our strong soil, & render it more fertile than any
other expedient yet in practice.

The house-martins have disappointed us again, as they did last
year, with respect to their Novem[r] visit for one day. On Nov: 5th
1779, & Nov: 4. 1777, they showed themselves all day along the
hanger in considerable numbers, after they had withdrawn for
some weeks: when, had they been properly watched, their place of
retreat¶ in the evening, I make no doubt, might have been easily
discovered. Once in a few years they make use a visit of this sort,
some time in the first week in November.

Sunday 11.
29 2/10½; 55¾; SW;
58.
Rain, dark & warm,
rain.

Rain all night.
My well rises.

Monday 12.
29 2/10; 51½; W.
Grey, mild & still, sun,
grey, red even:

Tuesday 13.
29 3/10¾; 48; W, S.
Sun, soft & pleasant,
rain.

Wells rise.

Wednesday 14.
29; 52; SW; 85.
Rain, rain, rain, dark,
rain.

One vast shower.

Thursday 15.
28 7/10½; 50; SW;
79.
Sun, grey, & windy,
shower, bright *aurora*.

Vast rain in the night, with strong wind.
My well is risen near six feet.
Thomas begins to dress the vines. The crop of grapes is just over;
having lasted in perfection more than ten weeks.

Friday 16.
29 1/10; 47; W.
Sun, & strong gale,
grey & still.

Saturday 17.
28 9/10½; 46½; SW.   *Antirrhinum Cymbalaria* flourishes, & blows.
Grey, small rain, sun,
bright.

Sunday 18.
29 1/10½; 42; E,
NW.
Frost, ice, sun, still &
pleasant, red even:

Monday 19.
29 7/10½; 41½; NW.   Planted two Cypresses in the garden.
Grey, still, &   They come from S: Lambeth.
agreeable.

Tuesday 20.
29 6/10½; 40½; S.   *Phalaenae* fly under hedges.
Frost, ice, grey & still.

Wednesday 21.
29 2/10; 49; S; 50.   Finished dressing the vines. The new wood was small, & not
Dark & brisk gale,   highly ripened; so it was laid-in the shorter. It covers the walls
rain, rain.   regularly.

Thursday 22.
29 5/10; 45; NW.
Sun, bright & cold, red
even: bright *Aurora.*

Friday 23.
29 ½/10; 42; S.
Dark & blowing, rain,
rain.

Saturday 24.
29 5/10; 44½; N, NE;   Cascades fall from the fields into the hollow lanes.
48; 2.
Rain, grey & mild,
fog.

Sunday 25.
29 7/10; 42; E, SE.
Fog, wh: frost, sun,
soft & bright.

As the fog cleared away, the warm sun occasioned a prodigious reek, or steam to arise from thatched roofs. In the evening picturesque partial fogs come rolling-in up the Lithe, from the forest.

Monday 26.
29 6/10½; 42½; S.
Frost, sun, mild, &
grey.

Planted against the fruit-wall three well-trained trees, that are to begin to bear fruit next year: viz: 1 Peterboro' nectarine: N:E: end: 1 Montaban peach: 1 red Magdalen peach. Against the scullery, 1 Elrouge Nectarine.
These trees came from Mr Shiells's nursery at Lambeth, & cost 7s 6d apiece on the spot. They have healthy wood, & well-trained heads. Planted a Virginian creeper against the wall of my house next the garden.
The planet Venus now is visible at Selborne over the hanger.

Tuesday 27.
29 4/10½; 47; S.
Grey, mild & still, still
& moist.

Began to use some of the advertised Celeri, which, I think, is crisper & finer flavoured than any sort that I have met with.

Wednesday 28.
29 7/10; N; 29.
Rain, rain, rain.

This month proved a very wet one, more so than any month since Decem^r 1779: in which fell 6 inc: 28; in this 6.18.

Thursday 29.
Dark & hazy, deep fog.

OXFORD

Friday 30.¶

DECEMBER 1781

Saturday 1.

Sunday 2.

Monday 3.

Tuesday 4.
† 30.

Wednesday 5.
† 35.

---

† Rainfall.

Thursday 6.

Friday 7.

ALTON
The weather was dark, still, & foggy, all the time that I was absent, & the wind mostly NE: & E.

Saturday 8.
29 3/10; 39; E.
Rain, rain, rain.

SELBORNE

George Tanner's bullfinch, a cock bird of this year, began from it's first moulting to look dingy; & is now quite black on the back, rump & all; & very dusky on the breast. This bird has lived chiefly on hemp-seed. But T: Dewey's, & – Horley's two bull-finches, both of the same age with the former, & also of the same sex, retain their natural colours, which are glossy & vivid, tho' they both have been supported by hemp-seed. Hence the notion that hempseed blackens bull-finches does not hold good in all instances; or at least not in the first year.

Sunday 9.
29 3/0¾; 41; E; 35.
Dark & still, small rain, dark & moist.

Hares continue to eat all my pinks, which they have now near destroyed.

Monday 10.
29 4/10; 39; E.
Grey & still, sun, grey.

Yellow-water-wagtail.
My well is shallow, & does not rise.

Tuesday 11.
29 4/10; 38; E, NE.
Frost, ice, sun, soft & still, red even:

Antirrhinum Cymb: continues to blow.
Trenched some ground in the meadow for carrots.
The planet Venus now makes a splendid appearance over the hanger.

Wednesday 12.
29 5/10½; 38, 41; NE. Grey, & mild, deep fog.

Larby now digs & double trenches a weedy spot in the great meadow. The ground is black, & mellow, & fit for carrots, for which it is intended.

Thursday 13.
29 4/10¾; 42; E.
Fog, grey & mild, rain.

My well sinks, & when much water is drawn, soon grows foul.

Friday 14.
29 4/10; 46½; SE.
Warm, deep fog.

Trees condense the vapour, & drip much.
The dew lies on the outsides of the windows.
Walls sweat much.

Saturday 15.
29 2/10; 48, 50, 51; S, SE.
Grey, sun, soft, clouds, & rain.

Some of my friends have sported lately in the forest: they beat the moors & morasses, & found some jack & whole snipes, most of which they killed, with a teal, a pheasant, & some partridges. The flight of snipes is but small yet. There is now, I hear, a flight of woodcocks in the upland coverts.

Sunday 16.
29 4/10; 51, 51½; SW.
Sun, soft, bright & pleasant.

Flies, & some butter-flies come out.
Beetles hum.

Monday 17.
29 4/10; 50½; SW.
Grey, sun, mild, small scud, soft, & still.

Heards well is now dry: it is of a vast depth.

Tuesday 18.
29 3/10½; 50½; 51; S.
Dark, moist, & warm, rain.

Earth-worms lie-out on the turf during these moist, mild nights.

Wednesday 19.
29 2/10½; 52; SE; 72.
Rain, rain, rain.

Thursday 20.
29 7/10; 50; W; 7.
Sun, soft & pleasant.

Friday 21.
29 7/10; 46½; S, SE.
Dark, small rain, dark & moist.

Furze is in bloom.
Several young lambs at the Priory.
Shortest day.

Saturday 22.
29 5/10; 46½; SE.
Grey & mild, moist, fog & small rain.

Sunday 23.
29 4/10½; 51; S.
Dark & moist, dark & blowing.

Monday 24.
29 4/10⅓; 52, 53;
SW; 30.
Rain, rain, sun &
clouds.

Soft & mild.

Tuesday 25.
29 7/10¼; 49; SW, S.
Sun, bright, &
pleasant.

A gardener in this village has lately cut several large cauliflowers, growing without any glasses.
The boys are playing in their shirts.

On this day Admiral Kempenfelt fell in with a large convoy from Brest, & took a number of French transports.

Wednesday 26.
29 2/10¼; 48; SE; 45.
Dark & windy, rain,
rain, rain.

Much wind in the night.

Thursday 27.
29 6/10¼; 48½; SW,
W; 42.
Sun, fine day, grey,
windy.

Friday 28.
29 4/10¾; 52; W; 28.
Rain, & wind, sun,
clouds, & wind, moon-
shine.

Saturday 29.
29 6/10; 47½; SW.
Grey, sun, showers, &
wind, moonshine.

Antirrhinum Cymb: in bloom.
Snow-drops & hepaticas blow.

Sunday 30.
29 1¾/10; 47; S; 43.
Dark & mild, showers
& wind.
Full moon.

Helleborus foetidus blows.

Monday 31.
29 3/10¾; 45; NE, S.
Grey, showers, wet.

JANUARY

— 1782 —

Tuesday 1.
29 5/10⅓; 45; SE; 30.
Rain, rain, rain.

SELBORNE
Winter aconites blow.

Wednesday 2.
29 4/10¼; 50; W.
Rain, rain, rain.

Thursday 3.
29 7/10½; 46; SW;
28.
Sun, clouds, dark &
mild.

Mezereon blows. *Viola tricolor*, red lamium, & grounsel blow.
Hazel catkins open.

Friday 4.
29 6/10; 49; W.
Dark & windy, rain, &
wind.

Saturday 5.
29 5/10⅓; 47; W; 38.
Sun & wind.

Wind & rain in the night.
Much damage has been
done at sea lately by storms.

Viola tricolor.
The Wakes
Early June.

Sunday 6.
29 8/10; 46½; SW, S,
SW.
Sun, bright & pleasant.

Wells now rise considerably.
Bees come out of their hives.
Gnats play about.

Monday 7.
29 3/10; 45; W; 40.
Heavy showers, sun &
clouds.

Tuesday 8.
29 5/10; 41; SW.
White frost, wind, &
sun, sun, small
showers.

Wednesday 9.
28 8/10; 45; S, NW;
80. Stormy with much
rain, dark, blowing.

The wind blowed-down the rain-measurer.
Wells rise very fast, & are now up to their usual pitch.

Thursday 10.
29 8/10½; 39½.
Shower, wind, & sun,
frost.

The earth is well-drenched; streams run; & torrents fall from the fields into the hollow lanes.
Wood-laurel blows.

Friday 11.
30 1/10; 32½; N, NE;
S.
Hard frost, sunny &
still.

Saturday 12.
30 1/10; 40;
W, NW.
Gentle thaw, deep fog.

Sunday 13.
30 1/10⅓; 40; W.
Foggy & moist.

Monday 14.
30; 44½; S, SE.
Dark, still & moist.

Missel-thrush, & song thrush sing.
Grass springs.

Tuesday 15.
29 8/10½; 43; W,
NW.
Grey, sun & mild, wet
fog, star-light.

Daiseys blow.

On this day Sr G. Rodney, after having been wind-bound for several weeks, sailed to the W. Indies from Torbay.

Wednesday 16.
29 2/10; 40; W, NW.
Dark, cold showers
with wind, bright &
sharp.

Thursday 17.
29 2/10; 37; W, NW.
Frost, sun, & strong
gale, flight of snow.

Friday 18.
29 5/10; 37; NW, W.
Frost, sun, pleasant,
cloudy.

Saturday 19.
29 5/10¼; 42, 46;
SW.
Grey & mild, sun, &
soft air, grey & still.

Sunday 20.
29 2/10; 48, 49; SW;
43.
Dark & showery,
stormy with driving
rain.

Monday 21.
29 6/10½; 42; W,
NW. Grey, sun, mild,
dark & cold.

Tuesday 22.
29 7/10; 43; SW; 11.
Rain, rain, dark &
moist.

Wednesday 23.
29 7/10½; 48; SW.
Grey, mild, & spring-
like.

Thursday 24.
29 4/10; 50; SW.
Dark, blowing & wet,
rain, rain, wind all
night.

Friday 25.
29 4/10¾; 45; 42; SW:
49. Showers, wind,
snow-storm, sun,
bright & cold.

Saturday 26.
29 5/10; W, NW; 70.
Rain & wind all night,
sun & brisk gale,
bright.

Several crocus's in bloom.
Some ivy-berries near full grown.
Birds sing.

Winter Aconite
in a Selborne garden.
15 January.

Snow-drops, hepaticas, & winter-aconite in full bloom. Green
Hellebore emerges, & blows. Hazels show their female
blossoms.

Hyacinths emerge & bud for bloom. Tulips shoot. Honey-
suckles shoot, & have leaves.
Antirr: Cym: looks gay & grows much.

Sunday 27.
28 9/10¼; 42; W; 33.
Rain & wind in the
night, shower, sun &
strong gale, grey &
still.

The earth is now full of water which runs from the fields into the hollow lanes.

Monday 28.
28 9/10; 42; NW.
Blowing all night, sun
& hail-storm, grey &
mild, rain & sleet.

Water-cresses come in.
The χειμαρρος, or winter-spring, or lavant, runs from the hanger into gracious street.

Tuesday 29.
28 7/10; 37; SW, S, E.
Grey, sun, frost, sun,
grey & still.
Full moon.

Wednesday 30.
29 3/10½; 38; N; 42.
Rain, snow & rain,
grey, sun, bright, sleet.

No snow lies.

Thursday 31.
29 7/10¾; 34; N.
Frost, bright & sharp
frost.

FEBRUARY 1782

Friday 1.
29 8/10; 33; N; SW.
Severe frost, sun,
pleasant, mackarel sky,
grey & still.

The wheat-fields so hard that they carry a waggon & horses.

Saturday 2.
29 4/10; 36; SW; 32.
Small driving rain.

Sunday 3.
29 1/10½; 37; SE, S.
Frost, sun, dark & still.

Monday 4.
29 1/10; 40; NW; 47.
Snow, snow, thaw,
frost, bright.

Snow melts very fast.

Tuesday 5.
28 9/10; 37; NE.
Frost, grey & cold.

Snow still on the ground.
Knee-holly, or butcher's broom blows.

Wednesday 6.
29 6/10; 36½; N.
Frost, sunny & sharp.

Thursday 7.
29 6/10½; 34½; NW.
Hard frost, sun, dark
& cold.

Friday 8.
29 6/10½; 33; NE,
NW.
Severe frost, grey &
sharp, bright.

Venus shadows very strongly, showing the bars of the
windows on the floors & walls.

Saturday 9.
29 6/10½; 34; NW,
N. Frost, grey,
clear, frost.

Venus sheds again her silvery light on the walls of my chamber,
&c: & shadows very strongly.

Sunday 10.
29 7/10½; 34; N.
Severe frost, driving
snow, grey & sharp,
snow.

Monday 11.
29 5/10; 32½; N.
Snow, frost, grey &
sharp frost.

Made a seedling cucumber-bed.

Tuesday 12.
29 7/10⅓; 32, 33;
NE.
Severe frost, flying
snow, hard frost.

Thermom.ʳ abroad 21.

Wednesday 13.
29 6/10½; 32; NW.
Severe frost, sun,
flights of snow.

Things froze in the pantry.
Shallow snow: ground very hard.

Thursday 14.
29 7/10; 37; NE.
Frost, sun, sunny &
still.

Friday 15.
29 8/10½; 37; NE.
Dark with cutting
wind, flights of snow.

Snow on the ground.

Saturday 16.
29 9/10¾; 30; NE.
Severe frost, sun &
clouds, bright & sharp.

Things freeze within doors.

Sunday 17.
30 ½/10; 30½; NE.
Severe frost, grey with
sleet, bright sun, clear
& frosty.

Last night the moon was mid way between Mars & Venus: she is
this evening just above, close above the former, at the seeming
distance of two feet.

Monday 18.
30 ¾; 29; NE, NW.
Severe frost, grey &
still, thaw.

ALTON

Thomas kept an account of the rain in my absence.

Tuesday 19.
NW.
Snow, dark & still,
grey, shower.

S. LAMBETH
Snow on the ground.
Chaf-finch, & hedge-sparrow sing.

Wednesday 20.
30 4/10; 40; E.
Dark & still, grey &
still.

Thursday 21.
30 1/10; 32; S.
Hard frost, sun, grey
& still, rain.

Bees play about.

Friday 22.
29 4/10; 43; SW; 47.
Sun & wind, sun & clouds, clear & still.

Storm & shower in the night.

Saturday 23.
29 3/10½; 44; S; 34.
Rain.

Sunday 24.
29 7/10; 44; SW.
Blowing, bright & mild.

Monday 25.
30; 45; SW; 38.
Blowing & wet.

Tuesday 26.
30 2/10; 48; SW.
Blowing & dark.

Wednesday 27.
30 1/10; 48; SW.
Dark & blowing, sweet sun.

Thursday 28.
30 3/10; 38; W.
Wh: frost, sunny & still.

MARCH 1782

Friday 1.
30 1/10½; 40; SW.
Frost, thin ice, sun, bright & pleasant.

Saturday 2.
29 8/10; 42; S, NW; 62.
Mist, rain, rain, rain.

Soft rain.

Sunday 3.
30; 40, 31; N.
Fair & still.

LONDON
Daffodil opens.
Missel-thrush sings.

Monday 4.
30 2/10; 33; SW.
Fair & still.

White frost, ice.

Tuesday 5.
29 8/10; 46; SW.
Clouds & wind.

Birds pull-off the blossom-buds of Apricot-trees.

Wednesday 6.
29 9/10; 39; SW.
Dark & louring.

Almond tree in bloom.

Thursday 7.
29 8/10; 40; W.
Fair, strong gales.

Friday 8.
29 4/10; 40; W; 82.
Bright, strong wind,
storms of snow.

Saturday 9.
29 4/10; 37; W.
Bright, strong gale.

S. LAMBETH
Vivid N: Auroras.

Sunday 10.
29 9/10; 40; W.
Fair & still.

Monday 11.
29 8/10; 50; SW; 11.
Wind & clouds, stormy.

Tuesday 12.
29 4/10; 44; W.
Stormy, sun, hail
showers.

Wednesday 13.
30 2/10; 35; NW.
Frost, ice, cold.

Thursday 14.
30 1/10; 31; N.
Frost, ice, bright &
sharp.

Friday 15.
30 2/10, 29 8/10¾;
37½; N.
Frost, ice, sun &
clouds.

SELBORNE
Some small flights of snow.
Roads very dusty. *Aurora*.

Saturday 16.
29 7/10¼; N, NW.
Frost, ice, sunny &
sharp, small flights of
snow.

Peaches, & Nect: forwarder in bloom than apricots.

Sunday 17.
29 7/10; 39; NW.
Frost, ice, dark & still,
sun, still & cold.

Monday 18.
29 7/10; 41; NW, SW.
Frost, ice, sunny &
mild, grey.

Made the cucumber-bearing bed, & put on the frames.

Tuesday 19.
29 3/10⅓; 46; SW.
Dark & mild, rain,
rain.

Cleaned-up the alleys, & borders of the k: garden.

Wednesday 20.
29 5/10¼; 41; NW,
W; 18.
Sun, sunny & pleasant,
grey.

The wheat-ear is seen on our down.

Thursday 21.
29; 41; SE.
Snow & sleet, snow.

Vast flocks of large Fieldfares appear: they are probably intent on
the business of migration.
Snow covers the ground.

Friday 22.
28 6/10; 39; NE; 95.

Much snow.

Snow & rain, snow &
rain.

Saturday 23.
29; 36; N; 35.   Snow all night.
Deep snow, bright sun,   The birds eat the ivy-berries, which begin to ripen.
frost.

A farmer tells me he foresaw this extraordinary weather by the
prognostic deportment of his flock; which, when turned-out on a
down two or three morning ago, gamboled & frolicked about like
so many lambs.

Sunday 24.
29 3/10¾; 33; N, SW;   Much snow on the ground.
7.
Severe frost, snow,
swift thaw.

Monday 25.
29 5/10; 39½; W,   Snow lies on the hills.
NW, N.
Snow, frost, sun &
clouds, bright & still.

Tuesday 26.
29 6/10½; 39½; S, S;
18.
Snow, rain, sun, hail,
showers.

Wednesday 27.
29 4/10¾; 44; S.
Showers, showers, mild
rain all night, stormy.

Thursday 28.
29 2/10; 49; 50; S, W;   Poor Timothy was flooded in his hybernaculum amidst the laurel-
174.   hedge: & might have been drowned had not his friend Thomas¶
Vast rain with wind,   come to his assistance, & taken him away.
rain, floods, wet &
warm, rain.

Friday 29.
29 2/10; 49; SW; 40.
Showers, strong wind,
sun, showers, bright.
Full moon.

Saturday 30.
29 2/10¾; 48; SW;
39.
Clouds, & sun,
showers, hail, still, &
warm.

Yellow butterfly appears. Violets blow.
Apricots show hardly any bloom: they exhausted themselves with
bearing last year. Peaches & Nect: abound with blossoms just
opening, as do the new, trained trees planted last Novʳ.
Earthed the bearing cucumber-bed, which is still full hot.
The small uncrested wren, the chif-chaf, is heard this day. They
are usually in good weather heard about the 20th. This is the first
summer bird that we hear.

Sunday 31.
29; 47; SW; 57, 16.
Rain in the night,
showers, great
hailstorm, bright.

The earth is glutted with water.

APRIL 1782

Monday 1.
28 1/10¾; 45; S; 91.
Rain, rain, rain.

Vast rains!

Tuesday 2.
28 8/10½; 44; W; 25.
Rain & snow, strong
gale.

Wednesday 3.
29 1/10¼; 44; W,
NW; 18.
Snow & rain, sun &
clouds, fine afternoon.

Peach, & Nect: blooms do not advance.
The prospect at Newton was most lovely; as usually is the case
after much rain, &c.

Thursday 4.
29 1/10; 40; SW; 35.
Wh: frost, sun, rain,
rain.

Friday 5.
42; SW; 12.
Showers, rain-bow,
showers, showers.

Bat appears.

Saturday 6.
29 4/10¾; 42; SE, E,

The wind veered about to every black storm.

NE, NW, W; 11.
Sun, showers, many
hail-storms about,
sunny evening,
pleasant.

On this day the lavants began to break at Chawton,¶ two fields above the church.

Sunday 7.
29 6/10¾; 47; N, N;
18.
Rain & hail, fog, sun,
massy clouds, thunder
& hail-storms.

Peter Wells's well runs over.¶ Strong lavant thro' Cobb's court-yard.
Some swallows, or bank-martins over Bins-pond.

Monday 8.
6/10½, 29 7/10; 44,
48; N; 21.
Rain, sun, dark with
strong gale.

The wall-fruit bloom is injured, & kept-back by the wet black season.
Lap-wings haunt the down.

Tuesday 9.
29 5/10½; 44½; N.
Dark & cold, shower,
dark.

Cucumber-plants are strong, & shew rudiments of fruit.

Wednesday 10.
29 2/10; 43; N, NW.
Dark & cold, dark &
mild.

Swallow appears over the streams near Alresford.

Thursday 11.
29 1/10; 46; S.
Grey & mild, rain.

Forked the asparagus-beds, & planted some firs in the outlet.

Friday 12.
28 9/10½; 44; SE, E;
39, 42.
Snow, rain, hail &
sleet.

A person thought he heard a black-cap.

12. On this day Sʳ George Rodney in the W: Indies obtained a great victory over Admiral de Grasse, whom he took in the *Ville de*

Blackcap.
Selborne village
Late April.

Paris. He also captured four more French ships of the line, & sunk one. On the 19th Admiral Hood, who was detatched with his division in pursuit of the flying enemy, took two more line of battle ships, & two frigates in the passage of Mono, between Porto Rico, & Domingo.

Saturday 13.
29 2/10; 42; NW, W, SW.
Grey, sun, showers about, rain.

Sunday 14.
29 1/10; 42; NW; 17, 11. Dark, cold, sleet, & rain, snow, clear.

Monday 15.
29 3/10; 40; NE, N.
Frost, ice, sharp air, sun & clouds, clouds, clear.

Showers about.

Tuesday 16.
29 2/10; 42; N.
Sleet, grey & chill, cold rain.

Wednesday 17.
29 3/10½; 43; N; 21.
Cold, misty rain.

Several Black-caps are heard to sing.
Shell-snails begin to come forth.

Thursday 18.
29 4/10¾; 44; NE, E; 21, 21.
Rain, rain, bright gleam.

Friday 19.
29 4/10; 42; NE.
Sleet, dark & cold.

Two swallows.

Saturday 20.
29 3/10½; 45; E, SW.
Grey, sun, pleasant, vast clouds about.

Swallow in the village.
Sowed flower-seeds, several sorts.
Cucumbers blow.
Bombylius medius, the hairy fly with a long proboscis.

On this day Admiral Barrington discovered a convoy newly from Brest. His fleet took 12 or thirteen transports; a French man of war of 74 guns, called the *Pegasus*; & a 64 gun ship named the *Actionnaire, armée en flute.*

Sunday 21.
29 4/10; 48½; SW, W.
Grey, sun, pleasant, shower, grey, shower.

Cuckow as heard in the hanger.
Nightingale sings.

Monday 22.
29 4/10¼; 47; W, S.
Sun, sweet morning, grey, bright to the N.

Swallows about. Pheasants crow.
Wry-neck pipes.
Vast halo round the moon. Bat. Toad.

Tuesday 23.
29 4/10; 48; SW, S, SE.
Shower, sun & clouds, rain, rain.

Laughing willow-wren sings.
Shivering willow-wren.

Wednesday 24.
29 1/10; 50½; SE, S; 37.
Grey, sun, showers about, rain, rain.

Distant thunder.
House-martins appear.
Swift appears.

Thursday 25.
29 2/10; 51, 55; W, N; 17.
Sun, pleasant, dark & cool.

Grass grows much.
Began to weed the pavements.

Friday 26.
29 4/10½; 49; NW, NE.
Dark & cold, dark & moist.

Saturday 27.
29 5/10½; 47; NE, N, NE.
Dark, moist & cold, dark & cold.
Full moon.

No hirundines appear this cold, black weather.
Vines barely begin to bud. Beeches yet quite naked.
Hyacinths in full bloom. My sort is very fine.
Sowed garden-seeds, carrots, onions, lettuce, parsnips, &c.

Sunday 28.
29 5/10½; 45; NE.
Dark, & moist, dark &
cold.

One swift.
One swallow.

Monday 29.
29 6/10½; 44; NE.
Dark, & sharp.

Planted potatoes.
Strong, cutting wind.
No hirundines appear.

Tuesday 30.
29 7/10; 42; NE.
Sun, cloudless, sharp
wind.

Strong gale all day. Sharp wind.
Planted one bed of asparagus.
Nightingale sings in my fields.

The quantity of rain that fell at Selborne between May 1st 1781, &
May 1st 1782.

				Hund.
In May 1781	.	.	.	172
June	.	.	.	278
July	.	.	.	202
August	.	.	.	215
September	.	.	.	245
October	.	.	.	33
November	.	.	.	624
December	.	.	.	367
1782 January	.	.	.	464
February	.	.	.	198
March	.	.	.	654
April	.	.	.	457
				3 909

39 inch: & 9 hund:

MAY 1782

Wednesday 1.
29 6/10¾; 42; NE.
Frost, ice, sun &
clouds, dark.

Thursday 2.
43½; NE.
Dark & cold, dark &
cold, dark.

Swallows about.
One beech in the Lith, which is always forward, in full leaf. The
beeches in the hanger are naked, but the buds are opening.
Nightingale sings in my fields; but no cuckow is heard.
House-martins are withdrawn for some time.
One swift.
Two swifts at Nore hill passed by me at a steady rate towards this
village, as if they were just arrived. Saw one h: martin.

Friday 3.
29 4/10¼; 43; NE.
Frost, ice, sun &
clouds, clear.

Bees keep within their hives. No gnats appear. One swift.
Redstart is heard.
Sowed the dug plot in the great mead with carrots.

Saturday 4.
29 3/10; 43; N.
Dark & sharp.

Three swifts now. Some few swallows, & h: martins. Vegetation
is at a stand, & Timothy the tortoise fast asleep. The trees are still
naked.

Sunday 5.
29 3/10¾; 44; N.
Dark & harsh.

Some swallows, & h: martins.

Monday 6.
29 4/10½; 43; N; 32.
Snow, sleet, cold, rain.

No swifts. Some swallows.

Tuesday 7.
29 6/10½; 43¼; N,
NW.
Dark & cold, sun &
clouds, pleasant even,
distant clouds.

White-throat appears. No swifts.
Cucumber sets, & swells.
Two Nightingales sing in my outlet.

Wednesday 8.
29 4/10½; 44; SE, S.
Frost, ice, sun &
clouds, louring.

Mowed the grass-walks for the first time.
Some swallows. No swifts. Tortoise awakes.

Thursday 9.
29 2/10⅓; 49; E.
Grey & mild, dark &
mild.

A few beeches in the hanger show leaves.
Swallows on every chimney.
Seven Swifts. Radishes.

Friday 10.
29 4/10; 51½, 55½;
NE, NW, S, W.
Sunny & hot, heavy
clouds, bright & chill.

14 or 16 swifts.
The tortoise weighs 6pd 11 oun 2dr.
he weighed Spring 1781 6: 8: 4
          & May 1780 6: 4: 0

Saturday 11.
29 1/10¼; 54, 55½;
S, SW. Dark & louring,
rain, rain.

Peach & Nect: bloom scarce over yet: no fruit seems to be set.
Vine-buds do not open at all.

One of my neighbours, an intelligent, & observing man informs me, that about ten minutes before 8 o'clock in the evening he discovered a great cluster of house swallows, 30 at least he supposes, perching on a willow that hung over the verge of James Knight's upper pond. His attention was first drawn by the twittering of these birds, which sate motionless in a row on the bough, with their heads all one way, & by their weight pressing down the twig so that it nearly touched the water. In this situation he watched them 'till he could see no longer. Repeated accounts of this sort spring & fall induce us greatly to suspect that house swallows have some strong attatchment to water independent of the matter of food; & that, if they do not retire into that element, they conceal themselves¶ in the banks of pools & rivers during the uncomfortable months of winter.

An uncommon, & I think a new little bird frequents my garden, which I have great reason to think is the Pettichaps.¶ It is common in some parts of the kingdom, & I have received formerly several dead specimens from Gibraltar. It much resembles the white throat, but has a more white, or rather silvery breast & belly; is restless & active like the willow-wrens, hopping from bough to bough, & examining every part for food. It also runs up the stems of the crown-imperials, & putting its head into the bells of those flowers, sips the liquor contained in the *nectarium* of each petal. It sometimes feeds like the hedge-sparrow, hopping about on the grass-plots & mown walks.

Sunday 12.
29 3/10; 52; SW.
Showers, showers, sun
& gale, chill even:

Fern-owl chatters.

A pair of white owls breed under Mr Yalden's roof of his house: they get in thro' the leaden-gutter that conveys the water from the roof to the tank. They have eggs.

About this time many swallows were found dead at & about Fyfield: Some were fallen down the chimnies, & some were lying on the banks of brooks, & streams.

Swifts kept-out all day, playing about in the rain: they seem to be more than 20 in number. Rain with wind they avoid, & are not seen in such weather.

Monday 13.
29 3/10; 53, 58½; S, SW.
Sun, summer
weather.

Fly-catcher appears. When this bird is seen the naturalist hopes the summer is established.

Tuesday 14.
29 1/10¾; SE, SW; 63, 56.

Lined the cucumber-bed. White cucumbers come-up well under a hand-glass.

Rain, rain, rain, rain.

Tortoise eats the leaves of poppies.

Wednesday 15.
55; SW, SW.
Grey, sun, showers,
fine.

The hanger improves in verdure very fast.
Grass grows. Cut a cucumber.
Warm, growing weather.

Thursday 16.
29 2/10; 55; SW, W.
Showers, showers,
showers.

Black-thorns, wild-cherries, & pear-trees blow.
Planted-out many ten-weeks stocks, & China hollyhocks.
The hanger more than half in leaf.

Friday 17.
28 7/10; 55; SW; 73.
Heavy showers, &
wind, rain, rain.

My tall hedges still naked.

Saturday 18.
29 1/10¾; 50; W; 18.
Dark, cold, &
windy.

Cut grass the first time for the horses, in the orchard.
Wild cherries in bloom are beautiful.

Sunday 19.
29 5/10¼; 48; N,
NW.
Dark & cold, showers,
bright even:

Monday 20.
29 3/10½; 47; SW,
SE; 9.
White frost, grey,
showers, sun, showers.

Men pole their hops.
Growing weather.

Tuesday 21.
29 3/10; 48; N, SW,
W; 39.
Showers, sun, rain, vast
showers.

Much hail in the neighbourhood.

Wednesday 22.
29 2/10¾; 48; SW,
W; 72, 30.
Wh: frost, sun,
showers, showers.

Men pole their hops, which are backward, but strong.
Some hail.

Thursday 23.
29 4/10; 49; SW, SE;
29.
Showers, sun & clouds,
showers, showers.

The hanger nearly in full leaf.
Maples naked.
Some hail.

Friday 24.
29 6/10; 50; NW; 19.
Frost, fog, sun,
showers, showers,
bright, & cold.

Vine shoots only one inch long! Lime-trees just opening their
buds. Oaks & ashes naked.
Hazel-leaves just expanded.

Saturday 25.
29 7/10, 5/10; 47½;
SW, SE.
Bright & cold, sun,
cold wind, dark, rain.

Early tulips blown. Hanger in full leaf.
Apple-trees begin to blow. The leaves of the old peaches, & nect:
sadly shrivel'd.

Sunday 26.
29 6/10¼; 49; SW,
W; 8.
Cold, sun, dark & cold,
small rain.

Monday 27.
29 5/10¼; 52; SW;
36. Rain, rain, dark
& warm, moist &
dark, fog.

Men have not been able to sow all their barley.

Tuesday 28.
29 3/10½; 56, 61; S,
SE, E, SE.
Fog, sun, sultry, vast
clouds, rain & thunder.

Wheat grows yellow, & looks sadly.
Swifts in great numbers dash about.

Wednesday 29.
29 4/10¾; 60; SW;
31.
Rain, rain, sun, grey.

Tulips blow.

Thursday 30.
29 3/10; 56; S; 21, 23.
Rain, rain, rain, gleam
of sun.

Plenty of asparagus.

Friday 31.
29 3/10¼; 55; S, SW;
11.
Shower, sun, showers
about, fine afternoon.

From Jan: 1: 1782 to May 31 D⁰ inclusive, the quantity of rain at
this place is 24 inch: 7 hund: This is after the rate of about 58
inch: for the whole year!!
This evening Chafers begin to fly in great abundance. They suit
their appearance to the coming-out of the young foliage, which in
kindly seasons would have been much earlier.

JUNE 1782

Saturday 1.
29 5/10½; 54; N; 18,
11.
Showers, rain, rain, sun
& clouds.

Some vine shoots are 3 or 4 inches long.
Black weather to the W: & N:W.

Sunday 2.
29 7/10; 51, 55; W,
NW.
White dew, sun,
shower, sun & brisk
gale.

House-martins build.
Apple-trees in full bloom.
Mʳ Pink is obliged to leave 26 acres of barley-ground unsown.

Feverish colds begin to be very frequent in this neighbourhood, &
indeed the country over. Within the bills of mortality this disorder
is quite epidemic, so that hardly an individual escapes. This
complaint seems to have originated in Russia, & to have extended
all over Europe. The great inclemency of the spring may best
account for this universal malady.¶

Monday 3.
29 8/10; 50; NW.
Sun, & flying showers.

Cucumbers abound. Wheat looks yellow.
Grass grows, & the clover-fields look well.

Tuesday 4.
29 8/10; 52; NW.
Dark, sun & clouds,
fine afternoon.

Made the hot-beds for the hand-glasses.
Kidney-beans in a poor way: they have all been in danger of
rotting.

Wednesday 5.
29 8/10; 51½; W.
Grey, still & mild.

H: Martins build.

My Broʳ Thomas White nailed-up several large scallop-shells under
the eaves of his house at South Lambeth to see if the house martins
would build in them. These conveniences had not been fixed half
an hour, before several pairs settled upon them; &, expressing
great complacency, began to build immediately. The shells were

nailed on horizontally, with the hollow side upward; & should, I think, have had a hole drilled in their bottoms to let-off moisture from driving rains.

Thursday 6.
29 8/10; 54½; 59; NW.
Sun, sun, summer, sweet even:

Tulips begin to go out of bloom.
Sycamore blows. Hawthorn begins to bloom.
Farmers turn out their horses to grass all night. Grass grows.
Wheat mends in colour. Tortoise feeds eagerly.
Apple-trees have much bloom.

Friday 7.
29 7/10¼; 55; S, SW, S.
Cold dew, sun, summer weather.

Crab Apple blossom
The Wakes
25 May.

Saturday 8.
29 5/10½; 59; SE.
Gret dew, sun, dark & hot, small shower.

Dressed the borders round the garden.
Flesh-flies begin to appear.

Sunday 9.
29 4/10; 62; S.
Dark, & sultry, sprinkling, brisk gale, dark & moist.

Horse-chestnut begins to bloom.

When the servants have been gone to bed some time, & the kitchen left dark, the hearth swarms with young crickets about the size of ants: there is an other set among them of larger growth: so that it appears that two broods have hatched this spring.

Monday 10.
29 3/10; 60½; S, W; 60.
Heavy showers, sun & clouds, bright even:
Apis longicornis.

Strong wind with the showers. Fine rain.
Corn & grass grow.

Tuesday 11.
29 4/10; 59; SW; 46, 20. Showers, strong gale, showers, thunder, showers.

Haw-thorn begins to blow. Wall-honeysuckles bloom. Standard honeysuckles, having lost their first shoots by the frost, will produce little bloom this summer.

Wednesday 12.
29 3/10; 57; S, SW.
Grey, gale, heavy clouds about.

The dearling-apple-tree is covered with bloom.
Wallnut-trees open their catkins, or male bloom.

Thursday 13.
29 6/10½; 56½; SW;
20.
Dark, strong gales,
cold, driving rain.

Hirundines hawk for food along behind my tall hedges.
A house-martin drowned in the water-tub: this accident seems to
have been owing to fighting.

Many people droop with this feverish cold: not only women &
children, but robust labourers. In general the disorder does not last
long, neither does it prove at all mortal in these parts.¶

Friday 14.
29 7/10½; 57½, 62;
SW, S.
Dark, cold, & blowing,
sun, sweet afternoon.

Sᵗ foin begins to blossom. Orange lilies open. Grass grows very
fast in the meadows.
Ephemerae, mayflies, appear, playing over the streams: their
motions are very peculiar, up & down for many yards, almost in
a perpendicular line.

Saturday 15.
29 9/10; 61½; 71; S,
SW.
Grey, sun, summer
cloudless, sweet even:

Hung-out my pendent meat-safe.
The martins over the garden-door have thrown out two eggs: they
had not been sat on.
A pair of partridges haunt Baker's hill, & dust themselves along
the verge of the brick-walk.
Kidney-beans now thrive. Pionies blow. Garden straw-berries
blossom well.

Sunday 16.
29 8/10; 62, 75½;
NE, SE, NE.
Sun, cloudless, sultry,
golden even:

This hot weather makes the tortoise so alert that he traverses all
the garden by six o'clock in the morning. When the sun grows
very powerful he retires under a garden-mat, or shelter of some
cabbage, not loving to be about in vehement heat. In such
weather he eats greedily.
Chafers abound.

Monday 17.
29 6/10½; 64, 76½;
NE, E, NE, N.
Great dew, sun,
cloudless, strong gale,
sultry, golden even,
distant thunder.

Tuesday 18.
29 7/10¾; 70½, 77;
SW, W.
Distant thunder SW,
sprinkling, thunder,
sultry, strong gale, red
even:, gale.

The hawthorns blossom in a beautiful manner in my fields. Vines
now shoot away.
Apis longicornis swarms in my walk down Baker's hill, & bores
the ground full of holes, both in the grass, & brick-walk.

On this day there was a great thunder-storm at London.

Wednesday 19.

29 9/10; 65, 71; NW.
Cold dew, sun,
cloudless, cool gale,
chilly, & red even:

Fiery lily blows.
Men shear their sheep.
Peat begins to be brought in.

Martins hatch in old nests: when the eggs open, the dams throw out the shells.
   Probably much rain fell this day at some distance to the S:W: While the thunder was about, the stone-pavement in some parts of the entry & kitchen sweated, & stood in drops of water.

Thursday 20.

29 9/10¼; 65, 71;
NE.
Blue mist, sun, blue
mist, cool breeze, sweet
weather, red even:

Medlar-tree blows finely.
The smoke from lime kilns hangs along the forest in level tracks for miles.

The farmers say, that the chafers, wch abound in some parts, fall off the hedges, & trees on the sheeps backs, where being entangled in the wooll they die, & being blown by flies, fill the sheep with maggots.

Friday 21.

30 1/10; 65½, 70;
NE.
Dew, sun, sun, & cool
gale, sweet even.

Rasps blossom.
Nightingale sings in my outlet.
Kidney-beans begin to climb their sticks.

Saturday 22.

30 1/10; 66; NE.
Sun, brisk gale, sun,
red even:

Young wall-nuts appear.
Began to tack the vines.
Some wheat begins to show ears.
Lovely midsummer weather.

The epidemic disorder rages in an alarming manner in our fleet. Sr John L: Ross has left the N: sea, & is returned to the downs, not being able to continue his cruize on account of the general sickness of his crews.¶

Sunday 23.

30; 65½, 68½; NE.
Sun, brisk gale,
cloudless, gale, golden
even:

The hawthorns are in beautiful bloom.

Jupiter makes, & has made for some weeks past a beautiful & resplendent appearance every evening to the S:E: Saturn, who is very near, is much obscured by the brilliancy of the former.

Monday 24.

29 8/10¼; 67, 73;
NE. Blue mist, sun,
cloudless, & brisk gale,
sweet even: red.

The by-roads begin to grow dry.
The disorder seems rather to abate in these parts.¶ Some few sufferers have had relapses.

Tuesday 25.
29 6/10¼; 67½; 78½;
NE, SE, S.
Fog, sun & brisk gale,
cloudless, still, &
sultry, red even:, a
great dew.

Thomas continues to thin & tack the vines: they show the
rudiments of much bloom. Elders begin to blow. Fraxinels blow.

The sun at setting shines along the hanger, just in these long days,
& tinges the stems of the tall beeches of a golden colour in a most
picturesque, & amusing manner!!
    Just at the summer solstice the sun at setting shines directly up
my broad walk against the urn, & tall fir.

Wednesday 26.
29 6/10; 71, 75½; W.
Great dew, sun, grey
clouds, sultry, gale,
clouds to the N:W.

Lines show their bracteal leaves, & rudiments of bloom.
Ants begin to appear at the foot of the stairs.
Serapias latifolia blossoms in the Hanger, & high wood.
Finished tacking, & thinning the vines. Bees swarm.

Thursday 27.
29 7/10; 64, 64; N, W.
Cool air, sun, sun, fine
even:, cool.

Wheat blossoms.

Friday 28.
29 7/10; 62; E, S, SW.
Dew, sun, cool, sun,
red even:, some broken
clouds.

Began to cut my meadow-hay: the crop is good.
Young red-breasts.
Fox-gloves, thistles, butterfly-orchis, blow in the high wood.
In the garden roses, corn-flags, Iris's, red valerian, lychnis's, &c:
blow.

Saturday 29.
29 7/10; 61; SW.
Sun, louring with cool
gale, sun, mist on the
hills, golden stripe in
the W.

Hay makes slowly.
Double catch-flies make a lovely show.

Sunday 30.
29 6/10¾; 62½, 66½;
S, SW, W.
Grey, sun, louring with
brisk gale, & some
scuds, sun & mackerel
sky, red & cool even:

Neither veal nor lamb is so fat this summer as usual: the reason is
because the cows, & ewes were much reduced by the coldness &
wetness of the last very ungenial springs.

JULY 1782

Monday 1.
29 6/10; 59; 62; W.

Hay makes slowly.

Cold air, clouds with stiff gale, clouds.

The crop of carrots in the great meadow will be good.

We have had no rain since June 13. The ground is bound as hard as iron, & chopped & cracked in a strange manner. Gardens languish for want of moisture, & the spring-corn looks sadly.
The ears of wheat in general are very small. The wetter the spring is, the more our ground binds in summer.
Garden flowers do not make a fine appearance this summer for want of rain.

Tuesday 2.
29 4/10, 5/10; 60, 62; W, W; 14.
Small rain, showers, grey, showers, rainbow.

Cut my S! foin, & sold it to John Carpenter.
This is the 15 crop. It continues as good as it has been for some years.

Wednesday 3.
29 6/10¼; 55, 62; W.
Cold dew, sun, clouds & strong cold wind, louring.

Ricked my meadow-hay, that received no manner of hurt from the showers of yesterday, in delicate order. If any thing was wrong, the produce of the little mead was scarce made enough: but it was put at the top.

Thursday 4.
29 6/10; 58, 62; W.
Grey, sun & clouds, sprinkling, bright even:

Many showers about.
Grasshopper-lark whispers.

Friday 5.
W, S, E.
Sun & clouds, dark, rain, rain.

WORLDHAM
My flower bank now in high beauty.
Rain all night.

Saturday 6.
29 5/10; 62¼; E, E; 101.
Rain, rain, dark & moist.

SELBORNE
These fine, still, soft rains will be of vast service to the country, which was quite parched up.
Several titlarks nests were mowed-out in the S! foin.
Martins in old nests have got young half fledged. Swallows now are very assiduous in collecting food for their young. No young swallows flown yet.

Sunday 7.
29 5/10¾; 61½, 62; N.
Dark & moist, small rain.

Monday 8.
29 6/10; 60; N, SW.

BRAMSHOT PLACE

Dorton,
Late July

Dark & still, sultry, dark.

Rode to Firgrove in the parish of Bramshot, & saw the house & garden. The south wall of the kitchen-garden is covered with a range of vines of the sort called the miller-grape. Each vine was trained within a very narrow space, & their boughs upright: yet they had fine wood, & promised for much fruit, & were in almost full bloom. Mr Richardson's vines, my sort, did not blow then: but Fir-grove is much more sheltered than Bramshot-place. The soils are the same, a warm sandy loam.

    When we came to Evely-corner, a hen partridge came out of a ditch & ran along shivering with her wings, & crying out as if wounded, & unable to get from us. While the dam acted this distress, the boy who attended me, saw her brood, that was small & unable to fly, run for shelter into an old fox-earth under the bank. So wonderful a power is instinct!

Tuesday 9.
29 6/10½; 57; S, SW.
Dark & moist, sun & gale.

Hay ricked.

Wednesday 10.
D°; 60; S.
Dark & still, red even:

Thursday 11.
29 5/10½, 29 5/10; 62; SE.
Grey, scud, cloudy, rain, rain, rain.

Much rain, & wind.

Lapwings.
Looking from Selborne Common.
12 August.

Friday 12.
29 5/10½; 62½; W, S; 87.
Sun, dark, sun & clouds, fine afternoon.

SELBORNE
Wood straw-berries begin to come.
A great flock of lap-wings passes over us from the uplands to the forest. They frequent the uplands at this season.
Young partridges.

Saturday 13.
29 6/10; 60; SE, E, NW.
Dark & moist, rain, rain, rain, thunder.

My vines barely begin to blow.
Much hay will be spoiled.

Sunday 14.
29 6/10¼; 61½; SW; 101.
Rain, rain, sun & clouds, cool even:

This weather will occasion much after-grass.
Field-pease, & spring corn thrive.

Monday 15.

29 6/10¼; 59½; E,
SE, E.

Sun, summer-day,
heavy clouds, soft even:

Began to cut my tall hedge.
White cucumbers begin to swell.
Wood straw-berries abound.
Heavy showers, & distant lightening.

Tuesday 16.

29 6/10, 5/10; 64, 69;
E, NE, N; 70.

Sun, hot, sultry, distant
thunder, shower,
showers about.

A covey of young partridges frequents my out-let.
Young martins put their heads out of nests.
Vines blow. Stone-floors sweat.
Hops do not yet cover their poles, nor throw-out any side-shoots.

Wednesday 17.

29 8/10; 63½; NE; 87.
Rain, rain, rain.

The great Portugal-laurel is in most beautiful floom. *Tremella nostoc* abounds.
Hay in bad state.

Some young swallows come-out, & perch on twigs, where the dams feed them. In kind seasons they usually appear about the beginning of July; & a few the last week in June. Saw very few young swallows in the whole.

Thursday 18.

29 9/10; 61½; NW,
W, SW.

Dark & heavy, sun &
clouds, dark & moist,
fine even:

Began stopping the vines, which are in full bloom, & will have much fruit.
Hay did not make at all.

Friday 19.

29 8/10¾; 68; N,
NW.

Sun, sun & clouds,
sweet afternoon, dew.

Young martins fly.

Haw-thorns had much bloom, but will have little fruit.

Saturday 20.

29 8/10¾; 63½; NE,
SE.

Fog, sun, summer
weather, sweet even:,
dew.

Wood straw-berries almost over.
Much damaged hay ricked.
Creeping mists over the meadows.
Vivid N: Auroras.

Sunday 21.

29 7/10; 63½; E, E.
Dew, sun, cloudless,
gale, sweet even:

Artichokes come in.
Wood straw-berries over.

Monday 22.
29 5/10; 65, 72; E, S,
SW.
Fog, sun, cloudless,
sultry, sprinkling, dark
& threat'ning.

The swifts are numerous, & seem to have brought out some of
their young.
Damaged hay ricked. Distant thunder to the S.

Tuesday 23.
29 6/10¼; 69; S.
Clouds & strong gale,
sun, cool & pleasant.

Began to cut some large white cucumbers.
Phallus impudicus stinks.
Much meadow-hay cutting. Solstitial flowers fade.

Will: Tanner shot a sparrow-hawk, which had infested the village
for some time. It had made havock among the young swallows &
h: martins, which are slow & inactive: the dams insult all hawks
with impunity.

Wednesday 24.
29 7/10; 65; SW.
Sun & clouds, & brisk
gale, sun, pleasant even:
Full moon.

Lime trees blossom.
Whortle-berries ripen.
Bought an aged brown Galloway of Mr Bradley of Alton.

Thursday 25.
29 6/10; 64; SW, S.
Sun, glorious sun-
shine, dark & soft.

Much hay ricked.

Friday 26.
29 6/10; 66; E, SE.
Rain, rain, dark &
mild.

Roses continue in full bloom. Orange-lilies, white lilies, & lark-
spurs figure.
Rasps ripen: white cucumbers bear.

Saturday 27.
29 5/10; 63½; N,
NW; 189.
Vast rain, dark &
moist, rain, rain.

Swallows-nests with their young washed down the chimney.
Many ricks of hay unfinished.

Sunday 28.
29 4/10; 63; SW, S;
42.
Showers, sun & clouds,
showers.

Monday 29.
29 5/10½; 60½; N,

Fine wood straw-berries again.

W; 18.
Grey, sun & clouds,
heavy showers.

A strong stream of water runs in Norton mead among the hay-cocks.

Tuesday 30.
29 6/10; 59; E, N, W.
Sun, clouds, dark &
still, showers about.

Jasmine begins to blow. Orange, & white lilies make a great show. White hellebore blows.¶
Grapes swell a little.
Some few swifts.

Wednesday 31.
29 4/10; 58½; N,
NW.
Grey & still, dark &
moist, small rain.

Kidney-beans blow but the leaves are spotted & distempered.
Swifts seem to be withdrawn.

AUGUST 1782

Thursday 1.
29 3/10; 60; S, SW.
Dark, grey, sun, dark
& moist.

Dark & damp.
One pair of swifts.

Timothy the tortoise weighed seven pounds & three ounces.

Friday 2.
29 1/10; 32; SW; 47.
Showers, sun, showers,
rain, rain.

People gather mushrooms.
The blossoms of the limes hang in beautiful golden tassels.

Saturday 3.
29 3/10; 62; SW.
Sun & clouds, showers
about, fine even.

Hay making.
One swift.
Vast shower at Petersfield.

Sunday 4.
29 5/10; 60½; SW.
Sun & clouds, shower.

Five swifts.

Monday 5.
29 5/10½; 58; SW;
47.
Sun, showers, heavy
showers, chill even.

Wheat turns colour.
Trenched-out several rows of Celeri.
Five swifts.

Tuesday 6.
29 7/10½; 60; SW; 86.

Five swifts.

Heavy showers,
showers, heavy
showers.

Red martagons blow.

Wednesday 7.
28 7/10; 60, 56; S, W;
130.
Rain & wind, rain &
strong gales.

Vast rains in the night.
The quantity of rain since Jan: 1st 1782, is 36 in: 1h.!!!
Eight swifts.

Thursday 8.
29 2/10½; 57; NW;
65.
Strong gales with cold
showers.

Rasps rot. Mushrooms come.
One swift.
Much *Tremella* on the grass-walk.
The wind has torn & broken many flowers, & strawed the walks
with leaves, & twigs.

Friday 9.
29 3/10; 56; W.
Grey & warm,
sprinkling, red even:

Hops are injured by the late winds.
Swifts about Reading.

Saturday 10.
29 5/10; 56; NW, W.
Dark & cold, strong
gale, sprinkling, dark
& cold.

Wheat green & backward.
Grapes hardly grow at all.
Sowed two plots of winter-spinage.

Sunday 11.
29 5/10½; 54;
W, S.
Grey & mild, sun,
sweet afternoon.

One swift.
Trenched-out the last row of Celeri.
Five swifts at E: Tisted.

Monday 12.
29 1/10; 58; SE, E,
NE, N.
Dark & still, rain, rain,
rain.

Three swifts.
Some men have begun to cut wheat.
Swifts about Windsor. Vast showers.

Tuesday 13.
29 2/10½; 56; W;
115.
Grey, sun & clouds,
dark, rain.

Showers about.
Bro: Tho: White & daughter came.

Wednesday 14.
28 9/10½; 60½; SW;
72, 13.
Rain, rain, rain.

The lavant runs by the side of Cobb's court-yard.
Strong gales.
Swifts about High Wycomb.

Thursday 15.
29 3/10¾; 59; SW.
Grey & mild,
sprinkling, dark, rain.

† [?] for the first time.
The celeri in the trenches looks red, & stunted from the wet &
cold.
Some wheat cut.
The hay is all totally spoiled; & men begin to fear that the wheat
will grow as it stands. That which is lodged is in much danger.

Thirteen swifts over the Lythe: seven at Hartley. Do they not at
this season move from village to village?

Friday 16.
29 2/10½; 63; SW,
W; 35.
Rain, showers, strong
gale.

No kidney-beans: the bad season prevents their bearing.
One swift. Swallows sculk about to avoid the bad weather.
Wood straw-berries. Mushrooms.

Saturday 17.
29 2/10; 59; SW; 43,
13.
Heavy showers,
thunder, showers, sun,
& strong gales.

Cranberries, but not ripe.
Six swifts at least feeding along the side of the hanger.
The field-pease, both hacked, & growing, are in danger of
spoiling. The crop is good.
Hops look miserably.
Whortle-berries.
Gathered one handful of kidney-beans. The ground is quite
glutted with rain.
The wheat is miserably lodged.

A fledged young swift was found alive on the ground in the
church-yard: it was full of *hippoboscae*. We gave it two or three
flies, & tossed it up on the church.

Sunday 18.
29 4/10¾; 58; NW,
W.
Sun & clouds, with
strong gale, bright,
shower.

Linnets congregate, & therefore have probably done breeding.

Saw a *Papilio Machaon* in my garden: this is only the third of this
species that ever I have seen in this district. It was alert, & wild. It
is the only swallow-tailed fly in this island.
   Many pairs of martins repair their nests, & some build new.
These preparations are with a view to a second brood, which must
be late.

---

† Word illegible.

Monday 19.
29 4/10½; 57½; W, SW.
Sun, vast dew, sun & white clouds, fine still afternoon, grey even:

16 swifts dashing & squeeking about the church.
Some men begin to reap wheat.
Mushrooms look very pale.

Tuesday 20.
29 5/10; 59; SW, S.
Small showers, sun & clouds, bright, heavy in horison.

Wheat-harvest becomes pretty general.
Several swifts.
Pease housed. Spoiled hay rick'd.
Tyed-up the first endive.
Fly-catchers about.
Some wheat shocked.

Wednesday 21.
29 4/10¼; 63½; SW, S.
Sun, & soft weather, grey, dark, misty rain.

Some swifts.
Turnips are hoeing.
Hay, of cow-grass, is housing.
Wheat-sheaves are bound in single bands.

Thursday 22.
29 4/10; 62; SE, S.
Sun, moist clouds, sun, rain, thunder, vast shower.

Goody Hammond goes off from the garden to glean wheat.
Much cow-grass ricked from the N. field.

8 or 9 swifts. It appears as if the hirundines kept pace with the backwardness of the year. These birds have probably all young: but whether they are their first brood, a late one, or a second, not come to maturity, is not so easy to determine; most likely the former.
  From circumstances, house-martins will be late with their second broods.

Friday 23.
29 6/10; 60; SW; 95; 11.
Thunder in the night with heavy showers, grey & moist.
Full moon.

The pond on Selborn-down is brim-full, & has run over.
Men turn their wheat. Ground very wet.
The quantity of rain from Jan: 1st 1782 to Aug: 23rd is 40 inc: 52 h:

Saturday 24.
29 4/10; 63; SW.
Grey, sun, soft gleams, dark, rain.

Newton great-pond runs over.
The first broods of martins congregate on sunny roofs.

Sunday 25.
29 6/10; 62; SW.
Grey, sun, sun, shower.

Clays-pond runs over.

Not one wasp or hornet to be seen: nor if there were, is there any fruit to support them. On such a summer, it seems quite a wonder that the whole race is not extinct. In great plum years, that fruit seems to be their principal food.

Monday 26.
29 6/10¾; 61; SW.
Dark & moist, small showers, brisk gales, dark & moist.

Wheat harvest is general; but the wheat is very green. Much hay lies about still.
Some pease are housed.

Tuesday 27.
29 3/10½; 59; SW, W.
Shower, sun, showers, rain, rain.

No wasps or hornets.
Several swifts.
Miserable harvest-weather!

These were the last Swifts. Not one straggler has been seen since. On this day last year the late swift, & two young withdrew. Vid: Aug^st 1781.

Wednesday 28.
29 3/10¾; 56; NW; 56.
Shower, sun, sun, cold air.

Wheat grows as it lies: & the lodged wheat uncut is in a bad state.
Cold & chilly.

Thursday 29.
29 3/10½; 54½; SW.
Red morn: rain-bow, sun, shower, bright & cold.

The store sheep on the down are in good case.
Some men began to house wheat before the shower. Were forced to light a fire in the parlor.

On this day the *Royal George*, a 100 gun ship, was unfortunately over-set at Spithead, as she was heaving down. Admiral Kempenfelt, & about 900 people, men, women & children, were lost. The lower port-holes being open the ship filled, & sunk in about 8 minutes.

Friday 30.
29 6/10; 54; NW, N.
Sun, sun & clouds, sun, red even:

Much wheat housed all day long.
The air is chilly, & has an October feel.
Thistle-down flies.
A few kidney-beans.

Saturday 31.
29 8/10; 54; W.
Sun, sun & clouds, shower, heavy clouds.

Swallows & martins settle on sunny roofs.
China-pinks, African-Marigolds, China-asters begin to blow.
Wheat housed.

Began to turn the horses into the great meadow: there is a fine
head of grass.

In the month of Augst there fell 8 inch 28 h: of rain!

SEPTEMBER 1782

Sunday 1.
29 9/10; 56; W.
Fog, sun & clouds,
chill air.

The swifts left Lyndon in the county of Rutland, for the most part,
about Augst 23. Some continued 'till Augst 29: & one 'till Septem^r
3rd!! In all our observation Mr Barker & I never saw or heard of a
swift in Septem^r tho' we have remarked them for more than 40
years. All nature this summer seems to keep pace with the
backwardness of the season.

Monday 2.
30; 58; NW, NE, N,
S.
Cold dew, sun, sweet
autumnal weather,
bright gleam.

Contrary to all rule the wheat this year is heavy, & the straw
short: last year, tho' so much heat prevailed, the wheat was light
& the straw was long.
Ladies-traces bud for bloom.

Tuesday 3.
29 8/10; 57; E, SE.
Grey, sun, sweet
harvest weather, red
even.

Wheat ricked.
Flying ants come forth.
Nep^s Thomas Holt White, & Henry Holt White came from
Fyfield.

Wednesday 4.
29 6/10¼; 56½; 64;
E.
Deep fog, vast dew,
sweet day, mackarel
sky, red even:

Shooters complain there are no partridges.
Began to cut the first endive: finely blanched.
Wheat housed in good order, much.
Curlews clamour.

Thursday 5.
29 7/10; 59; NE.
Fog, sun, sweet
autumnal weather, red
even:

Lapwings in a vast flock on the upland fallows.
Vast flock of martins & swallows. The air is full of flying ants &
the hirundines live luxuriously.
Much wheat housed.

Friday 6.
29 8/10; 60, 67; NE,
E. Fog, sun &
clouds, cloudless, sweet
even: red.

Young martins cluster on the tower, by hundreds.
Planted several Ladies-traces, & Serapias's from the long Lithe,
in the bank near the alcove.
Sister Barker & Nieces Mary & Eliz: Barker came from Lyndon

in Rutland.
Much wheat bound. The latter-housed wheat in nice order.

Saturday 7.
29 8/10; 60, 68; NE,
E.
Fog, sun, cloudless,
sweet autumn weather!

Colchicum blows.
Titlarks haunt the walks, & grass-plots.
Hops are very small.
Therm! in the sun – 104.
Wheat housed. Many Selborne farmers finished wheat-harvest.
The latter housings are in delicate order: the early housed will be
cold, & damp.

Sunday 8.
29 7/10½; 61½; 69½;
NE, N, NE.
Fog, cloudless, brisk
gale, red even:

People complain of harvest bugs.
Therm! in the sun – 110.

On this day M⁽ʳˢ⁾ Brown of Uppingham in the County of Rutland,
eldest daughter of my Sister Barker; was brought to bed of a
daughter, her third child.
    My nephews & nieces living are now 17 nephews: 15 nieces: 2
grand nephews: 2 grand nieces: 2 nephews by marriage. total 38.
One Niece since, 39.
    8 nephews & nieces dead.

Monday 9.
29 8/10; 62; NE.
Fog, cloudless, cool
gale, red even:

Some oats are mowed.
Partridges are more plenty on the verge of the forest in the sand.

Tuesday 10.
29 7/10½; 62; NE.
Fog, cloudless, strong
cool gale, red even:
still.

Martins congregate on roofs.

Wednesday 11.
29 6/10½; 63; NE.
Fog, blue mist, brisk
gale, dark & moist, red
even:

Goody Hammond returned to weed in the garden.
Got-in two loads of peat at last in good order.
The perfoliated yellow centaury in seed on the bank above Tull's
cottage. *Chlora perfoliata.*

On this day Lord Howe sailed from Spithead with 34 ships of the
line, as is supposed for the relief of Gibraltar.

Thursday 12.
29 7/10¼; 62; N.
Dark, sun & clouds,
strong gale, dark &
chill.

Got-in one load more of peat.
Hop-picking begins in the Hartley garden.
No rain now for a fortnight.

Friday 13.
29 6/10½; 60; N.
Dark, still, & heavy.

Some few orleans-plums.
Ravens about the hanger.
All the Selborne wheat in, except some turnip-wheat at the priory.

Saturday 14.
29 5/10; 50; N.
Sweet grey weather,
dark.

Vast flock of lap-wings in the forest.
Barley housing on the sands.
Hop-picking stops, because the hops are not ripe.
Five ring-ouzels were seen on Hindhead on their autumnal
migration.

In reading Dr Huxham's "*Observationes de aere, &c*", written at
Plymouth, I find by those curious, & accurate remarks, which
contain the weather from the year 1727, to the year 1748
inclusive, that tho' there is frequent rain in that district of Devon,
yet the quantity is not great; & that some years it is very small. For
in 1731 the rain was only 17:266; & in 1741 – 20:354: and again
in 1743 only 20:908.
   Places near the sea have frequent scuds, that keep the
atmosphere moist, yet do not reach far up into the country.
   In the wettest years they had at Plymouth only 36 & odd: &
once, viz: 1734–37 – 114; a quantity that has been exceeded at
Selborne of late.
   The D^r remarks that frequent small rains keep the air moist;
while heavy ones render it dry, by beating down the vapor. He also
supposes that the dingy, smoaky appearance in the sky in very dry
seasons arises from the want of moisture sufficient to let the light
thro', & render the atmosphere transparent: because he has
observed several bodies more diaphanous when wet than dry; &
has never remarked that the air has that look in rainy moist
seasons.

Sunday 15.
29 1/10; 62½; SE.
Grey, shower, sun &
clouds.

The barley & oats are full of clover.
Barley in general not ripe.

Monday 16.
28 9/10; 64; SE, W;
28.
Dark, showers,
blowing & wet.

Hops are very small; but the haulm is clean & free from insects.

My brother Thomas White opened two of the most promising
tumuli on the down above my house. In the first, at about three
feet under ground, was found a blackish matter that had some
appearance of an *humus animalis*; in the second, at the same
depth, a greyish matter that looked like the first rudiments of a bed
of *pyrites*.

Tuesday 17.
29 1/10; 60; SW; 27.

Hop-picking begins. The storm last night injured the hops.

Sun, showers, showers, dark.

Wednesday 18.
29 ½/10; 60; SW; 59.
Heavy showers,
showers, blowing.

NEWTON
The woods & hangers still look very green: the tops of the
beeches are scarcely tinged.

Thursday 19.
29 7/10; NW; 37.
Bright, sun, cool air,
pleasant moonshine.

BASINGSTOKE, SELBORNE
Barley-mowing about the country.

Friday 20.
29 4/10; 52; SW.
Dark & windy, rain.

One little starveling wasp.
Hop-picking is general.

Saturday 21.
29 4/10; 59½; S; 33.*
Dark, driving rain.
Full moon.

Hops very small.
* The rain-measurer on Selborne-tower in the same space of time
only produced 20 hund.

Sunday 22.
29 3/10; 60½; SW.
Small rain, grey, dark
& moist.

Barley not cut at Faringdon.
Many martins & swallows.

Monday 23.
29 2/10¾; 60, 60;
SW; 25.*
Showery & blowing.

* The rain-measurer on the tower – 22.
Many swarms of bees have dyed this summer; the badness of the
weather has prevented their thriving.

Tuesday 24.
29 6/10½; 54; SW;
23.*
Bright, sun, dark, rain.

* The rain on the tower – 19.
Barley & oats in a bad way.

Wednesday 25.
29 6/10¾; 58; SW.
Wet & blowing,
dismal, & wet.

Many hirundines.
Sad hop & harvest weather!

Very few house-martins had any second broods this Summer.

Thursday 26.
29 6/10; 5/10; 62;
67½; SW. Soft &
pleasant, soft, & dark.

Barley grows in swarth.
Many hirundines.

Friday 27.

29 6/10; 62¼; SW;
30.
Showers, & gales,
showers, bright.

On the tower – 27.
Mich: daiseys, & other asters begin to blow.
Bro: Thomas White, his daughter, & two sons left Selborne.

Saturday 28.

29 8/10; 55; SW.
Vast dew, bright, grey
& pleasant.

Some grapes begin to turn colour!
Oats & barley lie in a sad state.
Young martins in a nest at Faringdon: they seem to be near
flying.

Sunday 29.

29 4/10; 57; SW, NW.
Dark & moist, grey,
heavy rain, blowing.

Young martins in the nest at Faringdon.
Hardly any barley or oats housed.
Began to light fires in the parlor.

Monday 30.

29 6/10; 57; NE; 90.*
Bright, showers, bright
& cold, bright N:
Aurora.

* On the tower – 85.
Many wasps at Lyndon in Rutland, tho' none in the great heats of
autumn 1781. So there is some mystery in their breeding that we
do not understand.

"You cannot tell what the mean rain at Selborne will be, 'till you
have measured it a great many years. If I had only measured the
rain the 4 years from 1740, to 43, I should have said the rain at
Lyndon was 16½ inch: for a year: if from 1740 to 50, 18½
inches. We had much less rain before 1763 than since. The mean
before was 20¼ inch: from 1763 & since 25½: from 1770 to
1780 – 26 inches. If only 1773, 74, & 75, had been measured,
Lyndon mean rain would have been called 32 inches. My greatest
twelve-months rain is from Oct: 1773, to Sept.ʳ 1774 – 39⅓
inches. We have had here near 29 inch: in the 9 months now past
this year: but I find there were in 1773, 74, & 75, times in which
the rain exceeded that of this year; except that the last 6 months
exceeded 6 months then. 1, 2, 3, 4, 5, 6, 7, 8, 9, in those years
exceeded the same number of months now."
                              "J. Barker."
"Lyndon: Sept: 30. 1782."
    At the autumnal aequinox the evenings are remarkably dark,
because the sun at that time sets more in a right angle to the
horizon, than at any other season. But of late these uncomfortable
glooms have been much softened by frequent N: Auroras.
    This circumstance of autumnal darkness did not escape the poet
of nature: who says
"Now black, & deep the night begins to fall,"
"A shade immense. Sunk in the quenching gloom"
"Magnificent & vast are heaven & earth";

"Order confounded lies; all beauty void;"
"Distinction lost; & gay variety"
"One universal blot: such the fair power"
"Of light, to kindle, & create the whole."

Thomson's *Autumn*.

It is remarkable that this wet cold summer produces no good mushrooms. A great plenty of the pale, coarse sort appeared early in the autumn; but I have seen none with the salmon-coloured *laminae* which only are the true edible sort.¶

OCTOBER 1782

Tuesday 1.
29 7/10½; 49, 53;
NW, W. Cold dew,
bright, dark & sharp.

Several hirundines.

Wednesday 2.
28 9/10¾; 53; W; 50.
Heavy showers &
strong gales, showers.

Some hirundines.
Ivy begins to blow. Elder-berries ripen.

Thursday 3.
29 6/10; 52, 53; N; 28.
Shower, cold, &
blowing, showers, cold
& blowing, *Aurora*.

Two or three swallows.

Rain 78 in my garden, on the tower 59.

Friday 4.
29 7/10; 45; N.
White frost, sun,
pleasant afternoon.

A few swallows.
Men house some spring corn.
Numbers of pheasants at Inne down-coppice.

Saturday 5.
29 5/10; 44; N.
Wh: frost, very cold,
sweet sunshine.

Ice.
Men house oats, & make oat-ricks.
No hirundines.

Sunday 6.
29 5/10; 49; N.
Bright & cold, pleasant

Several swallows at Farindon.
No barley housed at D⁰
Wood-cock returns, & is seen in the hanger.
Young martins in a nest at Little Worldham; probably Ward le ham.

Monday 7.
29 4/10; 49; N.

Men have housed oats all day.

Dark, still & moist.

Many swallows over Dorton, & Coomb-wood-pond.
Deep autumnal darkness.

Tuesday 8.
29 4/10¾; 52; NE, N.
Dark & moist, soft
rain.

Sad weather for the barley.
All the hops of this parish this year are carried to Wey-hill in two
waggons: good crops require four or five. No hirundines.
Gathered two or three bunches of grapes: they have some colour,
but are crude & sour.
By the evening being so light, there must be great N: Auroras.
Mr Yalden finished moving his barley.

Barley housed at Bramshot, & other places, being green & damp,
has heated violently, & endangered the firing the barns.

Wednesday 9.
29 9/10¾; 52½; E.
Grey, sun, flying
showers, dark & mild.

Several swallows round the village.

Few pheasants in Selborne manor this year.

Thursday 10.
29, 28 9/10; 52; SE;
23.
Heavy clouds, sun,
warm, star-light.

Several swallows.
We make tarts, & puddings with the crude unripened grapes.
Gathered-in the Virgoleuse, & Chaumontelle pears, a good crop:
some what has gnawn many of the former like wasps or hornets.

Friday 11.
28 9/10; 52; NE.
Dark & moist, blowing,
grey even: blowing.

Wood-cocks about.
Began to light fires in the great parlour.

Lord Howe arrived in the straits of Gibraltar.

Saturday 12.
29 4/10; 48; N.
Sun & drying wind,
pleasant starlight.

No Hirundines.
The paths are dry & crisp.
Much barley housed on the downs this day.
Men housed barley 'till between ten & eleven at night.

Sunday 13.
29 7/10; 45; NE.
White frost, sun, fine
autumnal weather.

The great farmer at Newton has 105 acres of barley abroad.
Many h: martins, & some swallows at Faringdon.
Mr Pink has still 40 acres of barley abroad.
Red-wings appear.

Monday 14.
29 7/10¾; 43; NW.
White frost, deep fog,
sun, pleasant, chill
even:

Several martins at Faringdon.
Much barley housed.
Partial fogs.
Sister Barker & her two daughters left Selborne.

Tuesday 15.
29 8/10; 43½; W,
SW. Frost, dark, grey
& still.

Fine autumnal weather.
Much barley housed.

Wednesday 16.
29 8/10½; 48; SW,
SW.
Great dew, grey, sweet
autumnal weather.

Gathered-in my apples, Knobbed russetings, & nonpariels, a
few. Near four bushels of dearlings on the meadow-tree: fruit
small.

Thursday 17.
30; 49½; W, NW.
Scud, sun, soft & still.

No baking-pears. Gathered-in medlars.
Dug-up carrots, a good crop, but small in size.
Paths dry & pleasant.
Bat appears.

The beeches on the hanger are beautifully tinged. My tall hedges
exhibit most lovely tints.

Friday 18.
29 7/10; 46; W.
Frost, dark & cold,
strong wind.

Leaves fall from the trees.
Barley-harvest finished.
Earthed up celeri, which looks better than it did.

Young martins in their nest at Faringdon fed by their dams.
　Lord Howe compleated the relief of Gibraltar.

Saturday 19.
29 3/10¼; 50, 48; W.
Strong gale all night,
shower, blowing,
moon-light.

Martins twittering in their nest at Dᵒ [Faringdon] after it was
dark.

The tortoise not only gets into the sun under the fruit wall; but he
tilts one edge of his shell against the wall, so as to incline his back to
it's rays: by which contrivance he obtains more heat than if he lay
in his natural position. And yet this poor reptile has never read,
that planes inclining to the horizon receive more heat from the sun
than any other elevation! At four P:M: he retires to bed under the
broad foliage of a holyhock. He has ceased to eat for some time.

Sunday 20.
29 5/10½; 41½; W.
Strong gale, sun,
blowing & sharp air.

No corn abroad but a few vetches.
Ground dry & crisp.

Lord Howe had a skirmish with the combined fleet, in which he
had 68 killed, & 208 wounded.

Monday 21.
29 5/10; 49, 54; W;
22.
Shower, dark & warm,

Planted-out cabbages to stand the winter.
Planted out 3 rows of small lettuces under the fruit-wall.
Bat, & beetles appear.

& still.
Full moon.

Grapes very eatable.

Tuesday 22.
29 4/10; SW.
Dark, & mild, & wet.

FYFIELD
My hedges are finely tinged.

Wednesday 23.
29 7/10; 49; NW.
Vast dew, sun, pleasant.

Rain in the night.
My brother's children & plantations strangely grown in two
years.
On the downs the green wheat looked very chearful & pleasant.
Some wheat & turnips covered with charlock in full bloom.

Thursday 24.
29 9/10, 30½; 47;
NW.
White frost, sun,
pleasant.

Therm: abroad 28.
Grapes at this place eatable: the sort, black-cluster, came from
Selborne.

This proves, it seems, but a poor trufle-year at Fyfield: so they fail
some times in very wet years, as well as in very dry ones.

Friday 25.
29 9/10½; SW, NW.
Wh: frost, dark & wet,
D°

A few vetches abroad.
The gold & silver-fish lie sleeping all day in their glass bowl
towards the surface of the water: people that have attended to
them suppose this circumstance prognostic of rain.
Jupiter & Saturn approach to each other very fast.

Saturday 26.
29 9/10; 58; N.
Sun, warm & pleasant,
red even:

For the time of year the foliage on the trees is very perfect.
Paths are dry.

Two of my brother Henry's gold-fish have been sick, & cannot live
with the rest in the glass-bowl: but in a tin-bucket by themselves
they soon become lively, & vigorous. They were perhaps too much
crouded in the bowl. When a fish sickens it's head gets lowest; so
that by degrees it stands as it were on it's head; 'till getting weaker
& losing all poise, the tail turns over; & at last it floats on the water
with it's belly uppermost. Gold & silver-fishes seem to want no
aliment, but what they can collect from pure water frequently
changed. They will eat crumbs, but do better without; because the
water is soon corrupted by the pieces of bread, & turns sour. Tho'
they seem to take nothing; yet the consequences of eating
frequently drop from them: so that they must find many
animalcula, & other nourishment. With their *pinnae pectorales*
they gently protrude themselves forward or backward: but it is
with their strong muscular tails only that Fishes move with such
inconceivable rapidity.

The common notion is that the eyes of fish are immoveable: but these apparently turn them forward or backward in their sockets, as their occasions require. They take little notice of a candle, tho' applyed close to their heads: but flounce & seem much frightened by a sudden stroke of the hand on the support whereon the bowl stands; especially when they lie motionless, & are perhaps asleep. As fishes have no eye-lids, it is not easy to discern when they are sleeping or not; because their eyes are always open.

Nothing can be more pleasing than a glass-bowl containing such fish: the double refractions of the glass & water represent them continually in a shifting variety of shapes & colours; while the two mediums magnify them vastly. Not to mention, that the introduction of an other element, & it's inhabitants into a parlor, amuses the fancy in a very agreeable manner.

Sunday 27.
30; 52; N, SW, NW.
Dark, mild, & still.

True autumnal weather.

Monday 28.
29 3/10; 52; SW.
Dark & still, rain.

Tuesday 29.
29 4/10; N; 40.
Strong gale, sun &
clouds, bright, red
even:

The strong wind has almost stripped the beeches of all their leaves.

Wednesday 30.
29 7/10; 34; NW, SW.
Frost, grey, rain.

Wallnut-trees are naked.

Thursday 31.
29 2/10; S, NW; 30.
Rain, rain, rain & wind.

Rain from the tower in my absence 64.

NOVEMBER 1782

Friday 1.
NW.
Hard frost, thick ice,
warm sun, shower,
bright & cold.

SELBORNE
Some flocks of starlings on the wide downs between Andover, & Winton.

Several martins were playing about over the chalk-bank at the E: end of Whorwel village. Can any one suppose but that they came-out of that bank that morning to enjoy the warm sunshine, & would retire into it again before night?

Saturday 2.
29 1/10; 49; S, SW.
Rain, rain, rain.

Flock of starlings.
The Plestor.

Sunday 3.
29; 45; W, NW; 145.
Small rain, grey.

Rain on the tower 138.
Vast rain in the night.
The hanger is almost naked.

Monday 4.
29 3/10; 40, 41¼;
NW.
Frost, sun, pleasant.

I watched the S:E. end of the hanger, hoping to have seen some
house-martins, as they sometimes appear about this day: but was
disappointed.

Tuesday 5.
29 2/10¼; 41; NE, N;
54.
Rain, snow, dark &
raw.

Much rain in the night.
Wild wood-pigeons appear.

Wednesday 6.
29 9/10; 38; W.
Frost, ice, sun, cold air,
frost.

Thursday 7.
29 9/10½; 36; N.
Hard frost, sun, sharp
air, frost.

Leaves fall very fast.
Large field-fare.

Friday 8.
29 8/10; 37; N.

Men are interrupted in their wheat-sowing in the mornings by

Hard frost, sun,
pleasant, frost.

hard frost.

Saturday 9.
29 7/10; 36; N.
Hard frost, sun, frost.

Sunday 10.
29 4/10; 36; NW.
Hard frost, dark &
cold, thaw, wet.

Men have put up their hogs to fat.
Oak-woods carry a good foliage still.

Monday 11.
29 6/10; 39; NE, N.
Dark, still & cold.

Planted 50 tulips, which I bought of Dan: Wheeler, in the
border opposite to the great parlor-windows. They are, I think,
good flowers.

Tuesday 12.
29 8/10½; 40; N.
Dark, sun, pleasant,
wet.

Men are busy in sowing wheat.
Grapes improve, & are tollerable.

Wednesday 13.
30 2/10½, 3/10; 41;
NW, W.
White frost, sun, sweet
day, red even:

Paths dry.
Insects swarm under sunny hedges.

Thursday 14.
30 2/10; 36½; W,
SW.
Hard frost, sun, sweet
day, grey.

Vast dew. Paths all mire from the frost, & thaw.
Flocks of great field-fares.
Lord Howe arrived at Portsmouth with 16 men of war. He was
absent just nine weeks.

Friday 15.
29 8/10; 47; W, SW.
Grey & mild, blowing,
wet.

The torrent down the stoney-lane as you go towards Rood has run
all the spring, summer & autumn, joining Well-head stream at
the bridge.

If a frost happens, even when the ground is considerably dry, as
soon as a thaw takes place the paths, & fields are all in a batter.
Country people say that the frost draws moisture. But the true
philosophy is, that the steam & vapours, continually ascending
from the earth, are bound-in by the frost, & not suffered to escape,
'till released by the thaw. No wonder then that the surface is all in a
flood, since the quantity of moisture by evaporation that arises

daily from every acre of ground is astonishing. Dr Watson, by experiment, found it to be from 1600 to 1900 Gallons in 12 hours, according to the degree of heat in the earth, & the quantity of rain newly fallen. – See Watson's *Chem: essays*: Vol: 3: p: 55; 56.

Saturday 16.
29 7/10; 41, 46; SW, NW.
Grey & mild, gales, flying showers, grey.

Paths dry: pleasant gleams.

Sunday 17.
29 7/10½; 41; NW.
Grey, sun, pleasant, grey & mild.

Monday 18.
29 6/10; 39½; NW.
Dark, still & moist.

No hogs have annoyed us this year in my outlet. They usually force in after the acorns, nuts, beech & maple-mast; & occasion much trouble.

Tuesday 19.
29 6/10¼; 41; W, SW.
Grey & mild, still, wet fog.

Began to dress & tack the vines. After so bad a summer their wood is crude & ill-ripened, & will hardly produce a good crop next year. One way or other we have used most of the grapes.

Wednesday 20.
29 7/10; 41; N, NE.
Grey & still, dry air, bright.
Full moon.

Thursday 21.
29 7/10¼; 36½; N.
Hard frost, sun, cloudless, red even: frost.

Vast white frost, which lay all day in the shade.

The conjunction of Jupiter & Saturn is over: & the former, which lately was just below the latter, is now to the E. of him, in a line parallel with the horizon. These planets are so near the sun at setting as to be visible but a small time: & are so low as not to be seen at all at Selborne, because of the hill.

Friday 22.
29 4/10; 32; NW, E.
Hard frost, sun, fog & rime, thaw, light clouds, frost.

Vast white frost.
Blackbirds steal the grapes off the vines.

Saturday 23.
29 2/10; 35; E.
Frost, grey & thaw,
frost.

*"Praehabebat porro vocibus humanis, instrumentisque
harmonicis, musicam illam Avium: non quod aliâ quoque non
delectaretur; sed quod ex musicâ humanâ relinqueretur in animo
continens quaedam, attentionemque & somnum conturbans
agitatio; dum ascensus, excensus, tenores, ac mutationes illae
sonorum, & consonantiarum euntque redeuntque per phantasiam;
cum nihil tale relinqui possit ex modulationibus Avium, quae,
quod non sunt perinde a nobis imitabiles, non possunt perinde
internam facultatem commovere."¶*

De vitâ Peireskii per Gassendum.

This curious quotation strikes me much, by so well representing
my own case: & by describing what I have so often felt, but never
could so well express. When I hear fine music, I am haunted with
passages therefrom night & day, & especially at first waking,
which by their importunity give me more uneasiness than pleasure.
In particular this autumn my Nieces M: & E: Barker played many
elegant lessons in a very masterly manner from Niccolai & others,
which still teize my imagination, & recurr irresistably to my
memory at seasons: & even when I am desirous of thinking of
other matters.

Sunday 24.
29 1/10; 35; NE.
Frost, sun, grey & still,
hazy, frost.

Roads get dry.

Monday 25.
29 3/10½; 35; NE.
Sleet, snow, snow,
snow.

Snow covers the ground.

Tuesday 26.
29 7/10; 35; NW.
Frost, sun, hazy sun,
frost.

The woods, & hedges are beautifully fringed with snow.
Ordered Thomas carefully to beat-off the snow that lodges on the
South side of the laurels & laurustines. Snow covers the ground.
Snow melts on the roofs against the sun.

Wednesday 27.
29 6/10; 33; E, SE.
Fierce frost, rime,
hazy, grey, snow.

Rime hangs all day on the hanger.
The hares, pressed by hunger, haunt the gardens & devour the
pinks, cabbages, parsley &c.
Cats catch the red-breasts.

Timothy the tortoise sleeps in the fruit-border under the wall,
covered with a hen-coop, in which is a good armfull of straw. Here
he will lie warm, secure, & dry. His back is partly covered with
mould.

Thursday 28.
29 4/10¾; 36; SE.
Thaw, thaw, thaw.

Dark & moist: snow melts apace.

Friday 29.
29 3/10¾; 39; W; 52.
Small frost, sun &
clouds, gale, bright &
mild.

Rain in the night: snow all gone.
One of the keepers of Wolmer-forest sent me a peregrine falcon
which he shot this day on the verge of the forest, as it was
devouring a wood-pigeon it had just taken. See over leaf.

The *Falco Peregrinus*, or Haggard Falcon, mentioned in the last
page but one, is a noble species of Hawk, seldom seen in the
southern counties. In winter 1766 one was killed in the
neighbouring parish of Faringdon, & sent by me to Mr Pennant in
N: Wales. Since that time I have met with none 'till now.

The specimen before me is in fine preservation, not being at all
injured in the shooting. It measures 42 inches & upwards from
wing to wing, & 21 from bill to tail: & weighs 2 pounds & an half
standing weight.

This species is very robust, & wonderfully formed for rapine: it's
breast is plump, & muscular; its thighs long, & thick, & brawny;
it's legs remarkably short, & well-set: the feet are armed with most
formidable sharp talons. The eye-lids, & *Cere* of the bill are yellow;
but the *Irides* of the eyes are dusky: the bill is thick, & hooked, &
of a dark colour, & has a jagged process near the end of the upper
mandible on each side. It's tail is short in proportion to it's bulk:
but the wings tho' long, when closed, fall short of the train. From
it's large & fair proportions it may be supposed to be a female.
Probably it was driven from the mountains of N: Wales, or
Scotland, where it is know[n] to breed, by the late deep snows, &
rigorous weather.

The plumage answers well to *Brit: zoology* 4to vol: 1: p: 156.

For a bird of prey, this was in high case: it's intestines very fat.
In it's craw were many barley-corns, which probably came from
the crop of the wood-pigeon on which it was feeding when shot.
Voracious birds, when devouring their quarry, swallow feathers, &
bones, & all parts indiscriminately.

Saturday 30.
29 3/10½; 39; NW.
Dark & mild, shower,
dark, wet.

Thomas has finished the vines, & finds the new wood,
circumstances considered, better than could be expected.
Phalaelae fly under the hedges.

DECEMBER 1782

Sunday 1.
29 6/10; 39; N.
Sun, pleasant, red even:
frost.

Monday 2.
29 6/10; 36; E.
Frost, rime & fog,
dark, fog & rime.

Tuesday 3.
29 7/10½; 36; E.   Beautiful rime on the hedges, & hanger.
Frost, rime, sun, thaw,
bright, frost.

Wednesday 4.
29 7/10; 35; NE.   Farmer Lassam's lambs begin to fall.
Frost, dark, thaw,
dark.

Thursday 5.
29 5/10; 36½; E, SE.
Frost, dark & still,
mild & dark.

Friday 6.
29 4/10¾; 37; SE, S,   Nights lately very dark.
SE. Dark, still, mild
& moist.

Saturday 7.
29 5/10; 39; SE.   Perfect thaw, & the paths very dirty.
Dark & mild, gleam of
sun, dark.

Sunday 8.
29 7/10; 37; E.   Ground loose, & dirty.
Dark & still, fog.

Monday 9.
29 5/10; 36, 36; SE.   Rime on the hill.
Dark & moist, deep fog.

Tuesday 10.
29 4/10; 36½; E, N.
Fog, dark & moist,
deep fog.

Wednesday 11.
29 6/10½; 36½; N.   Weather like February.

Dark & still, D°

Frost on the hill.

Thursday 12.
29 3/10½; 36, 39; W.
Dark, & still, sun,
moist, rain.

Paths dry. Pleasant & spring-like.

Friday 13.
29 4/10; 37; SW.
Frost, sun, thaw, wet &
mild, rain, rain.

Saturday 14.
29 3/10; 37; W; 44.
Frost, sun & wind,
bright.

Sunday 15.
29 4/10; 37½; W.
Frost, sun & showers,
frost.

Hare
Coomb Wood
20 May.

Monday 16.
29 4/10; 37; NW.
Frost, thaw, rain.

A hare frequents the garden, & eats the celeri-tops, the spinage,
young cabbages, pinks, scabious's, &c.

Tuesday 17.
29 6/10; 43, 46; W;
47.
Dark & wet, mild &
wet.

Wednesday 18.
29 8/10; 47, 48; SW.
Dark, blowing, & wet.

Vast condensations on walls, & wainscots.
Vast halo round the moon.

The rain on the tower, since Nov.̣ 3.ͬ ͩ – 142: on the ground, in my
garden, – 197.

Thursday 19.
30 1/10¼, 2/10½; 43;
SW
Wh: frost. Sun. Gale.
Mild, & still
Full moon.

Friday 20.
30 2/10; 42; W.
Mild with brisk gale,
grey & mild.

Paths dry.

Saturday 21.
30 1/10; 44; SW.
Grey, brisk air, sunny
& pleasant.

Paths dry.

Sunday 22.
30 1/10½; 42; NW.
Sun, sweet, cloudless
day, grey.

Flesh-flies come forth in rooms.

Monday 23.
29 8/10½; 40; W.
Grey, brisk air, dark,
bright & cold.

Tuesday 24.
29 7/10½; 43; W.
Grey & dry, D⁹ cold
wind.

Paths dry & pleasant.
Beetles flie.

Wednesday 25.
30; 45, 47; NW.
Dark & mild, scud,
dark & mild.

Rooks frequent their nest-trees.
The boys at Faringdon play in the churchyard in their shirts.
They did so this day twelvemonth.

Thursday 26.
30 2/10; 45½; NW.
Dark, still & mild.

Crocus's shoot.
Feb:- like weather. The Plestor, & street dry & clean.

Friday 27.
30 ½/10; 44; NW.
Dark, still & mild.

Large flock of Wood-pigeons in the N: field.

Saturday 28.
29 9/10; 41; NW.
Dark, still, & mild.

Paths dry like spring.
Boys play at Marbles on the Plestor.

Sunday 29.¶
29 8/10¼; 43½, 45;
W. Dark, mild & still.

Some gleams of sun.
The ground quite dry.

Monday 30.
29 8/10; 43, 43; NW.
Dark, mild, & still,
dark & moist.

Sweet weather.

Tuesday 31.
29 9/10; 42; NW.
Frost, sun, pleasant.

Rain in Decʳ 0 in: 91.

The quantity of rain¶ that fell at this place in the year 1782 was –
50 inc: 26 hund.
The greater part was caught in the first 9 months: Octʳ Novʳ &
Decʳ being comparatively very dry.
    The very wet months were, Jan: – 4 inch: 64. March – 6: 54!
April 4: 57. May – 6: 34. July – 7: 9! Aug: – 8: 28! Sept: – 3:
72.

in 1782		1782		1782	
Rain at Lyndon		Rain at Selborne		Rain at South Lambeth	
Jan:	2:333	Jan:	4:64	Jan:	223
Feb:	0.636	Feb:	1.98	Feb:	56
Mar:	1.923	Mar:	6:54	Mar:	249
April	6:125	April	4:57	April	214
May	5:722	May	6:34	May	410
June	1.295	June	1:75	June	49
July	2:697	July	7: 9	July	688
Aug:	3:114	Aug:	8:28	Aug:	
Sept:	5:151	Sep:	3:72	Sep: }	780
Oct:	1:502	Oct:	1:93	Oct:	
Nov:	1:074	Nov:	2:51	Nov:	124
Dec:	0:517	Dec:	0:91	Dec:	72
	32:089		50:26		28:65

Baromʳ in 1782 at S: Lambeth
Lowest April 1 . . 28 5/10
Highest Nov: 13 . . 30 13/20
            or 6 ½
Therm: lowest
        Feb: 12 . . 23
Highest June 18 . . 81.

JANUARY   — 1783 —

Wednesday 1.
30; 34; NW.
Hard frost, bright &
cold.

SELBORNE

Thursday 2.
29 9/10; 28; N.

Vast hoar frost.

Severe frost, bright & sharp.

Frost comes within doors.

Friday 3.
29 6/10½; 35; SE, S.
Dark, snow, sleet, thaw.

Saturday 4.
29 5/10; 48; S.
Dark & wet, rain, swift thaw.

The dew on windows is on the inside.
Vast condensations on walls, & wainscot.

Sunday 5.
29 4/10; 48, 49; S.
Dark & moist, gleam of sun, fog & rain.

Vast condensations on looking-glasses, walls, &c.

Monday 6.
29 5/10; 49½; SW; 62.
Rain, grey, & mild, mild.

Tuesday 7.
29 5/10½; 47½; W, NW, W.
Grey, sun & soft.

Heavy rock-like clouds.

Wednesday 8.
29 2/10; 45, 49; SW.
Wind, dark & moist, blowing with driving rain.

Walls sweat again.

Thursday 9.
29 2/10½; 46; SW.
Blowing, bright, wind.

Blowing all night.
Walls dry.
Strong gales.

Friday 10.
Sunny & mild, wet.

ALTON

Saturday 11.
29 4/10; 48; SW.
Sunny & soft, moist.

SELBORNE

Sunday 12.
28 8/10½; 49½; S.
Rain, wet & blowing,
rain, blowing.

Winter-aconites blow.
Linnets flock.

Monday 13.
29 ½/10; 44; SW, W;
55. Sun, & brisk gale,
bright, still & mild.

N: *Aurora.*

Tuesday 14.
28 8/10¾; 42; SW.
Grey, rain, strong
gales, thunder.

Wednesday 15.
28 7/10; 45; SW; 40.
Showers & wind,
showers.

Hail-storm in the night.

Thursday 16.
29; 41½; NW.
Sun, grey, still & mild,
moonshine.

Friday 17.
29 3/10; 39; N, NW.
Frost, sun & clouds,
frost.
Full moon.

Saturday 18.
29 ½/10; 36; W, NW.
Snow, snow, bright,
frost.

Sunday 19.
29 2/10; 32; NW.
Hard frost, sun,
bright.

Snow on the ground.
Vast halo round the moon.

Monday 20.
29 3/10½; 29; NE.
Fierce frost, sun, still
& frosty, snow.

Frost comes within door[s].

Tuesday 21.
29; 44; NE, S, W, N.
Dark & hazy, thaw,
rain, fog.

Snow in the night. Snow pretty deep.
Made a stout seedling cucumber-bed.

Wednesday 22.
28 9/10; 36; SW.
Frost, sunny & still.

Snow covers the ground.
Heavy banks in the horizon.

Thursday 23.
29 2/10½; 34; SW.
Fierce frost, sun &
sharp wind, bright,
hard frost.

Snow on the ground.

Friday 24.
29 2/10; 36; S, SW;
62. Rain, rain, swift
thaw, bright.

Snow on the ground.

Saturday 25.
29 ½/10; 42; S; 18.
Rain, blowing, stormy
with much rain.

Snow gone.
The wryneck pipes.

Sunday 26.
29 3/10; 44; SW; 20.
Small frost, sun, mild
& pleasant.

Monday 27.
28 6/10½; 45; SW;
105.
Much rain, & wind,
windy, windy.

Rain & wind all night.

Tuesday 28.
29 2/10; 44; W; 19.
Strong gale, dark &
still.

Blowing all night.
Hepatica's, & snow-drops blow. Crocus's swell.¶ Hyacinths
sprout.

Wednesday 29.
29 3/10; 44; W.
Sun, shower, sun,
shower.

Brisk gale all day.

Thursday 30.
29 2/10; 44; SE, S; 62.   Lambs fall apace.
Dark, wet, & blowing.   Ground full of water.

Friday 31.
29 5/10; 48½; SW.
Grey, shower, sun,   Rain that fell in Jan: − 4 inch 43.
shower, bright.

FEBRUARY 1783

Saturday 1.
29 7/10; 47½; S.
Wh: frost, grey, sun,
dark & mild.

Sunday 2.
29 7/10; 49; SW.
Wet, & blowing, wet,
& wind.

Monday 3.
29 6/10; 49; SW.   Condensations on walls, &c.
Driving rain, deep
fog.

Tuesday 4.
29 4/10; 49; SW.   Potted several cucumber-plants.
Driving rain.

Wednesday 5.
29 2/10; 49, 51; SW;
80.
Rain, rain, dark &
blowing.

Thursday 6.
29 4/10½; 47½; SW.   Halo round the moon.
Sun, sun & gale.

Friday 7.
28 8/10; 45; SW; 75.   Much rain in the night.
Rain, rain, wind, sun,   Flood at Gracious street.
stormy.

Saturday 8.
28 4/10½; 42½; SW; 72.
Rain, rain, rain, dark.

Sunday 9.
28 2/10¾; 46½; SW;
85. Sun, dark &
blowing, shower, dark.

Vast rain in the night, with some thunder, & hail.
Peter Wells's well runs over.

Monday 10.
29; 46½; SW; 29.
Showers, showers, sun,
& wind, bright.

Sheep rot very much.
Ewes & lambs
are much distressed
by the continual wet.

Tuesday 11.
29 3/10½; 44; S, SE.
Sun, sun & clouds,
dark & blowing.

Thunder.

Wednesday 12.
29 3/10; 46; S, W; 42.
Sun, showers, sun, bright.

Thursday 13.
29 1/10; 45; S.
Dark, rain, rain, rain.

Dorton.
7 February.

Friday 14.
29 6/10¼; 46½; SE, E,
NE; 85. Showers,
showers with hail, showers.

A perfect & lovely
rain-bow.¶

Rain that fell from Jan: 24: to Feb: 14: inclusive – 5 inc: 22.

Saturday 15.
30; 44; N. Dark &
cold, grey, cold wind.

Drank tea at Newton by day-light.
Sheep on the down look deplorably!

Sunday 16.
30 2/10½; 42; NE, N.
Bright, & cold, bright,
grey.

Monday 17.
30 2/10; 41; NE.
Grey, sun, grey, &
cold. Full moon.

Partridges are paired.
Footpaths in many places very clean.

Tuesday 18.
29 9/10½; 41½; N.
Grey, sun, sweet
weather, sun & clouds,
deep fog.

Cleaned-up the borders in the garden.
Sowed radishes & a few carrots under the fruit-wall. Some
Crocus's blow.

Wednesday 19.
29 8/10½; 38; W,
NW. Frost, rime, sun
& cold air.

Men busy in plowing for pease
Timothy the tortoise awakes.
Peter Wells's well runs over.

Thursday 20.
29 8/10; 38½; W, W.
Wh: frost, sun, dark &
cold.

Men sow pease in their fields, & horse-beans.

Friday 21.
29 5/10; 45; W, SW.
Dark, wet & blowing.

Ashed the two meadows.

Saturday 22.
29 4/10½; 48½; SW.
Dark & moist, & wet,
blowing.

Walls sweat.

Sunday 23.
29 2/10½; 50; SW.
Driving rain, windy.

P: Wells's well runs over.

Monday 24.
29 6/10¼; 41½; W,
NW.
Stormy with hail,
blowing, sleet, bright
& chilly!

Tuesday 25.
29 5/10; 39; S, W,
NW; 24.
Sleet, snow, sun, frost.

Snow melted.

Wednesday 26.
29 9/10; 31½; NW.
Fierce frost, sun, sharp
frost.

Venus begins to appear above the hanger.

Thursday 27.
29 5/10¾; 34½; SW.
Hard frost, wind, &
thaw, rain, stars.

Friday 28.
29 9/10; 41; SE, E, N.   Rain in Feb: – 5 in: 4 hund:
Rain, rain, rain.

MARCH 1783

Saturday 1.
29 ½/10; 44; N; 67
Shower, dark & harsh.   Peter Wells's well ceases to run over. It is only 36 feet in depth, &
continues almost full all the winter in wet seasons. A lavant from
the hanger fills it. The wells in this part of the street are 63 feet
deep.

Sunday 2.
29 1/10; 36, 38; SW.   Large flock of fieldfares.
Hard frost, sun, sun &
clouds.

Monday 3.
28 5/10, 6/10; 38, 38;   Deep snow on the ground.
SE, E, NE.
Snow, snow, heavy
snow, snow, snow.

Tuesday 4.
29 4/10½; 36½; N.   Snow on the ground, 4 or 5 inc: deep.
Frost, icicles, bright,   Snow melts on sunny roofs.
sun, cloudless, frost.

Wednesday 5.
28 7/10; 33; SE.   Vast rock-like clouds over the hanger.
Frost, clouds, snow,   Snow 7 inches deep: no drifting.
vast snow, gentle rain.   Swift thaw.

Thursday 6.
28! 28 3/10; 43; W; 25.   Flood at Gracious street.
Stormy, swift thaw, sun   All the fields full of water.
& clouds.   Snow much gone.
        Worms come forth on the grass-walks.

        The barometer strangely low!
            A slight shock of an earth-quake at this time at Paris.

Friday 7.
28 7/10; 41; W; 132.
Strong gales with
showers.

Snow gone except on the hills.
The air smells spring-like.

Saturday 8.
29 1/10¼; 40; W.
Wh: frost, sun,
showers, hail.

Made the bearing-cucumber-bed for four lights.
The crocus's make a gaudy appearance, & bees gather on y.ᵐ The
air is soft. Violets blow.
Snow lies under hedges. Men plow.

Sunday 9.
29 4/10; 45½; W.
Sun, sun & clouds,
showers about.

Some snow under hedges.

Mercury was visible all the first half of March: but partly thro' bad
weather, & partly for want of an horizon I never was able to get a
sight of him.

Monday 10.
29 4/10½; 41; E.
Ice, sun.

ALTON
Vast lavants at Chawton.

Tuesday 11.
29 7/10; 35; NE.
Sun, & clouds.

SOUTH LAMBETH
Mʳ Charles Etty sailed from Spithead for India.
Cellars flooded.

Wednesday 12.
29 6/10; 36; NE.
Grey, & harsh.

Dust begins to fly.

Thursday 13.
29 7/10½; 35; N.
Grey & harsh.

Friday 14.
29 9/10; 36; N.
Harsh, small snow.

Daffodil blows.

Saturday 15.
30 1/10; 34; NE.
Keen, & harsh.

Apricot blows.

Sunday 16.
30 3/10; 31; NE.
Keen, & bright.

Ice.

Monday 17.
30 5/10; 31; E.

Ice.

Bright & sharp.
Full moon.

Nect: & peach blow.
Moon totally eclipsed.

Tuesday 18.
30 3/10; 36; SW.
Bright & still.

Ice.

Wednesday 19.
30 3/10; 39; W.
Bright summer
weather.

Thursday 20.
30 2/10; 42, 47¾; NE.
Dark & mild.

Water sinks in Thomas White's field.¶

Friday 21.
29 8/10; 38; E.
Bright, wh: frost.

Saturday 22.
29 9/10; 39; SE.
Bright, fog, still.

Sunday 23.
29 9/10; 44; W. Dark.

Monday 24.
29 7/10; 42; NW.
Clouds, & sun, harsh.

Tuesday 25.
30; 40; W.
Ice, sharp.

LONDON

Wednesday 26.
29 3/10½; 44; W; 30.
Clouds, rain, wind.

Thursday 27.
29 2/10; 36; N. Mist.

Friday 28.
29 7/10; 35; N; 19.
Ice, snow, sleet.

Saturday 29.
30 3/10; 31.
Thick ice, bright &   Thomas kept the rain at Selborne.
keen.

Sunday 30.   S: LAMBETH
30 2/10½; 42; SW; 10.
Louring, wet, rain.

Monday 31.
30 2/10; 46; SW.   Cellars almost dry by pumping.
Over-cast.   Rain in March – 2 in: 16 h:

APRIL 1783

Tuesday 1.
30 2/10; 58; W   Field almost dry.
Soft, over-cast.

Wednesday 2.
30 4/10; 61; NE.   Timothy, my tortoise, came-out for the first time at Selborne.
Mist, summer weather.   *Aurora bor:*

Thursday 3.
30 5/10; 46; E.   Brimstone butter-fly.
Wh: dew, bright.   Bats.

Friday 4.
30 4/10; 45; E.
Mist, bright.

Saturday 5.
30 5/10; 44; NE.
Mist, bright.

Sunday 6.
30 6/10½; 39; E.   Dusty.
Bright, cold, & harsh.

Monday 7.
30 4/10½; 37; E, S.   Apricots swell.
Cloudless.   Vast dust.

Tuesday 8.
30 2/10½; 40, 60; W.
Cloudless.

Swallow appeared at Liss.

Wednesday 9.
30 2/10; 46, 67; E.
Cloudless, hot.

Red-start at Selborne.

Thursday 10.
72!!!
Cloudless, sultry.

Prodigious heat: clouds of dust.
Therm^r at Selborne only 62!
Nightingale at Bradshot.

Friday 11.
SW, S.
Small rain, good
showers, showers.

NEWTON
Several bank-martins near the great lake on this side of Cobham.
Two swallows at Ripley.
Ground well soaked.

Saturday 12.
29 4/10; 53; NE, N;
51.
Dark & mild, showers.

SELBORNE
Wheat mends. Barley-grounds work well.
My grass-walks begin to be mown.
Grass-lamb, six pence p^r pound: veal 5^d.
Fresh butter 9½^d.

Sunday 13.
29 9/10; 53; N, NW.
Dark, grey & moist,
grey.

Three swallows at Goleigh.
Cucumbers blow.

Monday 14.
29 8/10; 55; W, S.
Sun, sweet day, dark,
fine even:

Sweet gardening weather. The ground works well. Sowed crops,
& flower-seeds.
Peaches & nect: still in bloom.

Tuesday 15.
29 7/10; 54; NW.
Dark, shower, dark.

Transplanted lettuces from under the fruit-wall.

Wednesday 16.
29 9/10; 56; N.
Bright, sweet summer
weather, yellow
evening.

Fine barley-season.
Vast bloom of plums, & cherries.

Thursday 17.
29 9/10½; 60½; SW.
Wh: dew, bright,
summer weather.
Full moon.

Tortoise weighs 6 pd: 11¼ oun: He begins to eat.

Friday 18.
29 9/10; 63; SW, S.
No dew, sun, summer
weather.

A Nightingale sings in my fields.
Young rooks. Swallows at Faringdon.

Saturday 19.
29 6/10; 65; SE, SW.
Bright, sun & gale,
flisky clouds.

One house-martin about the stables.
Sultry out of the wind.
The garden is watered every day.

Sunday 20.
29 6/10½; 55; W.
Sun, brisk gale, &
clouds.

Some whistling-plovers in the meadows towards the forest.
Cool air.

Monday 21.
29 6/10½; 48; NW.
Strong gale, showers,
& hail.

Beeches in the hanger begin to leaf.

Tuesday 22.
NE.
Blowing & harsh, wet
& cold.

READING
Young goslings abound.
No hirundines.

Wednesday 23.
NE.
Wet & cold, sun.

OXFORD
No hirundines.

Thursday 24.
NE; 37.
Cold air, dry & cold.

No hirundines.

Friday 25.
NE.
Sun & clouds, dry air.

No hirundines.

Saturday 26.
E.

ALTON
Several swallows on the road.

Hot sun, & cold air.

Fine clover in Oxfordshire & Berks.
Barley-fields work finely.
Vivid *Aurora*.

Sunday 27.
29 7/10; 60; E.
Bright, brisk air,
cloudless.

SELBORNE
Many swallows.
Strong *Aurora*!!!

Monday 28.
29 7/10; 65; E, SE.
Wh: frost, cloudless,
hot summer weather,
red even.

Three nightingales sing in my outlet.
Cut two brace of good cucumbers.
Sowed kidney-beans, scarlet, & white dwarf.

Tuesday 29.
29 7/10; 66½; NE,
SW, NW.
Large dew, cloudless,
summer, sweet even:

Cut a brace of cucumbers.
Flesh-flies troublesome.
Martins clean-out their old nests.
Asparagus sprout.
N. *Aurora*.

Wednesday 30.
29 8/10¼; 65½; NE,
N.
Wh: frost, sun,
summer, blue mist,
flisky clouds, dark.

Gardens want rain. We water every day.
Peaches & Nectarines set. Apple-trees begin to bloom.
Cucumbers come.

Rain in April 0 in: 88 h:

MAY 1783

Thursday 1.
29 8/10¼; 65;
NE, N.
No dew, sun, brisk,
harsh gale.

Peat is brought in from the forest.
Cut some asparagus.

Friday 2.
29 6/10½; 54; N.
Dark & cold, gleams of
sun, dark & cold.

Rain wanted.

Saturday 3.
29 7/10; 50; NE, 10.
Severe wind, cold

Honey-suckles against walls begin to blow.
Early tulips blown-out: late begin to turn colour.

showers, severe wind.   No hirundines appear in this cold wind.

Sunday 4.
29 6/10½; 46; NE.   <u>Two swifts.</u>
Frost, ice, strong cold   Swallows & h: martins.
wind, cloudless, still,
red even:

Monday 5.
29 5/10½; 48; NE,   Ivy-berries ripen, & fall.
NW.   Two swifts.
Frost, thick ice,
cloudless, hot sun,
sweet even:

Tuesday 6.
29 6/10; 53; N.   Much Peat brought up from the forest.
Frost, sun & clouds,   Swifts not seen.
sharp air.   Some ponds, & ditches dry, & cleansed out.

Wednesday 7.
29 7/10½; 49; N; 27.   Snow covers the ground.
Snow, snow, hail, sun, Nightingales sing.
bright & sharp.   Cucumbers abound.

Thursday 8.
29 7/10½; 45; N.   Apple-trees in high bloom; in danger from the frost.
Hard frost, sun, & cold Swift.
air, bright & chill.

Friday 9.
29 4/10½; 46; N, SW.   Sowed more kidney-beans, scarlet, & white dwarfs.
Frost, sun & brisk air,
dark, hollow wind.

Saturday 10.
29 3/10, 5/10; 52; SW, Cucumbers abound.
W; 38. Rain, rain, sun, Three swifts.
fine even: Apple-bloom does not seem injured by the frosts.

Sunday 11.
29 3/10½; 53, 59; SW, Growing weather.
SE.   Apple-bloom stands.
Large dew, sun &   Fern-owl chatters.
clouds, fine even:

Monday 12.
29 6/10; 54; SW, S;
10.
Shower, sun & clouds,
sweet afternoon.

Cucumbers abound.
Growing weather.

Tuesday 13.
29 6/10; 56; SW.
Sun, sweet day, bark
clouds, lovely summer
even:

Tulips blow, & open.
Several swifts, 5 or 6 pairs.
Honey-suckles, stocks, & wall-flowers smell sweetly. Tulips
blow out; but their cups will be much larger.

Wednesday 14.
29 6/10½; 60; SW, W.
Sun, spitting rain, sun,
heavy clouds with gale.

Sowed a crop of kidney beans, large white Dutch. Planted some
basons in the field with China-asters, & China-pinks. Pricked out
many China-asters on a mild hot-bed.

The large Apricot-tree much infested with maggots, which twist &
roll-up the leaves: these we open, & destroy the maggots, which
would devour most of the foliage. These maggots are the produce
of small spotted *phalaenae*.

Thursday 15.
29 7/10; 57; SW, W.
Sun, hot & bright, dark
with gale.

Much watering necessary.
Rain much wanted.
Few asparagus for want of rain.

Friday 16.
29 6/10¾; 60½, 66½;
SW, S.
Sun, no dew, sultry,
sweet even., red
horizon, dew.
Full moon.

Watered much.

Saturday 17.
29 6/10¾; 62½, 65;
W, NW.
Grey, some dew, gleam
of sun, sweet even:

Wells sink. Benham's is dry.
Sprinkled & washed the foliage of the fruit-trees, that were
honey-dewed, & began to be affected with Aphides.
Stocks blow finely.
Tulips, thro' heat, will continue but a small time in bloom.

Sunday 18.
29 6/10; 57; N; 25.
Dark, rain, dark &
blowing.

Hawthorns blow.

Monday 19.
29 6/10¾; 52½; N;
56.
Rain, rain, dark &
cutting wind.

Strong wind.

Tuesday 20.
29 6/10¾; 52½; NE,
N; 14.
Sun, strong gale, red
even:

Peonies blow. Young red-breasts.
The wind injures the foliage.

Wednesday 21.
29 6/10½; 61; NE.
Sun, cloudless, strong
gale, red even:

Planted-out white cucumber-plants under the hand-glasses.

Thursday 22.
29 4/10, 3/10; 57½;
65; N, NW.
White dew, sun, hot,
cloudy, & blowing.

Tulips begin to fade.
Standard honey-suckles blow.
Some heads of Saint-foin begin to bloom.

Friday 23.
29 4/10; 54; N; 14.
Small rain, & strong
wind, heavy gale.

Stocks blow, & are very double & handsome!
Fly-catcher appears: the latest bird of passage.

Saturday 24.
29 6/10; 49¾; N.
Dark, cold, & blowing.

Horse-chestnuts, & other large-leaved trees much damaged by
the winds.
Honey-suckles in beautiful bloom!
In this harsh weather few Hirundines appear.
Kidney-beans come-up well. Planted-out some annuals.

Sunday 25.
29 5/10; 48; NE, E.
Grey & sharp, gleams
of sun, bright & sharp.

The late-sown barley does not come up.

Monday 26.
29 3/10; 48; N.
Severe frost, thick ice,
sun & sharp wind,
yellow even:

The frost cut-down all the early kidney-beans, injured the
annuals; & made the apple-trees cast much of their fruit.

Tuesday 27.
29 3/10½; 52; N, NW.
Cold, small rain.

Not one spring-chaffer this year.
No hirundines appear.

Wednesday 28.
29 4/10; 54, 50; N, NW; 23.
Rain, soft rain, rain, rain all night.

Orange, & fiery lilies blow. Sowed some more large white kidney-beans.
Hirundines do not appear.

Thursday 29.
29 4/10½; 48; NW; 67.
Rain, rain, pleasant even:

The late frost has cut the tops of the laurel-hedge.
No hirundines. Young redstarts. They appear again in the evening.

Friday 30.
29 6/10¼; 52; W, SW.
Sun & clouds, grey & cool, gleams of sun, sweet even:

The potatoe-shoots are injured by the frost.
Planted more white kidney-beans.
Goose-berries, & currans are coddled on the trees by the frost.

Gooseberries.
Hollow lane to Alton.
3 June.

Saturday 31.
29 6/10½; 62; NW, SW.
Sun & white clouds, sweet summer day.

Planted the basons in the fields with annuals.
Continue to put out annuals. Began to tack the vine-shoots: there will be a tollerable bloom. The potatoes in the meadow seem to be all killed.
Aphides prevail on many fruit-trees.
Medlar-tree blows.
The sun at setting shines up my great walk.

Rain in May – 2 inc: 84 hund:

JUNE 1783

Sunday 1.
29 6/10; 55; E, NE.
Large dew, sun, brisk
air, bright & cool.

The late frost cut-down the fern, & scorched many trees.
Wheat spindles for ear.

Male Fern.
Selborne Hanger
Late April.

Monday 2.
29 5/10; NE.
Dark, & harsh.

Continued to put-out annuals.

Dr Derham says, that all cold summers are wet summers: & the
reason he gives is, that rain is the effect not the cause of cold. But
with all due deference to that great Philosopher, I think, he should
rather have said, that most cold summers
are wet. For it is certain that sometimes cold summers are dry; as
for example, this very summer hitherto: & in 1765 the summer
the weather was very dry, & very cool. See *Physicotheol*: p: 22.

Tuesday 3.
29 5/10; 58, 68; NE,
S, SW, W, NW.
Fog, hot sun, summer,
vast clouds, thunder,
shower, golden even:

Turned mould for future hot-beds.
Showers about. Great rain at Farnham, Froil, &c. Clouds in the
horizon. Rain at London.

Wednesday 4.
29 5/10¾; 68; NE, S,
SW. Fog, vast dew,
sun, & vast clouds.
Sweet afternoon. Heavy
clouds in the horizon.

Continue to tack vines.
Distant thunder.
Cut the tall hedge down Baker's hill.

Thursday 5.
29 7/10; 66; S, SW.
Dark, shower, showers
about, sun, fine even:

Hops are very lousy, & want a good shower.
Washed the cherry-trees against the wall with a white-wash
brush: they are full of aphides, but have a vast crop of fruit.

Friday 6.
29 8/10; 60; SW, W.

Prickled out some celeri. Elder-trees blow.

Fog, sun & clouds, brisk gale, red even:

Watered much: the garden is very dry.
Great honey-dews.

Columbines.
The Wakes.
20 June.

Saturday 7.
29 8/10; 61; SW, N, NW.
Grey, sun & clouds, dark & warm.

Washed the cherry-trees: some of the fruit turns red. Tulips are faded. Honey-suckles still in beauty. Peaches, nect: & apricots swell.
My columbines are very beautiful: tyed some of the stems with pieces of worsted, to mark them for seed.
Planted-out pots of green Cucumbers.

Vast honey-dews¶ this week. The reason of these seems to be, that in hot days the effluvia of flowers are drawn-up by a brisk evaporation; & then in the night fall down with the dews, with which they are entangled. This clammy substance is very grateful to bees, who gather it with great assiduity; but is injurious to the trees on which it happens to fall by stopping the pores of the leaves. The greatest quantity falls in still, close weather; because winds disperse it, & copious dews dilute it, & prevent it's ill effects. It falls mostly in hazey, warm weather.

Sunday 8.
29 8/10; 60½, 65; N, S, SW.
Grey, hot gleams, sweet even:

S^t foin is very short.
The potatoes, killed-down by the frost, shoot again.

Monday 9.
29 7/10½; 60; NW, N.
Grey, sun, sun & clouds, warm even:

Hops are very lousy!
Rain much wanted.
Nightingale sings.

Tuesday 10.
29 6/10; 59; NW, S, SW.
White dew, sun &

Some fields of pease look finely.
Roses begin to blow.
Wych-elm sheds it's seeds, which are innumerable.

clouds, heavy clouds,
cool air, dark.

House-martins begin to hatch: they throw their egg-shells out of
their nests.

Wednesday 11.
29 1/10½; 60; SW,
NW; 65.
Rain, wind, rain, rain.

Honey-suckles still beautiful.
Soft rain all day.
Snails come forth in troops.
Mʳ Beeke came from Oxford.

Thursday 12.
29 3/10; 57; SW.
Sun, sun & clouds,
dark horizon.

The fields much refreshed by the rain.
Ophrys nidus avis, many in bloom on the hanger, along the side of
yᵉ Bostal.

Friday 13.
29 2/10¾; 60; S; 32.
Rain, rain, rain.

Serapias latifolia begins to blossom in the hanger. The Serapias's
transplanted last summer from the hanger to my garden grow, &
thrive.
Continue to plant out annuals.

Saturday 14.
29 2/10; 61; S; 48.
Rain, showers,
thunder, dark clouds to
the NW, yellow even:
Full moon.

Continue to plant-out annuals.
Distant heavy showers.
Cherries are eatable. The ground is well-soaked. The showers
have washed the hops, & trees infested with aphides.
Some bunches of grapes begin to blow.
Mʳ Beeke returned.

Sunday 15.
29; 62; SE, E; SW.
Rain, dark & warm,
rain, rain.

Some ears of wheat begin to peep.

Monday 16.
28 9/10; 59; S, SW;
51. Rain, rain, brisk
gale, rain.

Continue to plant-out annuals. Annuals do not thrive.

Tuesday 17.
29 1/10; 57; S, SW;
69.
Rain, rain, rain, cold &
blowing.

The potatoe-shoots, that were cut-down by the frost, all spring
again; the kidney-beans do not.
Lighted a fire in the parlor.

Wednesday 18.
29 3/10; 56; SW, SW.

Continue to plant out annuals.

Shower, strong gales, showers, chilly.

Thursday 19.
29 3/10; 57; SW.
Shower, cool & blowing, shower.

Friday 20.
3/10, 29 4/10; 58; NW, W; 17.
Dark, thunder, shower, moist & still.

Saturday 21.
29 8/10; 59; NE.
Dark, still & warm.

Sunday 22.
29 9/10¼; 59½; NW, SW.
Mild, still & grey.

Monday 23.
29 9/10; 60; S.
Vast honey-dew, hot & hazy, misty.

Tuesday 24.
29 8/10¼; 60, 69; SW, W. Vast dew, sun, sultry, misty & hot.

Wednesday 25.
29 8/10; 65; NE, NW, NW.
Small dew, dark & still, gale, misty & hot.

Thursday 26.
29 8/10; 65½, 69½; N, NW.
Great honey-dew, blue mist, rusty gleams,

*Flowers in the Wakes garden –
Convolvulus minor and Venus Looking Glass.
Late June.*

Vast crops of cherlock among the spring-corn.

Growing weather.

Growing weather.
The late ten dripping days have done infinite service to the grass, & spring-corn.

Cornflags, fraxinella, martagons, pinks, & dark-leaved orange-lilies begin to blow. Bees swarm. Cherries look finely, but are not yet highly ripened.

The blades of wheat in several fields are turned yellow, & look as if scorched with the frost. Wheat comes into ear.
Red even: thro' the haze. Sheep are shorn.

Began to mow my meadow-grass.
This is the weather that men think injurious to hops. The sun, "shorn of his beams" appears thro' the haze like the full moon.

Turned the swarths, but did not ted the hay.
Much honey-dew on the honey-suckles, laurels, great oak.

Tedded the hay, & put it in small cock.
Sun looks all day like the moon, & sheds a rusty red light.
Mʳ & Mʳˢ Brown, & niece Anne Barker came from the county of Rutland.

sultry, still & dark, sun
red at setting.

Friday 27.
29 8/10; 66½; NW.
Fog all night, dusky,
red rusty gleams!!

Hay makes pretty fast. Wheat blossoms.
Nose-flies, & stouts make the horses very troublesome.

Saturday 28.
29 8/10; 65, 71½; W.
Fog, grey, & sultry,
brisk gale, sweet even:

Large dew.
Ricked the hay of the great meadow in lovely order: six jobbs.
The little meadow is hardly made.

The country people look with a kind of superstitious awe at the red
louring aspect of the sun thro' the fog . . . *"cum caput obscura
nitidum ferrugine texit."*¶

Sunday 29.
29 9/10; 66; NW.
Fog, sun, sultry, hot
gleams, sweet even.,
fog.

Wheat blows finely.
Oestrus curvi-cauda follows horses, & lay it's nits on the
flanks, &c.

My garden is in high beauty, glowing with a variety of solstitial
flowers.

Monday 30.
29 9/10; 70¼, 72½;
NE.
Dark & louring, sultry,
sweet even.

Finished ricking my hay in most delicate order.
The portugal-laurel is in bloom, & makes a fine shew.

A person lately found a young cuckow in a small nest¶ built in a
beechen shrub at the upper end of the bostal. By watching in a
morning, he soon saw the young bird fed by a pair of hedge-
sparrows. The cuckow is but half-fledge; yet the nest will hardly
contain him: for his wings hang out, & his tail & body are much
compressed, & straightened. When looked at he opens a very red,
wide mouth, & heaves himself up: using contorsions with his neck
by way of menace, & picking at a person's finger, if he advances it
towards him.
    Rain in June was . . . 2 inc: 82.

JULY 1783

Tuesday 1.
29 8/10; 68, 76; NE,
NE.
Vast dew, sun & gale,
sultry, sultry, red
sunshine.

Turned out my cucumbers, housing the glasses, & frames.
Thatched the hay-rick.
Many trees shed their leaves.
Mr & Mrs Brown, & Niece Anne Barker left me.

Wednesday 2.
29 8/10; 69; E, S.
Sultry, mist & warm.

BRAMSHOT PLACE
Wood-strawberries abound, but are not ripe.
The foliage on most trees this year is bad.
Vast damage this day by lightening in many counties!!

July 1: & 2. Tremendous thunderstorms in Oxfordshire, &
Cambridge-shire!
Great thunder-shower at Lymington & in the New forest, & in
Wilts, & Dorset, & at Birmingham, & Edinburg.

Thursday 3.
71; SW.
Misty, hot gleams, hot
& gloomy.

Mr Richardson's garden abounds with fruit, which ripens a
fortnight before mine. His kitchen crops are good, tho' the soil is
so light & sandy. Sandy soil much better for garden-crops than
chalky.

Friday 4.
30; 71, 69; NW, N.
Gale & hot sun, fine
afternoon, misty.

SELBORNE
Much hay delicately made.
Young martins peep out of their nests.

The leaves of the wild cherries are turned red; my oaks are covered
with honey-dews. Few trees carry a good foliage this year: many
beeches, ashes & oaks were scorched by the frost in May.
Much upland hay ricked. Wheat looks well.

Saturday 5.
29 8/10½; 64; W, W.
Cloudless, brisk gale,
brisk gale.

Leaves fall much from many trees & hedges.
Tim: Turner bought, & carryed off my Saint-foin, the 16th crop.
It was over-ripe, & not so large a burden as the last. The S^t foin
was all run to seed.
The garden wants rain.
Stopped the shoots of the vines, which are almost out of bloom.
There will be fruit.
Water the garden daily.
Cucumbers set, green & white.
Kidney-beans begin to run up their sticks.
Lime-trees blow. Annuals grow a little, but are stunted.

Sunday 6.
29 7/10½; 67; W.
Dark & louring, with
gale, louring, gale,
broken clouds, gale.

Young martins come forth.
Some young martins came out of the nest over the garden-door.
This nest was built in 1777, & has been used ever since.

As the summer has been dry, & we have drawn much water for
the garden, I caused my well to be plumbed, & found we have yet
13 feet of water. When we were measuring I was desirous of trying
the depth of Benham's well, which becomes dry every summer; &
was surprised to find it 25 feet shallower than my own: the former
being only 38 feet deep, & the latter 63.

Monday 7.
29 8/10; 66; NW, S,
E. No dew, grey, sun,
hot summer, sweet
even: broken clouds.

Jasmine just begins to blow.
Watered much. Ground very dry.
The young cuckow sits out upon the nest, which will no longer contain him.

Tuesday 8.
29 7/10; 67; S, S, E,
NE.
No dew, sun, strong
gale, cloudless, blue
mist, red even:

Watered much. Rasps begin to ripen.
Watered the fruit-trees against the walls, & sheltered their stems from the fierce sun with boards, &c.
Young swallows come out of their nests.
The cuckow is flown.

Wednesday 9.
29 4/10½; 66, 75¼,
74; E, S.
Sun, little dew,
cloudless, brisk gale,
blue mist, thundrous
clouds, sultry.

Second crop of cucumbers come in apace.
Grass walks burn. Garden very dry.
Grapes swell.

Bees have thriven well this summer, being assisted by the honey-dews, which have abounded this year.

Thursday 10.
29 5/10; 71, 79¾! 78;
NE, E.
Dark, still, & sultry,
drops, blue mist, sun,
sultry, some great
drops.

White cucumbers swell. Kidney-beans run their sticks, but want rain. Watered much.
Thunder & lightening all round.

About 8 o'clock in the evening on the 10th A great tempest arose in the S:W. which steered off to the N:W: an other great storm went to the N:E: with continued thunder, & lightening. about 10 an other still heavier tempest arose to the S:E: & divided, some part going for Bramshot & Headley, & Farnham: & the rest for Alresford, Basingstoke, &c. The lightening towards Farnham was prodigious. It sunk all away before midnight. Vast showers around us, but none here.

Friday 11.
29 7/10; 74! 80! W,
NW, N.
Sun, sultry! sun, sun,
dark & sultry, much
lightening.

The heat overcomes the grass-mowers, & makes them sick.
Cut two long white cucumbers. By watering cucumbers abound.
There was not rain enough in this village to lay the dust.

Some of the standard-honey-suckles, which a month ago were so sweet & lovely, are now loathsome objects, being covered with aphides, & viscous honey-dews.
    Gardens sadly burnt.

Saturday 12.
29 7/10; 74! 78; E.
No dew, sun, & haze,

The water in my well rises!¶ tho' we draw so much daily!
Watered much.

rusty sunshine! hazy.

White lilies, scabious's, nasturtions, poppies, china holly-hocks blow.

The tempest on friday night did much damage at West-meon, & burnt down three houses & a barn. The tempests round on thursday, & friday nights were very aweful! There was vast hail on friday night in several places.

Sunday 13.

29 5/10½; 72, 78; NE. No dew, sun, & haze, brisk gale, red sunshine, dark & more cool.

Five great white sea-gulls flew over the village toward the forest.

Monday 14.

29 5/10; 69½, 72; E, N.
Dark & misty, cooler air, red sunshine, haze, sun sets red. Full moon.

When the owl comes-out of an evening, the swifts pursue her, but not with any vehemence.

Tuesday 15.

29 4/10; 68, 74; E, E. Great dew, sun & haze, with brisk gale, deep haze.

The drought is now so great that those hops that looked tollerably seem to be all going.
Some wheat begins to turn.

No rain since June 20th at this place; tho' vast showers have fallen round us, & near us.

Wednesday 16.

29 7/10; 68, 69; W, SW, S; 58. Still showers, grey, sun, haze, thick haze, damp.

A fine refreshing rain.
Large white kidney-beans begin to blow.
Rasps, currans, large American straw-berries abound.

Thursday 17.

29 9/10; 68½, 70; SW, SW.
Thick haze, rusty sun, thick haze, damp.

Some cherries left behind the net.
The jasmine, now covered with bloom, is very beautiful. The jasmine is so sweet, that I am obliged to quit my chamber.
Artichokes abound.
Larkspurs blow.
Trimmed, & dressed the vines for the last time by taking-off the side-shoots: the grapes are large, & forward.

Friday 18.

29 7/10½; 66, 73; S, W.

Trenched-out two rows of celeri: the ground is hard as iron.
Some backward meadows are now mowing: but the hay in general

Haze, rusty sun, yellow
sun set, sprinkling.

is delicately made.
Hot, ripening afternoon!
Some few solstitial chafers on the common.
Apricots begin to ripen.

Saturday 19.
29 6/10½; 69, 73;
SW, W. Sun, sultry,
sun & clouds, dark, &
warm, no haze.

Wheat turns colour very fast.

Men talk that some fields of wheat are blighted: in general the crop
looks well. Barley looks finely, & oats & pease are very well: Hops
grow worse, & worse.

Sunday 20.
29 4/10; 69, 75½; S,
W.
Haze, & sultry, rain &
thunder.

Hot, ripening weather. Apricots ripen, & fall.
Ferruginous fox-glove blows.
The thunder rose in the S: & parting off went round us in two
divisions, one to the N:W, & one to the E.

Monday 21.
29 4/10½; 68; W; 62.
Showers, sun, shower,
grey, cool, haze.

Scarlet martagons blow.
The garden is much refreshed by the showers.
Lapwings flock.
Lark-spurs figure.

Tuesday 22.
29 3/10¾; 65; SW, S.
Showers, sun, &
pleasant, dark & moist.

Goose-berries, & currans load the trees.
Many oaks abound with acorns.
China pinks blow.
Few swifts appear.

Wednesday 23.
29 6/10¼; 65; NW,
W; 25. Showers,
sun & showers,
bright & chill.

Dwarf kidney-beans are gathered: most of the plants were killed
by the frost.
Cucumbers abound.
Turnips (field) thrive, & are hoeing.

Thursday 24.
29 8/10; 63½; SW, W.
Dark, scud, dark &
mild, yellow sun-set.

Planted-out some endive.
Few swifts.
Few swifts.

Friday 25.
29 8/10½; 65½; W,
NW.
No dew, sun, dark &
moist, dark, still &
warm.

Trenched two more rows of celeri in the upper end of the plot by
W: Dewey's: the ground mellow.
Six or eight swifts.
We plant out the cabbage-kind some few at a time.
The boys bring me a large wasp's nest full of maggots.

Saturday 26.

29 6/10; 73; S, SE.
No dew, sun, sultry,
clear, sweet even:, no
haze.

Pease (field) are hacking.
Some wasps appear.
Four or five swifts.
Wheat turns. Some wheat reaped at Faringdon.
Boys bring two more wasps nests.

Sunday 27.

29 3/10¼; 73, 77½;
S, W.
Good dew, sun,
cloudless, gale, sweet
even: red.

Cob-webs on the grass, ripening weather.
Wheat turns very fast.
Fine gale.
Many swifts now.
No haze.

My china-holly-hocks, after standing a year or two, lose all their
fine variegated appearance, & turn to good common sorts, being
double, & deeply coloured.

Monday 28.

29 4/10½; 70½; 79;
SW.
Great dew, sun, sultry,
rocky clouds, clouds,
gales.

Wasps swarm so, that we were obliged to gather in all the
cherries under the net.
Several swifts.
Apricots all ripen together.
Distant thunder.
Wheat harvest begins in many places.

Tuesday 29.

29 5/10; 70, 72; S, W.
Deep fog, sun, hot,
dark with cool gale,
sprinkling.

Many blackbirds from the woods invade the garden.
Preserved a good quantity of currans, & some rasps, cherries, &
apricots.

Young swallows & house-martins begin to congregate, both in the
air & on roofs.

Wednesday 30.

29 7/10¼; 65, 69; W,
S.
Dew, sun & brisk gale,
cool gale.

Few hazel-nuts.
Men house field-pease.
Ponds are dry. Grass walks burn. Ripening weather.
This morning Will Tanner shot, off the tall meris-trees in the
great mead, 17 young black-birds.¶ The cherries of these trees
amuse the birds, & save the garden fruit.

Thursday 31.

29 8/10; 66, 72; W,
NW.
No dew, dark with
gales, sun & clouds, red
even.

The aftergrass in the great meadow burns.
Few swifts.
The sheep-down burns, & is rusty. Much water in the pond on
the hill!
Sweet harvest weather.

Rain in July was —— 1 inch 45 h.

AUGUST 1783

Friday 1.
29 8/10; 66½, 78; SE, E.
Great dew, cloudless, sultry, sweet even, red, gale.

Many swifts.
No haze.
Martins cluster on the tower.
Ripening weather.
Vast shooting star from E: to N.
My nephew Sam: Barker came from Rutland thro' London by the coaches.

Much smut in some fields of wheat.¶ Barley cut about the forest-side.
     We shot in all about 30 black-birds.

Saturday 2.
29 5/10; 71! 79¾; E, SW. Dew, cloudless, sultry, clouds, cloudless, red even:

Burning sun. Workmen complain of the heat.
Gardens burn.
Goody Hampton left the garden to go gleaning.

Sunday 3.
29 4/10; 71½, 69; NW, S.
Deep fog, small shower, dark & moist.

Thistle-down flies.
"Wide o'er the thistly lawn, as swells the breeze,"
"A whitening shower of vegetable down"
"Amusive floats. The kind impartial care"
"Of Nature nought disdains; thoughtful to feed"
"Her lowest sons, & clothe the coming year,"
"From field to field the feather'd seeds she wings."
                  Thomson's *Summer*.
     My white pippins come in for kitchen uses. The aphides, of various species, that make many trees & plants appear loathsome, have served their generation & are gone no more to be seen this year: perhaps are all dead.
     Wheat harvest general.

Monday 4.
3/10, 5/10; 67, 65; SW; 11. Shower, sun & clouds, scud.

Swallows, & martins repair their nests for a second brood. Swifts retire about the time that the other hirundines begin to prepare for a second brood. One swift.

Tuesday 5.
29 5/10½; 64; NE.
Grey, sun, dark & still, soft, misting shower.

Four swifts.
The grapes are very forward. Some of the leaves of the vines begin to turn purple.
Wasps devour the goose-berries, & currans. Rasps are over.
Young swifts still in one nest.
Wheat seems very good. Hops are quite gone. They have some weak side-shoots without any rudiments of bloom.

Wednesday 6.
29 5/10; 63½; SE, S.
Grey & mild, sun, dark
& soft.

Sweet harvest weather.
No swifts seen.
Much wheat bound.
Wasps encrease.
Mᴿ Barker came from Rutland¶ thro' Oxford on horse-back.

Our fields & gardens are wonderfully dryed-up: yet after all this
long drought Well-head sends forth a strong stream. The stream at
the lower end of the village has long been dry.

Thursday 7.
29 6/10; 64¼; W.
Broken clouds, flying
showers, sun, fine even:

Sarah Dewey¶ came to assist in the family.
Much wheat housed.
No swifts seen. White currans gone.

Friday 8.
29 6/10; 63½; SW.
Grey, clouds,
sprinklings, shower,
dark & mild.

Wasps lie very hard on the goose-berries.
No swifts appear.
Two swifts.

Saturday 9.
29 7/10; 63; SW, SW.
Clouds, & gale, sun,
sprinkling, clouds,
dark & mild.

Two swifts.
Flies come in a door, & swarm in the windows, especially that
species called *Conops calcitrans*.
Nep: John White came by the coach from London.

Sunday 10.
29 5/10½; 65; SW,
NW; 24.
Driving rain, dark with
gale, dark & warm.

Two swifts.
Wheat-harvest half over.

Creeping thistle
Nore Hill
August.

Monday 11.
29 5/10; 61½; NW;
12.
Showers, showers, sun,
chilly.

Vast rock-like
clouds.
Wheat housed.

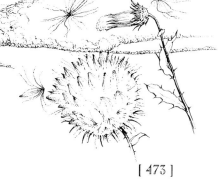

Tuesday 12.
29 7/10; 57; 62; N, N.
White frost, sun &
clouds, heavy clouds,
cool air. Full moon.

6 or 7 swifts.
Some showers about.

Wednesday 13.
29 8/10; 58; N, NW.
White frost, sun &
clouds, sun, fine even:,
haze.

One swift.
Much wheat housed.
Farmer Spencer of Grange finished wheat-harvest.
Mr Pink of Faringdon finished D^o

Thursday 14.
29 8/10¼; 56, 61; N,
NW. Fine dew, sun,
sweet day, chilly air,
red even.

Much wheat housed.
One swift.
Mr Yalden finished wheat-harvest. Farmer Bridger of Black-
more finished harvest of all sorts.

Friday 15.
29 9/10; 58½, 63; N,
NW.
Sun, sun, grey & mild.

Took this morning by bird-lime on the tips of hazel-twigs several
hundred wasps that were devouring the goose-berries. A little
attention this way makes vast riddance, & havock among these
plundering Invaders.

Saturday 16.
29 9/10; 63, 71½; N,
NW.
Sun, hot sun, sweet
even:

Farmer Knight of Norton finishes wheat-harvest.
Farmer Lassam of Priory D^o Farmer Hewet of Temple
finished D^o

Sunday 17.
29 8/10; 63, 71; NW,
S.
Sun, hot sun, sweet
even.

Hot ripening weather.
Goose-berries fail.
The boys brought me three large wasps-nests.
Young swallows & martins cluster on the tower.

Monday 18.
29 8/10; 65½; SW,
W.
Dew, sun, hot sun, hot,
grey & mild, haze.

The *Colchicum*, or autumnal crocus, blows.
Oats housed. Wheat-harvest seems to be over.
Caught many wasps with bird-lime.

4 swifts at Guildford. 1 swift at Meroe.
    On the evening of this day, at about a quarter after nine o' the
clock, a luminous meteor of extraordinary bulk, & shape was seen
traversing the sky from NW: to SE. It was observed at Edinburg,
& several other E^m parts of this Island. No accounts of it, that I
have seen, have been published from any of the western counties.
It was also taken notice of at Ostend.
    This meteor, I find since, was seen at Coventry, & Chester.

Tuesday 19.
29 7/10; 65, 71½; N,
S, W.

Few wasps: they seem to be much thinned.
Much spring-corn housed.

Great dew, sun, sultry, sweet even.

Distant thunder: some large drops.

1 swift at Dorking.

Wednesday 20.
29 6/10½; 64½, 73; NE, S. Vast dew, sun, hot sun, fine even:

Peaches & nectarines turn colour: plums turn. Rock-like clouds.

Thursday 21.
29 6/10½; 66, 70; NE, S, W; 23. Deep fog, dark & warm, thunder, soft showers.

Caught about 30 wasps: they are reduced very low. Vast shower in the Holt.

Friday 22.
29 6/10; 66; SW. Grey & warm, gleams of sun, dark, moist & warm.

Caught about 100 wasps in the fallen codlins, which were gnawn & scooped hollow.
Some bunches of grapes are turned almost black!

Saturday 23.
29 5/10; 64; SW, W. Grey, ruffling gale, sun & clouds, shower, cool air.

China-asters begin to blow.
Caught several wasps.
Orleans plums abound.

Sunday 24.
29 4/10; 60; SW. Dark, showers, showers about, showers, rainbow.

Paid for four wasps-nests.

On this day the *Duke of Kingston* India man, outward bound, Captin Nutt, was burnt at sea off the island of Ceylon. Mr Charles Etty,¶ one of the mates, was wonderfully saved, tho' he could not swim an inch, by clinging to a yard-arm that had been flung over board; by which he was kept above water for about an hour & ¼, 'till he was taken up by a boat, & carryed, naked as he was, aboard the *Vansittart* India-man Captain Agnew, who treated him with great humanity, & landed him in a few days at Madras.*

* This ship, cargoe, & more than 70 lives were lost by the carelessness of a mate in drawing rum, who permitted the candle to catch the spirits; so that the whole vessel was in flames at once, without any chance of extinguishing them. She burnt about four hours, & then blew up: so that nothing was saved except what cloaths some had on their backs. She had soldiers aboard, & some passengers, & a few women, & children.

Monday 25.

29 4/10; 59; SW; 41, 20.

Showers, heavy showers, thunder, & vast clouds, clear & cool.

Muscae domesticae swarm in the kitchen.
When the sun breaks-out, the roofs, & grass-walks reek.
Men cut their field beans.

Potatoes very fine, tho' the ground has scarce ever been moistened since they were planted. They were also very good last year, tho' the summer was mostly wet & cold.
  Nectarines ripen.

Tuesday 26.

29 5/10; 56, 64; SW.

Vast dew, chill, hot sun, thunder, vast clouds about.

Some fly-catchers haunt about the church, take the flies off the sides of the tower with much adroitness. Swallows do the same in the decline of the summer.
Showers about.

The boys broke up the arch of a bricked grave to get at a wasp's nest. Paid for 1 wasp's nest.
  Fern-owl glances, & darts about in my garden, in pursuit of *phalaenae*, with inconceivable swiftness.
  Great thunder-storm at London.

Wednesday 27.

29 5/10½; 59, 63; SW, S.

Great dew, sun, sweet day, cool.

Sowed a plot of spinage with 3 ounces of seed: the ground still too dry, & wanted much pressing down with the garden-roller.
Planted two rows more of celeri, six in all.
Peaches ripen.

Thursday 28.

29 4/10; 59½; S.

Fog, shower, sun & clouds, dark, rain, rain.

Caught several wasps.
Barley housing.

Friday 29.

29 5/10; 63; S, SW; 52.

Dark, shower, sun & clouds, clouds.

Sowed a crop of lettuce to stand the winter, brown Dutch.
Hops are picking under Hartley-hanger.

Saturday 30.

29 6/10; 63; SW; 17.

Fog, rain, dark & mild.

Ophris spiralis blows, ladies-traces.
Mushrooms begin to come. Last summer there were no good edible mushrooms, but only a coarse, white sort.
Planted-out in a bed a great number of Seedling-polyanths: seed f^m Bramshot-place.
P^d for 1 wasps's nest.

Sunday 31.

29 6/10; 61, 65; NE,

Mushrooms abound.

SE; 24.
Heavy shower, grey,
thunder, hazy & hot,
thunder, rain.

Red sun-shine.
Tremendous thunder-storm in London.

The stream which rises in James Knight's upper pond has failed all
this summer, as it does all very dry summers; so that the channel is
dry down to the middle of the short Lithe; from whence there is
always water running 'till it joins the Well-head stream at little
Dorton. This spring, which is at the bottom of the Church-litten-
closes, seems to rise out of the hill on which the Church is built.
Rain in Aug^st . . . 2 in: 24 hund.

SEPTEMBER 1783

Monday 1.
29 7/10; 63; NE, SE;
16.
Haze, hot, grey & soft.

Red sun-shine.
Sowed a bed of Coss-lettuce.
Timothy begins to frequent the border under the fruit-wall for
the sake of warmth.

Tuesday 2.
29 6/10; 61½; SE,
SW. Deep fog, grey,
dark & mild.

Red sun-shine.
Peaches not fine.
Wasps gnaw the grapes.

Wednesday 3.
29 3/10½; 61; SW,
SW.
Vast dew, sun, rain,
rain, rain.

Red sun-shine.
Asters begin to blow.
Nectarines, one of the new trees, the fruit delicate.
Two of the new peach, & Nect: trees this year are distempered,
& one barren: one nect: has a crop of small, but well-flavoured
fruit.

Thursday 4.
29 1/10¾; 57; W;
108.
Sun, showers, thunder,
sun, showers, sun, red
even: chilly.

Much rain in the night. The rain, & wind have injured the
flowers in the garden.
Gathered some bunches of grapes: they were eatable, but not
delicate.
Tremella nostoc¶ appears on the walks. Tho' the weather may have
been ever so dry & burning, yet after two or three wet days this
strange jelly-like substance abounds.

Friday 5.
28 9/10½, 29 3/10½,
56½; W; 83.
Rain, wind & clouds,
sun & clouds, rain.

Much rain in the night.
Plums are over. The crop of Orleans plums was very great.
Ponds fill. Flood at Headley-mill.
Planted 50 curled endive-plants, which we had from Daniel
Wheeler. The heat of the summer prevented our last sowings
from growing.

Saturday 6.
29 2/10; 58; W; 40.
Rain, & wind,
blowing, strong gales.

Garden-flowers much injured.
The wind has blown down most of the Cadillac pears.
Nep: John White left us, & went to London.
Sun-dew blows.

Sunday 7.
29 7/10; 55; W.
Blowing, blowing,
chill.

Ground dries very fast.
Strong gale all day.
Fly-catchers.
Mr Barker left us, & went to Fyfield.

Monday 8.
29 5/10½; 58¾; SW.
Cold & blowing, harsh,
& chill.

Ponds are filled. Leaves fall.
Men house beans, & oats.
Hirundines skulk about to avoid the cold wind.
Mr Sam: Barker left us, & went to Fyfield.

Tuesday 9.
29 1/10½; 58; SW.
Blowing, & wet, sun &
strong gales.

Mr Etty's well is still foul.
Began to light fires in the parlor.
Brother Thomas, & Molly White came.

Wednesday 10.
29 5/10; 54½; SW;
21.
Strong gales, showers,
gales, bright, & chill.

Gathered-in the white pippins, a great crop.
Cleansed-out the zigzag.
Tho: Holt White, & Henry Holt White came.
Bessy White, Sam White, & Ben Woods came from Fyfield.
Total eclipse of the moon.

Thursday 11.
29 3/10; 54½; SW, S.
Sun, vast clouds, soft &
pleasant.

Sam White, & Ben Woods returned to Fyfield.
Fly-catcher.
Harvest-moon.

Selborne hopping lasts only two days in Farmer Spencer's, &
Master Hales gardens: many gardens afford no pickings at all. M^r
Hale will have only about 200 weight. The great garden at
Hartley, late Sr Sim: Stuart's consisting of 20 acres, produced only
about 2 tons.

Friday 12.
29 3/10; 60; SW.
Grey & mild, sun,
pleasant.

Tyed-up endives: they are backward this year, & not well grown.
One sowing never came up.
The Virginian creeper is grown up to the eaves; but will probably
shoot no further as the leaves at bottom begin to turn red.

Saturday 13.
29 5/10¼; 56½; SW.
Sun, grey, showers,
dark & moist.

Began to mend the dirty parts of the bostal with chalk.
The barley about Salisbury lies in a sad wet condition.

Sunday 14.
29 5/10½; 62½; SW.
Driving rain, dark &
blowing, driving rain.

Mr Yalden's tank is full.

Brought down by Brother Thomas White from South Lambeth, &
planted in my borders: – Dog's toothed violets – Persian Iris –
Quercus cerris – Double *ulmaria*¶ – Double *filipendula* – Double
blue *campanula* – large pansies – double daisies – *Hemerocallis* –
white fox-glove – Iron-fox-glove – double wall-flower – double
scarlet *lychnis.*

Monday 15.
29 5/10; 60½; SW.
Grey, soft rain, grey &
mild.

Tuesday 16.
29 6/10; 58; NE, N;
91. Rain, rain, rain.

Rain in three days, 91.

Wednesday 17.
29 8/10; 56; N.
Grey, still & pleasant.

Fly-catchers in the garden.

Planted from Mr Etty's garden a root of the *Arum dracunculus*, or
Dragons: a species rarely to be seen; but has been in the vicarage
garden ever since the time of my Grandfather, who dyed in spring
1728.

Thursday 18.
29 5/10; 59, 62; N, E.
Grey, mild, fog, rain,
rain.

Earthed up the two forward rows of celeri.
Young swallows, & martins come forth.

Friday 19.
29 1/10½; 59, 62; S,
W; 24.
Sun, rain, rain, warm.

Ivy begins to blow on Nore hill, & is frequented by wasps.
Pd for a wasps nest, full of young.

Saturday 20.
29 2/10; 60½; W, S;
43.
Rain, sun, pleasant,
showers.

Pheasants on the commons.
Grapes are now good.
Mr & Mrs Richardson came.¶

Fungi on the hanger are *Clavaria* several sorts: *Boleti,* several.

Sunday 21.
29 3/10¾; 57; SW, S.
Sun, pleasant, mild,
rain & wind.

Green wheat up in the N: field.
Stormy wind all night, which has blown-down most of my
apples, & pears.

Monday 22.
29 3/10; 58; S, SW; 100,
22. Rain, rain, heavy
showers, sun, bright.

Thunder: rather the guns at Portsmouth.
Splendid rain-bow.
Mr & Mrs Richardson left us.

After three weeks wet, this vivid rain-bow preceded (as I have often known before) a lovely fit of weather.

Tuesday 23.
29 4/10; 56½; 60; SW, S; 5. Shower, sun, mild, sweet day.

Black snails lie out, & copulate.
Vast swagging clouds.

Wednesday 24.
29 7/10½; 52½; W, S. White frost, sun, sweet day.

Gossamer.
Some great clouds.

Thursday 25.
29 9/10½; 53½; S. Vast white dew, sun, sweet day, cool.

Many hirundines.
Some few wasps.

My wall-nut tree near the stable, which is usually barren, produces this year 5, or 600 nuts: the sort is very fine. The vast tree at the bottom of the garden bears every year, but the nuts are bad.

Friday 26.
29 9/10; 51½; NE. White dew, sun, sweet day.

Partial fogs.
Few hirundines.
Mich: daisies blow finely.

Saturday 27.
29 9/10; 59, 65½; NE. Wet fog, sun, hot, sweet day.

Few hirundines.
Endive comes in.
Grapes are good.
Thermom.ʳ in the shade abroad 70!
Charles White, & Harry Woods came from Fyfield.

Sunday 28.
29 8/10¼; 61, 67; NE. Dark, sun, sweet summer weather.

Very few hirundines.
Thermʳ abroad in the shade 70!

Monday 29.
29 8/10; 59; NE. Vast dew, sun, cloudless, sweet summer, red even:

Few hirundines.
Thermom.ʳ abroad in the shade, 69.
Gathered in the apples, knobbed russets, & non-pariels. Royal russets none. All the Baking-pears were blown down. No dearlings.

Tuesday 30.
29 8/10¼; 57½; 65½;
NE, SE.
Vast dew, sun, lovely
weather, red even:

One swallow. No martin.
True Michaelmass summer.

Endive now finely blanched.
Rain in Septemʳ – 5 inch: 59 hund.

OCTOBER 1783

Wednesday 1.
29 7/10½; 57½; NE,
S, NW.
Deep fog, sun, sweet
day, some clouds.

No hirundines observed.
Thermomʳ abroad 69.
The leaves of the Virginian creeper, turn red & fall.
Timothy, the tortoise, spends his whole time on the border under
the fruit-wall.

Thursday 2.
29 7/10; 57; N, NE.
Vast dew, sun, sweet
day, still & warm.

Gossamer. No hirundines.
Some thunder-like clouds.
Erected an alcove¶ on the middle of the bostal.
Charles Henry White, & his sister Bessey returned to Fyfield.

Friday 3.
29 7/10; 60; SW; S.
Vast dew, sun, sweet
day, still fine even.

The hanger is beautifully tinged. Leaves fall apace.
No hirundines. Dug up carrots.
Many flesh-flies: here & there a wasp.
The cat frolicks, & plays with the falling leaves.

Saturday 4.
29 4/10½; 61½; 63½;
SW, S.
Dark, clouds, sun, &
gale, soft & still.

Acorns innumerable. Grapes now finely flavoured.
This day has been at Selborne the honey-market: for a person
from Chert came over with a cart, to whom all the villages round
brought their hives, & sold their contents. This year has proved a
good one to the upland bee-gardens, but not to those near the
forest. Combs were sold last year at about 3¾ᵈ per pᵈ; this year
from 3½ᵈ to 4ᵈ.
No hirundines.
Black snails lie out. Shell-snails have withdrawn for some time.

Women pick up acorns. & sell them for 1ˢ: pʳ bushel. A splendid
meteor seen at half-hour past six in the evening: but not so large as
that on the 18th of August.

Sunday 5.
29 3/10½; 62½; SW;
39. Rain, sun &
clouds, small showers,
moon-shine.

Rain in the night.
No Hirundines.

In the High-wood. under the thick trees. & among the dead leaves.
where there was no grass. we found a large circle of Fungi of the

Agaric kind, which included many beeches within it's ring. Such circles are often seen on turf, but not usually in covert.

We found a species of *Agaric* in the high wood of a very grotesque shape, with the *laminae* turned outward, & the cap within formed into a funnel containing a good quantity of water.

Monday 6.
29 2/10¼; 58; SW,
SE; 10.
Rain, rain, rain.

Saw two house-martins.
Leaves fall.
Much rain in the evening.

Tuesday 7.
29 6/10; 55½; W,
NW; 50.
Grey, sun, sun,
pleasant, dry & chill.

No house-martins.

Wednesday 8.
29 9/10; 47; NW.
White frost, sun,
pleasant, cool air.

Neps: Th: H. & Hen: H: White went to Fyfield. Wood-cock returns.

Thursday 9.
29 8/10; 46½; 51; W,
W.
No dew, cold air,
shower, sun, cold air,
vast clouds.

Grapes now very delicate: the grapes are large this year on the bunches.
Just at the close of day a great many swallows & h: martins, perhaps an hundred, appeared round the church, & Plestor. Many of the swallows were young: the martins are not so easily distinguished.

Friday 10.
29 9/10; 48; SW.
Sun, cool, sun, &
clouds, pleasant, bright
& chill. Full moon.

Red-wings appear. Several swallows.
Sweet moon-shine.
Flies of many sorts swarm on the bloom of Ivy.

Saturday 11.
29 8/10; 48; N, SE, E.
Wh: frost, ice, sun,
pleasant, cloudless.

Some few swallows.
Mr John Mulso came.
Hunter's moon rises after sun set.
Muscae domesticae abound in the kitchen, & enjoy the warmth of the fire: Where they lay their eggs does not appear. The business of propagation continues among them.

Sunday 12.
29 5/10½; 49; E.
Wh: frost, sun,
cloudless, cold wind.

Great fieldfares on the common.
Several swallows at the same time.

Two swallows at Fyfield.

The crop of acorns is so prodigious that the trees look quite white with them; & the poor make, as it were, a second harvest of them, by gathering them at one shilling pʳ bushel. At the same time not one beech-mast is to be seen.

This plenty of acorns has raised store-pigs to an extravagant price.

Monday 13.
29 6/10½; 49, 56; N, SE, S.
Deep fog, sun, sultry, grey, & soft.

Dug up potatoes.
Thunder.
Some wasps on the Ivy-bloom.
Mʳ John Mulso left me.
Bats out.

Tuesday 14.
29 9/10¼; 56, 58; NW, N, NW.
Grey, sun, haze, still.

The potatoes in the meadow small, & the ground very stiff.
Low creeping fogs.

Wednesday 15.
29 9/10; 55; N.
Dark, still & warm.

Grapes delicate.
Planted-out on the border near the wall-nut trees many young polyanths, seed from Bramshot-place.
Nep: Harry Woods left me, & went to Funtington.
Black snails lie out.

Thursday 16.
29 9/10½; 54, 57½; N.
Wet fog, sun, lovely weather! grey, mild & still.

Rover finds pheasants every day, but no partridges.
The air is full of gossamer.
There is fine grass in the meadows. Wheat looks green.

... "see, the fading, many-coloured woods,"
"Shade deepening over shade, the country round"
"Imbrown:" ... Thomson.

Friday 17.
29 9/10; 54; NE.
Dark, still, gleams, grey, & mild.

Mowed, & burnt the dead grass in my fields.
Rooks on the hill attended by a numerous flock of starlings.
The ground is very dry.
Neps T:H: & H: Holt White returned from Fyfield.
The tortoise gets under the laurel-hedge, but does not bury himself.

Saturday 18.
29 8/10½; 53, 56; N, SE.
Wet fog, sun, grey & still.

Planted under the fruit-wall rows of Coss, & brown Dutch lettuce to stand the winter.

... "a crouded umbrage, dusk & dun,"
"Of ev'ry hue, from wan, declining green"

Sunday 19.

29 8/10; 55; S, W.
Dark & moist, grey,
dark & warm.

"To sooty dark" . . . Thomson.

As the tenant at the Priory was lately digging among the foundations of that convent for materials to mend the roads, his labourers discovered two large stones, which the farmer had vertù enough to be pleased with, & ordered them to be got out whole. One of these proves to be a large Doric capital worked in good taste; & the other the base of a pillar; both formed of soft stone. These fragments from their dimensions seem to have belonged to massy pillars, & shew that, probably, the church of this Priory was a grand, & costly edifice. They were found in the space which I have always supposed to contain the South transept of the priory-church. Some fragments of large pilasters were also discovered at the same time.

The diameter of the Column seems to have been 18 inch: & ¾:
The diameter of the capital 2 feet 3 inch: & ½.

Two years ago some labourers, digging among the foundations of the Priory, found a sort of rude vase of soft stone containing about two gallons in measure on the verge of the brook, in a space which from tradition has always been supposed to have contained the kitchen. This vase I was going to procure, but found that the labourers had just broken it in pieces for way-mending.

Monday 20.

29 7/10; 58, 59½; W, S.
Dark & warm, dark & moist, very warm!

The prospects tho' shady, are very distinct.
Celeri comes in: very fine.
The bright yellow in the maples of my hedges is very striking, & picturesque!!

Tuesday 21.

29 5/10; 56; SE.
Dark, & mild, sun, dark & still.

Nasturtiums in high bloom, & untouched by the frost!
Late Asters in full beauty.
Brother Thomas White, & daughter, & sons left us.

Wednesday 22.

29 4/10; 55; S, SW.
Dark & mild, sun, sweet afternoon, dark & heavy clouds, rain.

Leaves fall. Grapes delicate. The beech-woods are beautifully tinged!
Two truflers came with their dogs to hunt our hangers, & beechen woods in search of truffles; several of which they found in the deep, narrow part of the hill between coney-croft-hanger, & the high-wood; & again on each side of the hollow road up the high-wood, known by the name of the coach-road.

Thursday 23.

29 6/10; 55½, 58; W, NW; 9.
Sun, sweet day, red even:

The poor make quite a second harvest by gathering of acorns.
Timothy Turner has purchased upwards of 40 bushels.

Friday 24.

29 3/10; 55; S, SW.
Blowing, wet, rain,
rain, grey & mild.

The roads are dry.
Black snails lie out.

Saturday 25.

29 3/10½; 51; SW;
22.
Vast dew, sun, soft &
mild, clouds, still, &
star light.

Nasturtiums still untouched by the frost.
Leaves fall very fast: some trees in the hanger are naked. My
hedges begin to lose their beautiful tints.
Timothy comes forth.
The firing of the great guns at Portsmouth on this day, the Kings
accession, shook the walls & windows of my house.

Sunday 26.

29 5/10; 46; SW.
White frost, sun,
pleasant, yellow
evening.

Wheat comes up finely.
Grapes still very fine.

If a masterly land-scape painter was to take our hanging woods in
their autumnal colours, persons unacquainted with the country
would object to the strength & deepness of the tints, & would
pronounce, at an exhibition, that they were heightened & shaded
beyond nature.

Wonderful, & lovely to the Imagination are the colourings of our
wood-land scapes at this season of the Year!
"The pale, descending year, yet pleasing still,
"A gentler mood inspires; for now the leaf"
"Incessant rustles from the mournful grove,"
"Oft startling such as studious walk below,"
"And slowly circles thro' the waving air,"
"But should a quicker breeze amid the boughs"
"Sob, o'er the sky the leafy deluge streams;"
"Till choak'd, & matted with the dreary shower,"
"The forest-walks, at every rising gale,"
"Roll wide the wither'd waste, & whistle bleak."

Thomson's *Autumn.*

Monday 27.

29 2/10; 49; S, SW.
Sun, blowing, heavy
shower, dark.

A couple of wood-cocks were shot in the high wood.

Tuesday 28.

29 5/10½; 46; W; 31.
Sun, & wind, pleasant,
& cool, bright.

Planted many slips of pinks.

Wednesday 29.

29 4/10½; 47; W; 10.

Tortoise begins to bury himself in the laurel-hedge.

Grey, & blowing, sun, & showers, cold shower, bright.

Nasturtiums flourish still.
Just at the close of day five or six house-martins came scudding over my fields towards the village!! I have neither seen nor heard of any hirundines since the 12th of this month. Bat was out at the same time.

Thursday 30.
29 7/10; 48; W.
Sun, sun & clouds, pleasant, shower, bright.

Ashes, & wallnut-trees are naked: & beeches begin to lose their leaves very fast.
Grapes delicate.
Vivid rainbow.

Friday 31.
29 5/10½; 48; S.
Vast dew, sun, sun, & clouds, dark & mild.

The stream at Gracious-street still dry.
Many blossoms on the jasmine.

Rain in Octr: – 1 inc: 71 h.

NOVEMBER 1783

Saturday 1.
29 5/10; 50½; SE. Sun, still, sun & clouds, soft & pleasant, moon-shine.

Timothy comes-forth from the laurel-hedge.
Green wheat looks finely. Fine wheat-season.
Most of the wheat-fields sown.

Sunday 2.
29 5/10; 51; E, SW.
Deep fog, sun, soft, sweet weather.

Tortoise gone into his winter-retreat under the laurel-hedge.

Monday 3.
29 4/10; 50½; SE, NE.
Deep fog, sun, sweet afternoon.

FYFIELD
The roads dusty, & the chaises run on the summer tracks, on the downs.
Lovely clouds, & sky!
Turnips on the downs are bad. Wheat looks well.
Men chalk the downs¶ in some parts.

Tuesday 4.
29 4/10⅓; 57; NE.
Sun, hot sun, sweet even.

The stream at Fyfield is dry.

My brother Henry's crops of truffles have failed for two or three years past. He supposes they may have been devoured by large broods of turkies that have ranged much about his home-fields, & little groves.

Wednesday 5.
29 5/10¾; 52; NE.
Grey, & cold, sun,

Lapwings.
Wild greese appear. On the downs, & Salisbury plain they feed

sweet afternoon, &
even., moonshine.

much on the green wheat in the winter, & towards the spring damage it much, so that the farmers set-up figures to scare them away.

Thursday 6.
29 5/10½; NE.
Grey, cold, sun,
pleasant, red even.

Men pen their sheep on the green wheat.

Friday 7.
29 7/10; 48; NE.
Vast dew, sharp gale,
cloudless, sweet
moonshine.

Leaves fall.
A chaced hind ran thro' the parish, & was taken at Penton. She ran but two hours the ground being too hard for her feet. She was carryed home in a cart to Grateley.

Saturday 8.
29 8/10; 32; NE.
Frost, ice, cloudless
with sharp wind, red
even: moon-shine.

My niece of Alton, (Clement) was brought to bed of a girl. This child makes my 40th nephew & niece, all living; Mr Clement, & Mr Brown inclusive.

Sunday 9.
29 7/10½; 42; N. Frost,
ice, grey, & sharp,
red even. Full moon.

Beautiful mackarel sky.

Monday 10.
29 5/10½; 49; N, N.
Misty rain, heavy sky,
still, vast clouds, dark,
& still.

To this time a very dry autumn.
Rooks swarm.

Tuesday 11.
29 2/10½; 45; NW.
Dark & mild, heavy
clouds, grey, red even;
grey.

This country swarms with pigeons from dove-houses.
Millers complain for want of water.

Wednesday 12.
29 ½/10; 42; N.
Sun, small showers.

Rain in the night – 0 inc: 2½ h.

Thursday 13.
28 7/10; N, S, SW.
Rain, rain, rain.

– 2½
Mr Mulso's grapes at his prebendal-house are in paper bags; but

the daws descend from the Cathedral, break open the bags, & eat
the fruit.

Friday 14.
NW; 60.
Showers, sun, vast rain.

WINCHESTER
– 24
Grey crows returned, & appear on the downs.
Looked sharply for house-martins along the chalk-cliff at
Whorwell, but none appeared. On Nov! 3ʳᵈ 1782 I saw several at
that place.

Saturday 15.
29 2/10½; NW; 65.
Sun & brisk gale, sun,
shower.

SELBORNE
Wind all night.
At Selborne a storm about 11 A:M:
Sea-gulls abound on the Alresford-stream: they frequent those
water for many months in the year.

Sunday 16.
29 3/10; 47½, 53; SW.
Grey, sun, clouds,
driving rain, warm,
much rain & wind.

Millers want water.
Dew on the outsides of the windows. Walls sweat.

Monday 17.
29 4/10; 55; SW; 59.
Blowing, & mild.

Thomas gathered-in the grapes in my absence: they are still fine.
He began to dress the vines, which have much well-ripened
wood. Flies come out.

Tuesday 18.
29 4/10; 56, 57; SW; 70.
Blowing, & showers,
showers, soft air.

Walls sweat.

Wednesday 19.
29 4/10; 57; SW; 27.
Blowing, showers,
blowing.

Timothy lies at the foot of the wall-nut tree, under the laurel-
hedge.

Thursday 20.
29 7/10; 50; W; 20.
Showers, sun,
cloudless, pleasant.

Friday 21.
29 5/10½; 45; W.
White frost, sun,
showers.

Winter is established.
"Fled is the blasted verdure of the fields;"
"And, shrunk into their beds, the flowery race"
"Their sunny robes resign. E'en what remain'd"
"Of stronger fruits falls from the naked tree:"
"And woods, fields, gardens, orchards, all around"
"The desolated prospect thrills the soul."
                                        Thomson's *Autumn*

Saturday 22.
29 9/10¼; 44; N.
Frost, grey, sun,
pleasant, grey.

Sunday 23.
29 9/10½; 40¼, 40;
NW.
Frost, grey & still,
pleasant.

The stream in Gracious-street runs, after having been dry for many months.

Monday 24.
29 9/10½; 40; N.
Frost, sun, cloudless,
pleasant, red even:

Foot-paths are dry.
Insects swarm in the air.

Tuesday 25.
30; 39½; NW.
Hard frost, still, sun,
pleasant, clouded sky,
red even:

Paths sloppy.
Insects abound.
Beetles fly.

Wednesday 26.
30; 43; N.
Fog, dark, still & mild.

The vines are all trimmed, dressed, & tacked.
They have much well-ripened wood for next year's crop.
The farmers have long since sown all their wheat, & ploughed-up most of their wheat stubbles.

Thursday 27.
30 ½/10; 45; N.
Dark, mild & still.

Antirrinum cymbalaria still in full bloom, making a beautiful appearance on the walls.
Jasmine blows. Wall-flowers bloom.

Friday 28.
29 9/10; 43; NE, SE.
White frost, sun, dark
& mild.

Paths dry.
The peaches, nectarines, & apricots trimmed & tacked. Well-ripened wood, & show for bloom.

Saturday 29.
29 9/10; 46, 49; S.
Grey, sun, mild & still.

Beetles, & *phalaenae* fly.

Sunday 30.
29 8/10½; 49, 50; SE.
Grey, still & mild

Rain in Novemᵣ 3 inch 2 hund.

DECEMBER 1783

Monday 1.
29 8/10; 50, 51; S, SE.
Shower, wet fog, dark
& mild.

Some ivy-berries near full grown: others, & often on the same twig just out of bloom. Farmer Lasham has more than 20 young lambs: some fallen some days, near a fortnight.

Tuesday 2.
29 7/10; 50; SE, E.
Grey, mild, fog.

Apples rot very fast; & so they did after the hot summer 1781; while those of the cold, wet summer 1782 kept very well.

Wednesday 3.
29 7/10; 49; E.
Deep fog, sun, fine
afternoon.

Thursday 4.
29 5/10; 45; E, SE.
White frost, grey &
mild.

Mowed some of the grass-walks;
Farmer Lasham cuts some of his lambs; they are near a month old.

Friday 5.
29 3/10; 47; SE.
Deep fog, dark, mild,
& moist, rain.

Fetched some mulleins, fox-gloves, & dwarf-laurels from the high-wood, & hanger; & planted them in the garden.

Saturday 6.
29 6/10½; 48, 48½;
SW, W; 14.
Grey, sun, soft &
pleasant.

Sunday 7.
29 7/10; 43; W, N.
Wh: frost, ice, sun,
cloudy.

Monday 8.
29 9/10; 44; N.
Dark, wet, dark &
moist. Full moon.

Ivy berries.
16 January.
Dorton.

Tuesday 9.
29 8/10; 41½; NE.
Dark & still.

Wednesday 10.
29 8/10½; 40½; 38;
E.
Frost, ground frozen,
sun, clouds, bright,
frost.

Thursday 11.
29 9/10½; 38; E.
Frost, dark, thaw,
grey, dark & still.

Planted 4 small spruce-firs, & 2 Lombardy poplars in Baker's
hill; & one spruce-fir in farmer Parsons's garden.

Friday 12.
30; 38½; NE, N:
Deep fog, bright,
frost.

Saturday 13.
30 ¾; 38; NE, NW.
Deep fog, sun, low,
creeping fog.

Sunday 14.
30; 38, 37; NW.
Vast, deep fog,
starlight, frost.

Helleborum foetidum blows.

Monday 15.
29 9/10; 37; NW, W.
Frost, thaw, fog, warm
fog.

Tuesday 16.
29 7/10; 39; W, NW.
Fog, soft rain, dark &
mild.

Laurustines are in bloom, & look beautifully.
The grass-walks, when rolled, make a fine appearance; are very
green.

Wednesday 17.
29 8/10¼; 42; NE; 21.
Fog, wet, wet.

Thursday 18.
29 9/10; 39½; E.
Dark, grey, sun,
bright.

Hares make sad havock in the garden; they have eat-up all the
pinks; & now devour the winter cabbage-plants, the spinage, the
parsley, the celeri, &c. As yet they do not touch the lettuces.

Friday 19.

29 8/10½; 35, 35; NE.
Severe frost, sun, hard
frost.

It froze all day in the shade.

Saturday 20.

29 8/10; 31; NW.
Severe frost, rime, sun,
thaw, dark.

Sunday 21.

29 6/10; 36; SW, NW,
E. Frost, dark, milder,
grey & still.

Monday 22.

29 5/10; 37; SW, NW.
Frost, sleet, sun, thaw.

Tuesday 23.

29 5/10; 38½; NW,
W.
Grey, still, sun,
pleasant, rain, hail.

Antirrhynum cymbalaria still in bloom, & flourishing on the
walls.

Wednesday 24.

29 1/10; 41, 39; W;
11.
Sun, pleasant, cold air.

A fine yellow wagtail¶ appears every day.

Thursday 25.

28 9/10, 8/10; 37; SE,
NW; 64.
Frost, dark! sleet,
snow, rain, bright,
frost.

White, & yellow water-wag-tails.¶

Friday 26.

28 6/10; 35, 34; NW.
Fierce frost, sun, dark,
small snow, dark snow,
sharp.

The ground is cased with Ice.

Saturday 27.

29; 33; NW.

Ground covered with ice.

Fierce frost, sun, dark
& cold.

Mr Churton came from Oxford.

Sunday 28.¶
29 2-½; 32½; NE, N.
Dark, fierce frost, small
flight of snow, dark.

Ground so icy that people get frequent falls.

Monday 29.
29 5/10; 31½; S! S!
Severe frost, sun, frost.

Some snow in the night.
Carryed some savoy head, endive, & celeri into the cellar: the
potatoes have been there some days.

Tuesday 30.
29 4/10; 29, 28, 14½
abroad; E, SE.
Fierce frost, sun, &
sharp wind, hard frost,
bright.

Red breasts die. Wag-tail.
Some sleet in the night.
Ground covered with ice, & snow.

Wednesday 31.
29 1/10; abroad 14,
16½; E.
Fierce frost, dark,
sharp wind.

Ice under people's beds. Water-bottles burst in chambers. Meat
frozen.
Wagtails two sorts appear in the street.
The fierce weather drove the snipes out of the moors of the forest
up the streams towards the spring-heads. Many were shot round
the village.

Rain in Decemr . . . 1 inch 10 hund.

Rutland	Hants	Surrey
Lyndon	Selborne	South Lambeth
Rain in 1783	Rain in 1783	Rain in 1783
Jan: . .1: 805	Jan: . . 443	Jan: . . 151
Feb: . .2: 313	Feb: . . 554	Feb: . . 298
Mar: . .1: 604	Mar: . . 216	Mar: . . 93
Apr: . .0: 558	Apr: . . 88	Apr: . . 59
May . .4: 218	May . . 284	May . . 236
June . .3. 033	June . . 282	June . . 400
July . .2: 663	July . . 145	July . . 78
Aug: . .1: 102	Aug: . . 224	Aug: . . 223
Sept: . .1: 440	Sep: . . 553	Sep: . . 430
Oct: . .0: 658	Oct: . . 171	Oct: . . 72
Nov: . .1: 783	Nov: . . 301	Nov: . . 163
Dec: . .1: 602	Dec: . . 110	Dec: . . 122
22:779	33.71	23:25

N O T E S

In order to avoid repetition the following abbreviations have been used:
GW = Gilbert White
NHS = *The Natural History of Selborne*

1774 Events and journeys

This year begins with Gilbert remarking on fluctuations in the barometer pressure in a letter written in January to his brother John. There was a climax in April when the big landslide which damaged 100 acres of land occurred, and there were great floods reported in south and west England. Jack White, John's son, who had not yet been found an apprenticeship, remained at Selborne and at the end of April Gilbert's niece, Molly White, Thomas's only daughter, was also there.

By mid-July his friend John Mulso had settled back at Meonstoke and Gilbert visited him there in August. He had also promised to journey to Blackburn to see his brother John, but was apparently unable to find anyone to undertake his clerical duties for him. Elections at Oxford also kept him in the south, so he put off the visit. In the event John himself came down to London in November to try to settle Jack as an apprentice, unsuccessfully as it turned out. Gilbert, it appears, greatly enjoyed Jack's company, describing him in a letter to John White as 'of real service to me, and a companion in my solitude'.

In March, Gilbert visited his brothers in London, and at mid-summer was at Fyfield with brother Harry. At one stage, he had thought to accompany his brother John back north, but the journey was again put off.

January	29.	wolf's bane This vernacular name is most usually applied to monk's hood (*Aconitum napellus*), a summer-flowering plant, but here it refers to the winter aconite *Eranthis hyemalis*, one of the first flowers of the year.
February	21.	ews GW originally wrote 'yews' but erased the 'y'; he only rarely corrected his spelling. At times he chose archaisms, at others a more modern spelling, not bothered by writing a word in different ways. However, 'yews' is not an old form of 'ewes', so here it seems likely that he absent-mindedly wrote the homonym and then corrected the mistake.
	26.	The titmouse Vernacular names for the great tit include 'saw sharpener' (Roxb.), 'sharpsaw' (Norfolk) and 'sit-ye-down', and the marsh tit is in some places known as 'saw-whetter'. Exactly what names were used in late 18th-century Hampshire is not clear. The Journal observations here are reiterated in NHS Letter XL of September 1774 to Pennant and commentators note that if the names of the species had been transposed the descriptions would have fitted better. The great tit has a wonderful variety of calls, but the best known is a two-note sawing sound. GW's 'marsh tit' is probably the bird now known as the willow tit which has a ringing, triple-note song. However, the great tit's song often contains a merry grace note, thus giving 'three chearful notes', and the *willow* tit's spring call is double-noted, so it is possible GW was correct. The willow tit was identified separately from the marsh tit only in 1897, the last native British species to achieve recognition.
March	8–25.	Thomas Hoar, GW's manservant, kept weather and temperature notes but not the barometric readings, and occasionally the Journal notes when GW was absent. Six years older than his master, he was remembered in GW's will as 'my old servant Thomas Hoar', and outlived him by four years.
April	2.	The saxon word Playstow Signifies an area for recreation – a gymnasium or wrestling-school, a theatre.
	30.	Probatum est This has been proved.
May	9.	Regulus . . . A splendid description of wood warbler song and behaviour.
	11.	first lettuces . . . brown Dutch This variety of lettuce is now proscribed under EEC legislation on vegetables. They are excellent sweet winter lettuces, 'loafing' (heading up) well.
	24.	found . . . in the long Lythe A plantation which is still in existence today. It can be reached through Church Meadow.
June	9.	swifts mate A very early observation of this extraordinary piece of mating behaviour.
	11.	swifts . . . eggs They occasionally lay three eggs, but two is more usual. Linnaeus quotation 'Hawks make a truce with the other birds for as long as the cuckoo calls.'
	18.	It was made in swarth, and lay eight days When grass was cut for hay, it usually lay

		five or six days 'in swath' – that is, the space covered by a scythe stroke – but in this case it took longer because of the rainy conditions.
	24.	spindling for ear The barley was shooting up into the slender pointed stalks that later would bear the ears of grain.
July	2.	oaks . . . cloathed again . . . with a beautiful foliage This second sprouting is known as the Lammas growth.
	6.	swifts . . . do not . . . appear at all in blowing wet days Swift nestlings seem to sustain a torpid state in bad weather, their metabolism generally slowing down. They can thus manage with little or no food for much longer periods than the young of swallows or martins.
August	23.	'Wide o'er the thistly lawn . . .' From a poem *The Seasons* by James Thomson. Perhaps a pedantic point, but Thomson ends his 'summer' before harvest time, and before most thistles are in flower.
October	3.	autumn burgamot A pear variety of great antiquity, possibly going back to Roman times, but now little grown. The Chaumontel was raised at the place of that name in France in about 1660. It is best when grown on a wall, as GW is very probably doing here.
	9–22.	Between these dates the Journal notes on weather and observations on 11 and 12 October were written by GW's brother Thomas White, but GW has added a few extra observations, apparently later.
November	4.	spotted water-rail The spotted crake. Uncommon in GW's time, it is still rarer nowadays, most probably owing to the drainage of many of its damp haunts during the 18th and 19th centuries. A beautiful and elusive species (*Porzana porzana*), it is now protected under Schedule I of the *Protection of Birds Act*.
	8 & 19.	Both these dates are omitted from the Journal, throwing the weekday names wrong. They were corrected in the week of 6–12, but left uncorrected in the following week.
November to December	21 9.	GW left for London via Alton on 21 November, and the Journal pages are bare for this period apart from footnotes, very likely written in on his return to Selborne.
November	22.	sprats *Clupea sprattus* is a member of the herring family *Clupeidae*, but is not the same species as the herring.
December	9.	Dun-diver and sparlin fowl These are both names for the female goosander which occasionally turns up on inland waters in the south in the winter months and which is so different in plumage from the male that it was thought to be a separate species. (Sparlin = sprat).

1775 Events and journeys

This year Gilbert did not stir from Selborne until March, when he was in Fyfield for ten days to celebrate the christening of Edward, the latest addition to his brother Harry's family. He split his Oxford visit into two, with four days there in April and four in October, and he spent just over a fortnight with his aunt, Mrs Rebecca Snooke, at Ringmer in August. Also in August, Gilbert's nephew Jack, John White's son, was finally settled in an apprenticeship to a surgeon in Manchester, while earlier in the year another nephew who had been seeking a place, Benjamin's son Edmund, was apprenticed to a Fleet Street linen draper, a career he subsequently left in favour of the church.

John Mulso made a visit to Selborne at midsummer.

January	2.	grey and white water-wagtails The taxonomy of wagtails has altered several times since GW's day. Possibly he means one species here (that is, the grey-and-white), which would conform to the present-day wintering habits of the pied wagtail. On August 26 1776 there is an observation of 'broods of wagtails, white and grey' but this reference too is ambiguous. In NHS Letter I to Daines Barrington three species are clearly indicated, white, yellow and grey, with their scientific names. However, both the grey and the white (pied) wagtails overwinter and there is no reason why GW shouldn't have seen both species.
	21.	bramblings In modern times these birds are quite common winter visitors, but they are noted by GW on only a few occasions as 'seen seldom'.
	28.	Chaucer . . . Gossamer There is a folk legend which says that clouds are made of gossamer or cobwebs, as in the nursery rhyme of the old woman who went up on a broomstick 'to sweep the cobwebs out of the sky'.
February	16.	spoon-bill *Platalea leucorodia*. Nowadays this bird is a regular visitor to East Anglian coastal regions.

	23.	Willughby's Ornithol: *The Ornithology*, published in 1678 by Francis Willughby and John Ray. It was an important early book which described and classified British birds, and our first real ornithology.
	25.	Dipterous insects Belonging to the order *Diptera* which includes flies, mosquitos, craneflies and midges and is distinguished by having a single pair of wings and sucking or piercing mouth parts.
March	22.	horse-ants The adjective 'horse' prefixed to a name usually indicates a large size or coarseness. This large ant might be *Formica rufa*.
	27.	creeper A tree creeper, *Certhia familiaris*, known in Somerset as the tree mouse.
April	1.	Greek word 'Snail', literal translation: 'house carrier'
	26.	Greek word As above.
	27.	A pair of house martins House martins may return to the same nests, and those that do, breed earlier than those who have to build anew.
	28.	Parhelia Also known as 'mock sun', a parhelion is a bright spot on the parhelic circle or solar halo, caused by the diffraction of ice crystals in the atmosphere. Two or more parhelia are usually seen at once, especially at sunset.
May	13.	Papilio Atalanta Red admiral butterfly, now *Vanessa atalanta*. Those seen in the early part of the year are migrants; eggs laid in May and June will metamorphose in the autumn and migrate southwards.
	27.	small ponds Such small ponds are discussed in NHS Letter XXIX to Daines Barrington dated 7 February.
July	15.	fern owls . . . striking their wings During courtship and occasionally at other times nightjars have the habit of making a sharp cracking noise as they fly, thought to be made by them clapping their wings.
	22.	Coleopterae *Coleoptera* is an order of insects which includes beetles and weevils where the forewings are modified to form a snail-like protective covering.
		young martin becomes a flyer Sixteen days is an estimate rather on the short side. It is usually more in the region of 26 to 29 days.
		Greek word Prime of life.
September	2.	in the suds An idiomatic phrase meaning in difficulties, in bad condition.
	26–27.	golden-rennet Golden reinette is an ancient variety of apple, a crisp russet eater, known in England since the mid-16th century.
		royal russet This is a culinary russet, grown in England since 1597.
		knobbed russets Probably the kind known also as Winter apple, this is a later season sweet apple, although it was not brought to public notice until 1820.
	30.	Arundo donax Known as the 'giant reed', this is a robust exotic grass similar in appearance to phragmites, with stems 6 to 19 ft high and 11 to 22½-inch panicles.
October	7.	oak in Newton Lane Reference to this occurrence is made in NHS Letter XXIX to Daines Barrington.
	13.	Hops were a drug A figure of speech, meaning that they were no longer in demand and virtually unsaleable.
	26.	Gossamer on every bent Cobwebs on every grass stem. Nowadays the name 'bent' applies solely to *Agrostis* species, but in GW's time it referred to grasses in general, and particularly to the old, dying stalks.
	28.	Locus cultus . . . A place which is cultivated or inhabited.
November	2.	Columba oenas The stock dove. This species has extended its range markedly since the early 19th century. In fact, it is present all the year round, inhabiting farm and parkland. The birds are adaptable in their choice of nest sites, using holes in cliffs or buildings, old nests or even on the ground under bushes or in burrows, but the nests are not easy to find.
	5.	227 species in Gr: Britain Nowadays the total number observed in the United Kingdom and Ireland amounts to 524 species.
	23.	Baromⁿ dote Act foolishly: that is, they behave erratically.
December	9.	ravens . . . peculiarity Ravens roll in flight as a part of the courtship ritual, or in play.
	30.	Latin words *Cornu vel angulus* = angle or corner; *humilis* = low; *crus* = cross; *saltus* = woodland-pasture; *ovile* = sheepfold; *coux* (?*crux*) = cross; *sepes* = hedge; *salutatio* = a greeting; *blatta terrena* = a bug.

1776 Events and journeys

Early in 1776, Gilbert's brother Thomas White came into possession of property settled on him by the will of Mr

Thomas Holt, his maternal grandfather's half-brother who had died in 1745, when Gilbert as an executor and trustee had supervised the ordering of the estate. Thomas White left London and settled in South Lambeth, then a rural village. In a letter dated 4th January, Gilbert encouraged him to 'begin laying in a fund of material for the Natural History and Antiquities of this county' when he became more settled: that is for the whole of Hampshire including the Isle of Wight. In the same letter he mentioned that he was reading Priestley's *Electrical History*, drawing attention to a section relevant to his own investigations into dew ponds.

This was a winter of intense cold. Gilbert left Selborne on 22nd January and was in London for two months. He wrote to his brother John with some excellent advice on John's book on the fauna of Gibraltar, *Fauna Calpensis*, and also mentioned the forthcoming publication of the first volume of Gibbon's *Decline and Fall*, describing Gibbon as 'a Hants gentleman'.

Late in February, Gilbert again gives evidence of editorial skills and conscientiousness, noting the errors in Pennant's *British Zoology* where early mistakes had not been corrected and new ones had accrued. Gilbert, it seems, had undertaken to read and correct it, an increasingly wearisome labour – 'I must correct over again what I have corrected 'til I am quite sick.' Another letter to John has an interesting discussion of the selling points of the prospective *Fauna Calpensis*.

In May, brother Thomas and his daughter Molly stayed a week at Selborne, then with Gilbert accompanying them, went on to Fyfield to visit their brother Harry for ten days. From Fyfield, Gilbert wrote to tell John that he was asking the artist Samuel Henry Grimm to come to Selborne in July to undertake several views. Midsummer day saw the completion of the new hermitage on Selborne hanger (not the original hermitage close to the steep zig-zag path). It was described as 'strong and substantial and will stand a long while . . .'

Gilbert visited his friend John Mulso and his family at Meonstoke early in August and spent the latter half of the month with his aunt Mrs Rebecca Snooke at Ringmer. At the beginning of November Gilbert was again at Fyfield, from where he wrote describing the twelve drawings which Grimm had made, and expressing himself well pleased with them. At this time Gilbert's nephew Dick, son of his brother Ben, was under his wing and tutelage. Gilbert taught him to ride, but made little headway in teaching him the classics.

January	28.	Therm^r at Selborne The initial figures which head the entries for the next three days appear to be those for Selborne, the ones in the left-hand column, those for South Lambeth.
February	1.	Thames frozen The freezing of the Thames has always been the most potent symbol of deep cold in Britain. Here, GW describes a scene of cheerful excitement in 'people running about on the ice of the Thames'.
April	3.	Thomas began this day mowing the grass-walks Thomas Hoar, GW's manservant. See note for 8/3/74.
	5.	Blackcap whistles This refers not to the warbler we commonly call by this name today, but the bullfinch, for which 'blackcap' is a country name. The whistle and the cherry plundering are both characteristic of this bird.
	30.	The sycamore . . . affords great pabulum This is an expanded version of remarks made on 30th April. Possibly GW had made brief notes on a scrap of paper and inadvertently wrote them into the Journal twice.
June	1.	Dames violets, double The double form of this plant, *Hesperis matronalis* v. 'Plena', considered by Gertrude Jekyll to be 'one of the handsomest and certainly one of the sweetest of garden flowers', is now a rarity.
	2.	Paid for near 20 wasps GW regularly paid boys to bring him breeding wasps and wasps' nests in the hope of protecting his soft fruit later in the year.
	29.	vast insect . . . feeds on the wing in the manner of hummingbirds Almost certainly this is the hummingbird hawkmoth (*Macroglossum stellatarum*), which is attracted to gardens with a luxuriance of flowers – exactly as GW describes. The population of this moth present in Britain fluctuates from year to year but most individuals are seen between June and September.
		Omiah . . . is expected to sail this week with Capt. Cook Omiah, a Society Islander whose real name was Mai or Omai, had been brought back to England by Captain Furneaux, commander of the *Adventure*, on Cook's previous expedition to New Zealand and the South Seas. Described in the papers as 'the wild Indian', he became a great success in society circles where he dined in the best houses, was presented to the King, and became a favourite of Fanny Burney.
		Cook left Plymouth on 12th July on an expedition to the North Pacific to search for the elusive north-west passage. He went to New Zealand and the South Pacific, discovered the Sandwich Islands and sailed north along the North American coast before turning back.

July	3.	Black-caps are great thieves See note for 5/4/76 above.
	8.	Mr Grimm, my artist This was the artist Samuel Henry Grimm whose works illustrated the first edition of *The Natural History of Selborne*.
August	19.	see back Refers to the Journal entry for August 13th.
	31.	where wheat-ear traps are frequent . . . Wheatears were commonly caught for food. In 1654 John Taylor wrote an elegiac poem to the tastiness of roasted wheatear. They were generally caught about harvest time.
September	12.	Virgil quotation *Georgics IV 245* 'The fierce hornet joins issue with those whose weapons are no match for his.'
November	1.	Four swallows were seen skimming . . . this circumstance seems in favour of hiding The migration or hibernation of hirundines was a theme to which GW frequently referred, and a question which he never finally resolved. With martins, especially those that were hatched late in the season, he seemed to be more inclined to accept the idea of hibernation. This is discussed in the NHS Letter XXXVI of 1777 and Letter LV of 1781 to Daines Barrington.
	9.	Ventis vehementer spirantibus When the winds blow strong.

1777 Events and journeys

In the early winter months, Gilbert spent a longer than usual period in London, from mid-February until the second week in April. At the end of February he wrote to his brother John on the subject of the Gibraltar book, offering good though briskly expressed advice, and also indicating that comment on the 'cobweb shower', an event that occurred in 1741, had been intended for his own book. It eventually became Letter XXIII of *The Natural History of Selborne*, to Daines Barrington.

Gilbert suffered during May from gout in his left hand. In June he wrote to his brother Thomas describing how Dr Richard Chandler, who in 1777 had come to the livings of East Tisted and Worldham, near Selborne, was assisting him in his investigations into the antiquities of Selborne. The building of the new parlour continued apace and there are several references to its progress in the Journal – and also to the fortunes of bricklayers in the dreadful weather of this year. John White was down south during the summer, in bad health and spirits; he had given up work on his book.

In September, Gilbert's aunt Mrs Snooke had what seems to have been a stroke ('was seized with the palsy') and at once Gilbert set off for Rignmer and stayed with her for a fortnight. The Oxford visit took place in October and at the end of the month, back in Selborne, Gilbert wrote his brother John another letter on the subject of the Gibraltar book. This was intended as an encouragement to restart work, but nonetheless it contained some penetrating criticisms on style. This letter also noted the death of their relative Nanny White and her burial in the churchyard at Selborne.

Gilbert wrote a letter in November to his nephew Sam Barker, who had just been admitted as a pensioner to Clare College, Cambridge, in which he adds some observations on martins, which were seen on Selborne Hanger early in November after nearly a month's absence. Such behaviour seemed to him similar to that of bats, which are hibernating animals.

The Wakes grounds were augmented in the autumn by the purchase of the farm which had belonged to John Wells, but there is no mention of this in the Journal. Money for this enterprise was advanced by Thomas White, and Gilbert subsequently rented it from his brother.

February	3.	The Planet Mercury is now to be seen every evening GW's growing interest in astronomy can be seen in the increasing frequency of his references to the position of the planets and the stars, and records of the phases of the moon.
April	11.	The smallest uncrested wren, & the laughing D^e are heard The chiff-chaff (*Phylloscopus collybita*) and willow warbler (*Phylloscopus trochilus*); the latter is nicknamed 'laughing wren' because of its rippling song.
	20.	Greek word House-snail.
June	20.	Tremella nostoc abounds in the field-walks There are several observations on the appearance of the blue-green alga *Nostoc*. Elsewhere GW remarks on its strange, jelly-like substance (4/10/83). The name *Tremella* is now used for a group of jelly-like fungi. *Nostoc* was named by Paracelsus and there are many references to its having been an emanation from the stars, but by the mid-18th century more rational descriptions of its origin were being sought, for example by Chambers.
	24.	Virgil quotation *Georgics IV, 557–558* 'They stream together on the top of the tree and hang like clusters of grapes from the bending boughs.'
July	5.	Greek word Maturity.
	31.	Garden much torn by the wind A terse entry which a few years previously would

		have been elaborated in detail, but natural history rather than gardening is now well in the ascendent of GW's interests.
August	1.	Reared the roof of my new building This shows remarkable perseverance on the part of the builders, considering the floods and gales that were widespread at the time.
	26.	A spotted water-hen shot in the forest The spotted crake *Porzana porzana*, also described by GW as the spotted water-rail on 4/11/74. See note for that date.
September	6.	Wheatears . . . esteemed an elegant dish See note for 31/8/76.
	12.	The curious migration of cross-bills The first note about crossbills appears in the Journal in 1770. Sometimes they migrate to Britain in very large numbers. Neither Journal entry mentions numbers, but NHS Letter VII to Daines Barrington refers to 'considerable flocks' in 1770, and this later 1777 note implies that the migration had occurred over a period of time, so the sightings could well have been of the crossbill 'irruptions' which occur every few years. In recent times in the region of a hundred pairs have bred in the New Forest, but numbers there are very variable.
December	16.	black rat . . . a great curiosity The black rat *Rattus rattus* has always been confined to ports and a few inland towns. Shalden is a little north-west of Alton and well inland for this species to appear. Nowadays there are very few in Britain and were it not for the widespread prejudice against rats, it might have become a protected species.
	24.	side-plasterwork . . . done on battin-work Plastering on ceilings, cornices or decorative work was usually carried out on a base of wooden laths or 'battins'.

1778 Events and journeys

Early in the year Gilbert received grave news of his brother John, who was in very bad health. Gilbert travelled to London at the beginning of March and stayed with his brother Thomas and nineteen-year-old niece Molly, returning to Selborne after a month to find crocuses still in bloom in the late season. His annual Oxford visit took place in April.

Writing to his sister-in-law Mrs John White in mid-April he mentioned that his brother Harry White's children had been inoculated – this would be against the smallpox, a disease from which Gilbert himself had suffered in 1747. The practice of inoculation had been strongly advocated by Lady Mary Wortley Montagu earlier in the century; she had had her own son inoculated in Turkey in 1717 and had tried to introduce the practice in England.

Notes on the progress of the new parlour continue and 3rd July marked its debut as a living room. Another young niece, Anne Barker, daughter of Gilbert's sister Anne and Thomas Barker, stayed with him in the late summer, and in September he wrote to her mother saying how well pleased he was with her companionship. There was more sad news from Blackburn; brother John's health was no better, but in Cambridge Gilbert's nephew Sam Barker was taking great pleasure in university life.

In October Gilbert wrote to his niece Molly and described how a Selborne man had been press-ganged into service on a ship which had pirated a French India vessel. He rarely mentions politics, even in his letters, and in the journals the seething hostilities with France and America are only indirectly noted when reverberations reach Selborne, as in May when the fleet's salutations to the King and Queen were heard in the village.

In the autumn there was a drought on which Gilbert reported from Ringmer where he was staying with his aunt, Mrs Rebecca Snooke, as well as from Selborne. He visited the Mulsos in September.

January	2.	There is reason to fear that the plasterer has done mischief . . . by mixing wood ashes with the mortar GW's fears were probably misplaced: the hydroscopic salts in wood ash would probably not delay the drying out of the plaster to a significant degree. It is nowadays quite common to mix wood ash (or brick dust) with the plaster to make the mixture set more quickly; coal ash is not now recommended.
	28.	I now set a chafing dish . . . in the room An old-fashioned kind of portable heater, a vessel filled with burning charcoal.
February		The entries for this month are squeezed on to just over two pages of the printed index to the *Naturalist's Journal*. The reason for this is not clear.
May	2.	Latin translation There can be no doubt but that the Horn shown to me . . . belonged to the Genus of Ox: for it was hollow, bent forward, forming a crescent to the left: where as had it related to the Genus of goat, it would have been hollow, bent upwards, upright, rough. Neither can it by any means belong to the genus of deer, for then it would have been solid, covered with rough skin, growing to a point; nor for as strong reasons to the Genus of sheep; for then it would have been hollow, bent backwards, twisted, wrinkled.
June	29.	wild merry trees The wild cherry *Prunus avium*. Merry is a sixteenth-century

		anglicisation of the French *merise*, a wild cherry. GW also calls it meris, or merris.
July	7.	Greek word Maturity.
October	13.	near 40 ravens have been playing about This occurrence which GW related so affectionately in the Journal would make headline news if it happened today.
	17.	Gathered in the berberries The barberry *Berberis vulgaris*, a shrub native to Europe, produces piquant red berries which were often used for garnishes and sauces. It is now seldom seen having been largely destroyed because it is a secondary host of wheat rust.
November	17.	slippery jacks Probably click beetles, members of the family *Elateridae*, also known as skip jacks.

1779 Events and journeys

Gilbert was working hard on his book on the antiquities of Selborne, a course disapproved of by his old friend John Mulso who believed that 'the natural part will be the forte of the Performance', as he wrote in February, adding with even greater fervour in July: 'I fear the sweet and elegant simplicity of your observations be overwhelmed by the rubbish of the antiquities of your native place.' The only obvious outward sign of Gilbert's new interest was in the spelling of his home village 'Seleburne' in letters to his niece Molly White and his nephew Sam Barker.

From 23rd February until 20th March Gilbert was at South Lambeth with his brother Thomas, and in April he spent a week in Oxford. Brother Harry and his family at Fyfield had a visit from him in September, and in October Gilbert stayed with his old aunt Rebecca Snooke in Ringmer.

During this year Gilbert was offered the living of Ufton Nervett in Berkshire, about eight miles north of Basingstoke. He visited the place in September and then again in November before he finally turned it down.

January	10.	thermʳ broken No records were kept of temperature until the bright mild day of February 26th.
April	17.	Greek word Maturity.
	28.	Five long-legged plovers These were the black-winged stilts *Himantopus himantopus*. The sixth bird was 'suffered to remain unmolested'. Gilbert wrote about this incident in his NHS Letter XLIX to Daines Barrington, 7th May 1779. These birds bred in Britain for only the second time on record in 1987.
May	1.	Rainfall GW's brother John had given him a rain measuring device in April 1778, and this is the first record that was entered. The 49 indicates 49/100ths of an inch.
	24.	Fiery lily blows: orange lily blows Philip Miller names them the narrow-leaved bulbiferous lily (possibly *Lilium bulbiferum*) and the *Lilium purpureo-croceum*, probably the one now known as *Lilium bulbiferum croceum*.
June	2.	The sands by liming, and turniping produce as good corn as the clays 'Turniping' was acceptable as a verb in the late 18th century. The early ripening of cereals due to lack of soil water is still a common problem today. By growing wheat after a root crop such as turnips a higher yield can be achieved, since the dung added for the root crop will result in increased humus and therefore improved water retention in a light, sandy soil. This will be of benefit to the subsequent crop.
	5.	borders in the garden chop for want of rain An old usage of the word 'chop', meaning to crack.
July	24.	Fairy rings . . . in these the puff-balls thrive best See note for 14/10/80.
September	11–14.	Rainfall in absence 73 See note for 1/5/79.
October	16.	Thomas Hoar kept the measure of the rain in my absence GW was in Ringmer from the 12th to 29th October. However, since the Journal went with him and the notes relate to Ringmer, the wind direction records are probably those of Ringmer.
November	3.	Wood-pigeons appear . . . the last winter-birds of passage Wood pigeons do not in fact migrate, but GW may have been observing local movements, about which there is still little known.
December	26–31.	The entries for this period were written on the index pages of the printed *Naturalist's Journal*. As usual, there were few crossings out or corrections in the Journal for this year, but the entries extended to an extra three pages, ruled up by hand. Perhaps GW had taken out pages which he was displeased with or on which he had made mistakes and so found himself at the end of the year with too few pages.

1780 Events and journeys

The year began badly for the parish of Selborne. In February Gilbert notes 'eruptive fevers & sore throats lurk about the parish: some die of this disorder'. In 1780 baptisms exceeded burials by two only, a very low margin. On 8th March Gilbert suffered a personal bereavement when his aunt, Mrs Rebecca Snooke, died at Ringmer. Her bequest to him of Iping farm receives no note in the Journal but his adoption of her tortoise Timothy gives rise to many scientific and affectionately perceptive observations.

In July Gilbert's brother Thomas and niece Molly were at Selborne. Molly admired the new parlour and clearly also took an interest in botany, for Gilbert wrote to her enthusiastically about the lady's tresses in the Lythe. Another improvement was accomplished in September, this time on the beech hanger, where a new path known as the Bostal was made, financed by Thomas.

A disapproving note on the shooting of woodcock by his nephew Richard (Benjamin's son) occurs in a letter to Sam Barker in November, and another letter, to Ralph Churton in December, makes reference to Edward Gibbon whose Volumes II and III of *Decline and Fall* . . . were to be published the following year.

On 21st November Gilbert's brother John died, and was buried in the parish church at Blackburn.

There are many short references in the Journal for this year to the naval hostilities with the Spanish and French. From May onwards there are, unusually, a few words which are illegible and the Journal as a whole is difficult to read. Blotting appears to have occurred subsequent to the writing, which is, as always, neat. Perhaps the Journal was stored in damp conditions which caused the ink to run.

February	21.	Green hellebore emerges Remarks on the appearance and flowering of this plant are made regularly. Its arrival had a seasonal significance for GW, in the same way as the first sighting of martins and swallows.
March	4.	Thomas Thomas Hoar, who had kept the rain measurements on other occasions.
	14.	Chaffinches sing but in a shorter way than in Hants Despite increasing deafness, GW caught the regional differences in song. His perceptive skills were remarkable, even when the physical receptors were below average.
April	22.	house crickets *Acheta domesticus*, the house cricket, is no longer a familiar species around the house as it was in the 18th century. As GW surmised, a single female lays groups of large numbers of eggs in suitable crevices. These hatch a few months later.
May	6.	The quantity of rain This table shows that GW had been keeping rain records regularly for a whole year, although they had been entered only sporadically in the Journal. See note 1/5/79.
	31.	Master Etty Charles Etty, son of the Reverend Andrew Etty, Vicar of Selborne 1759–1784.
June	6.	Terrible riots in London These were the Gordon riots. General hatred of the government and economic misery was fuelled by a wave of anti-papist feeling on account of some concessions that had been given to the Catholics. The riots were fiercely put down by military action, with the cavalry charging down Downing Street. London did indeed look devastated and the government took advantage of the public revulsion at the scene.
	27.	Mr Curtis's botanic garden in George's fields William Curtis (later famous for his *Botanical Magazine*) was a local man born in 1746 at Alton. His garden at St George's Fields, Lambeth Marsh, was the second of three famous botanical gardens he established.
	29.	Jane White was married to Mr Clement Jane was the second child, born in 1755, of GW's brother Benjamin. She married Thomas Clement.
July	2.	Testudo Graeca of Linnaeus The carapace of Timothy the tortoise, preserved in the British Museum, has been identified as that of a female of the species *Testudo ibera*. Dr Chandler GW's friend, a clergyman and antiquarian, who had been assisting him in his work on the antiquities of Selborne since 1777.
	11.	Finished my great parlour By modern standards this seems a very long time after the work of constructing the room had been started. In a letter written during the summer of 1780 Molly White wrote of the parlour: 'My uncle's new room . . . looks very handsome indeed. The paper, a sort of light brown with a coloured border is extremely elegant, and the glass and other furniture are very neat and handsome; in short, the *tout en semble* has a very pleasing effect, and it is I think one of the pleasantest rooms I ever was in.'
August	2.	Papilio Machaon The swallowtail butterfly, about which GW made a journal note on September 14th 1769 when he was in Ringmer, but he did not say that he had seen the butterfly there himself. Latin translation A Machaon butterfly with tailed wings all the same yellow hue with a dark edge and yellow crescent-shaped marks and reddish-yellow at the angle of its posterior.
	11.	wheat in shock Sheaves of corn set up in a stook with six a side and two to cap them.

September	19.	Virgil quotation *Georgics IV, 245*: 'Or the fierce hornet joins issue with those whose weapons are no match for his.'
	24.	Seleburne Here GW is using the old-fashioned spelling of the name to head a fresh page of the Journal, in the same way as he used it in some of his letters in the previous year. It is an indication of his interest in antiquities during this period.
	27.	bostal Sometimes spelt borstall, an 1888 definition gives a Saxon derivation for these names, applied in downs country to paths which wind up to the summits of hills. Latin translation Ammonite.
October	14.	the cause . . . of fairy rings This is another example of GW's clarity of perception, leading in this case to the idea that there was a relationship between fairy rings and fungi, which is now known to be their cause.
November	12.	Seleburne See note for 24/9/80.
December	2.	Sir George Baker The eminent physician and long-standing President of the College of Physicians. He wrote an introduction to the *Pharmacopoeia* of 1788 and was author of *An Inquiry into the Merits of a Method of Inoculating the Small-pox in 1766*. This *Inquiry* may have been an influence on the Barkers having their children successfully inoculated against smallpox in 1778.
	12.	The barometer at S: Lambeth During this period there was an increased interest in science, and barometers became much more widely available. Skilled glass blowers from Milan came to Britain and large quantities of better quality instruments were produced. The standard instructions advised users to 'add 1/10 for each 100 ft above the sea' when making the initial adjustment to the mercury level. In NHS Letter LX to Daines Barrington, GW notes that 'the barometers at Selborne stand three tenths of an inch lower than the barometers at South Lambeth; whence we may conclude that the former place is about three hundred feet higher than the latter.' On 12th December the difference between the barometers in the two places shows 5/10 inch, which allowing for the difference in height above sea level gives a 2/10 inch lower pressure at South Lambeth.

1781 Events and journeys

Just as John White's death was not noted in the Journal, neither was the arrival of Mrs John White at Selborne, where she came to reside and keep house for her brother-in-law after her son Jack ('Gibraltar' Jack) had finished his apprenticeship. Gilbert himself spent March mostly at South Lambeth with his brother Thomas and niece Molly, and they returned the visit in late summer. There were short trips to see his friend Mr Richardson at Bramshott Place in July and to the Mulsos at Meonstoke in September, while his annual Oxford visit was made from November 29th to December 8th.

This year was one of considerable drought, with the Selborne farmers having to bring in water required for brewing in October, and local mills could hardly 'grind barley sufficient for men's hogs', so scanty was the flow of water. Rain eventually fell in November, and the year came to an extraordinarily mild close with a Selborne gardener cutting cauliflowers on Christmas Day.

The Journal for 1781 is heavily interleaved with blank sheets on which Gilbert jotted additional observations (usually dated), having found the space and columns of the ruled journal too confined for all he wanted to say. During this year there was an increase in his astronomical observations.

January	20.	Two of these three paragraphs are written on a sheet of paper interleaved into the Journal, a common occurrence during this year. The first observation about the box tree is written at the foot of the page containing January 14th to 20th; the following note on the same subject is on the facing interleaved page. GW seems to be trying out different styles of making the same remarks.
		My heliotrope An ancient sort of sundial, here used to measure the reach of the sun between summer and winter solstices. A full account of the making of GW's heliotropes is given in the NHS Letter XLIV to Daines Barrington.
February	27.	This storm GW was absent when this storm broke in Selborne. In a letter to his nephew Sam Barker he adds that the damage which grieved him most was the shattering of his walnut tree 'which they write word is almost torn to pieces'.
March	3.	Persian iris blows Persian iris appears in Miller's *Gardener's Dictionary* in the Xiphium section, 'greatly esteemed for its Beauty and Extream Sweetness of its flowers as also for its early Appearance . . .' It is known at present as *Iris xiphium*, originally native to Portugal and southern Spain (not the species which Parkinson describes under the name Persian Iris which had broader leaves and was very tender). GW refers several times to xiphium irises in earlier years and seems to have changed

his nomenclature to Persian iris. It is illustrated in the February plate of the famous *Twelve Months of Flowers* printed in 1730.

May   2.   Field crickets crink A noise in which chinking and cricking blend. The earliest OED example is Gosse 1860, so this may be a GW neologism or a vernacular usage which he appropriated.

June   3.   Boys bring hornets GW probably paid for the destruction of hornets as he did for wasps. However, there were still enough around to 'devour the nectarines' (21st August).

           30.   honey-buzzards built them a large shallow nest Probably never a common bird in Britain, it is now confined to only twelve or so pairs, in greatest concentration in the Hampshire forest areas, where a few pairs have bred regularly for several decades.

August   11.   A swift, or rather a pair Compared with the observation for August 9th this seems to be an exercise in style as much as a straightforward comment for the day. Matching accuracy of language to accuracy of observation, GW crossed out 'no doubt' and inserted 'have perhaps a brood of backward young'.

           21.   Vivid N: Aurora The *Aurora borealis* or northern lights is caused by charged solar particles entering the upper atmosphere of the earth making beautiful luminous displays visible from the higher northern and southern latitudes. The display may be a simple glow or spectacular arcs and curtains of coloured light, sometimes still, sometimes moving and varying. At times of sunspot activity the *aurora* is visible from southern England on about five per cent of all clear moonless nights. Not much is known about sunspot activity in the 18th century, although records show that 1778 and 1787 were years of great vigour, so GW's comments on the phenomenon are especially interesting. In 1773 the *Aurora australis* was noted for the first time by Captain Cook.

September 26.   Gathered knobbed-russetings Also known as knobbed russet, *The National Apple Register* (Muriel Smith 1971) gives its earliest reference as 1820. It is still grown in the neighbourhood of Selborne by the Earl of Selborne.

           27.   Cadilliac pears, dearlings and royal russets Dearlings are otherwise known as dearling pippins, a large sweet apple, grown since the 16th century and in the National Fruit Trials ground under the synonym 'Harvey' in 1971.

October   6.   white-rumped sand-piper Not the rare vagrant which now goes by this name and which is sometimes seen in Hampshire, but the green sandpiper, still called *Tringa ochrophus*.

            9.   grey hen A vernacular name for the water rail *Rallus aquaticus*.

           26.   Bro⸱ T: & M: went away GW's brother Thomas and his daughter Molly had been staying at Selborne since September 10th.

November   10.   house-martins . . . place of retreat This is one of GW's most direct remarks about the possible winter residence of this species, although he still makes it quite clear that he has never actually observed their retreat into hibernation.

           30–   There are no entries for this period while GW was in Oxford. Perhaps he had
December   7.   forgotten to take the Journal with him.

1782 Events and journeys

In mid-February, Gilbert and his widowed sister-in-law, Mrs John White, went off to South Lambeth to see his brother Thomas and niece Molly, and also to spend a few days with their brother Benjamin's household. When Gilbert returned his brother Harry visited him at Selborne. Both Thomas and Harry and some of their families stayed at Selborne for much of the summer, and Gilbert also entertained his friend the Reverend Ralph Churton. Gilbert's nephew 'Gibraltar' Jack (John's son) paid several visits to Selborne to see his uncle and mother, having set up in Salisbury as a surgeon.

Gilbert paid a return visit to Harry at Fyfield for a week at the end of October, but apart from this and his South Lambeth trip earlier in the year, he was absent from home for only a few days. He did not make his usual visit to Oxford.

Selborne's own routine was upset this year by the billeting of 26 Highland soldiers of the 77th regiment, who had been on their way to Gibraltar when they were driven back by cross winds. Gilbert continued to record military events during the year, and there are a few personal notes about the comings and goings of relatives. The occasion of the eldest Barker daughter giving birth to a daughter inspires an additional note from Gilbert on September 8th with an account of the total number of his nieces and nephews – made in as formal a way as if he had been making a count of house martins – and reaching a grand total of 39.

January   28.   Greek word Winter-stream.

March	28.	friend Thomas Thomas Hoar, GW's manservant and general helper in the garden.
April	6–7.	Peter Wells's well runs over This quantity of rain is in remarkable contrast to the conditions of acute drought that prevailed only six months before.
	6.	lavants began to break at Chawton This was the village which later was to become the home of Jane Austen, but the family did not move there until 1807.
May	11.	the Pettichaps The lesser whitethroat, *Sylvia curruca*, first described by Linnaeus in 1758. This passage with almost exactly the same wording appears in NHS Letter LVII to Daines Barrington. In the Journal the account appears on an interleaved sheet.
		house swallows . . . conceal themselves See note for 1/11/76.
June	2, 13, 22, 24.	this universal malady There was a widespread 'flu epidemic during this year, which disabled part of the naval fleet, as GW reported on June 22nd, although as he notes on June 13th it was not to prove fatal to anyone at Selborne, and was abating in its strength by the 23rd.
July	30.	White hellebore blows This is *Veratrum album*, now called white false hellebore or white helleborine: a hardy rhizomatous plant with pleated leaves and greeny white star-like flowers carried on stiff plumes surmounting the stem.
September	30.	mushrooms . . . with the salmon-coloured laminae which only are the true edible sort *Agaricus campestris*, the field mushroom. British ignorance of the large number of fungi which make excellent eating still surprises other Europeans.
November	23.	Latin quotation 'Human voices and harmonious instruments have a quality which simple bird-song lacks. It is not that one cannot also take pleasure in other kinds of music. Rather music made by humans leaves something lingering in the spirit – an agitation which disturbs concentration and sleep. For even after it is finished, the rise and fall of the music, the changes of pitch and tone come and go in one's fancy. Bird-song has no such quality and just as we cannot imitate it exactly, so it cannot affect our internal faculties in exactly the same way.'
December	29–31.	Again, the last page of the Journal is written on an index page which probably indicates that several pages have been torn out during the year.
	31.	This comprehensive comparative rain chart was the result of collaboration between GW and his brothers Thomas and Harry.

1783 Events and journeys

The *Naturalist's Journal* for this year gives the strong impression of a writer who has a happy and well-integrated life, an impression reinforced by the letters of the period. Gilbert wrote several poems and sent them to his friends. One of those which were based on observations recorded in the Journal is printed in the notes for this year.

Entries on the war at sea continue, as do the astronomical ones, and gardening and natural history observations sit unchallengingly next to comments on the comings and goings of friends and relations:

> Oct 8.   Th. H. & Hen: H. White went to Fyfield.
> Woodcock returns.

The Highlanders who had been billeted at Selborne were ordered back to Portsmouth on 22nd January, having impressed the villagers with their decorum and high vegetable intake. During March and April Gilbert was at South Lambeth visiting his brother Thomas and spending a few days with Benjamin. Later in the month he stayed three days at Oxford and at the beginning of July a few days with his friends the Richardsons at Bramshott Place. In November Gilbert spent almost a fortnight with his brother Harry and family at Fyfield, calling in at John Mulso's prebendal house at Winchester on the way home.

From the records of his visitors in the Journal it is easy to see that this year was an extremely sociable one with often large numbers of family and friends staying at the Wakes.

| January | 28. | Crocus's swell Gilbert's affection for these bright early flowers finds expression this year in verse: '*On the Early and Late Blowing of the Vernal and Autumnal Crocus*' |

Say what impels amidst surrounding snow,
Or biting frost the crocus-bloom to glow:
Say, what retards, amidst the summer's blaze,
Th' autumnal bulb, till pale declining days?
The God of seasons, whose pervading power
Controls the sun or sheds the fleecy shower;
He bids each hast'ning flower his word obey,
Or to each lingering bud enjoins delay.

  Gilbert sent these verses to his friend the Reverend Ralph Churton and also to John

Mulso with the signature 'Nobody', perplexing his old friend greatly since he had asked his niece Molly to send them to Meonstoke from London.

February   14.   A perfect & lovely rainbow This was also marked with a poem, written in the style of Milton.

March   20.   Water sinks in Thomas White's field Possibly this was part of the land purchased by Thomas in 1777 which previously had belonged to Farmer Wells.

June   7.   Vast honeydews The sweet, sticky substance found on the leaves and stems of trees and plants, which is the excreta of aphids, was formerly believed to be a natural phenomenon in origin like the dew, and on June 23rd GW therefore entered it in his weather column.

27.   Virgil quotation *Georgics I, 467* '. . . when he covered his shining head with dusky gloom'.

30.   cuckow in a small nest Edward Jenner's controversial work on the cuckoo which describes not only how the bird lays its eggs in other birds' nests, but how the young cuckoo ejects the other eggs or young, was published in 1788 and received with widespread disbelief and scorn. The veracity of his account was not accepted until Montagu's substantiation of it in 1808.

July   12.   The water in my well rises For once Selborne seems to have been especially fortunate in its weather. While the storms did widespread damage to neighbouring areas, Selborne escaped, yet the wells rose with the increased water.

30.   Will Tanner shot off the tall meris trees . . . 17 young blackbirds The gean or wild cherry, which Gilbert appreciated for its beauty in the spring, was regarded apparently as a decoy in the summer.

August   1.   Much smut in some fields of wheat A fungal blight of the order of *Ustilaginales* that attacks wheat and other cereals and reduces the grain to a blackish powder.

6.   Mr Barker came from Rutland 'He rode in three days from Lyndon through Oxford to this place 118 miles; and at every dining place, while the horses were baiting, walked four or five miles in the heat in his boots with his wig in his hand.' Gilbert sent this description of Sam Barker's energy in a letter to Mrs Mary White on August 27th, 1783.

7.   Sarah Dewey A local woman who came to serve at the Wakes as a maid when there were visitors. In this year, GW employed her for the autumn.

24.   Mr Charles Etty This was the son of the Reverend Andrew Etty. In the same August as his remarkable survival at sea, his daughter and his brother died of a long and debilitating illness. Both were young, and GW performed the funeral offices.

September   4.   Tremella nostoc See note for 20/6/77.
14.   Double ulmaria – double filipendula These are double forms of meadowsweet (*Filipendula ulmaria* "Plena") and dropwort (*Filipendula vulgaris* "Flore Pleno").

20.   Mr & Mrs Richardson came These were the friends from Bramshott Place with whom GW frequently stayed.

November   3.   Men chalk the downs Chalk was added to the land, just as lime is today.
December   24.   yellow wagtail Almost certainly the bird we now call the grey wagtail. In his list of species given in NHS Letter I to Daines Barrington, GW includes the yellow wagtail as one of the birds resident all year. In fact, the yellow wagtail (*Motacilla flava*) is a summer visitor to England, so GW's observations, made in the winter months, were probably of the grey wagtail *Motacilla cinerea* which has a yellow breast. This species was also noted in Letter I. The male grey wagtail differs from the female in having a black throat and being brighter yellow when in breeding plumage. It is possible that GW mistook the male and female for different species, calling the male the 'yellow water-wagtail'.

25.   White wagtail See note for 2/1/75.
28–31.   These entries were written on the Journal's index sheet.

The Anglo-Saxon lettering in the text of the Journal has been reproduced from Gilbert White's handwriting.

GLOSSARY·INDEX

Included in this glossary/index are words or ideas which might perplex the modern reader: scientific names, unfamiliar common names, archaic or idiomatic terms, and names of people and places. Some species may be mentioned frequently so only the first date reference has been given, unless another entry is particularly significant or is accompanied by reference to a note¶, in which case this date is also given.

In order to avoid repetition the following abbreviations have been used:
GW = Gilbert White
NHS = *The Natural History of Selborne*

Entries are indexed as they appear in the text, with their date. Then follows the present-day common name and scientific name, with other names also used by Gilbert White shown afterwards in brackets.

Examples
Churn-owl: 1/5/77 Nightjar *Caprimulgus europaeous* (Goatsucker, fern owl)

i.e. The bird referred to by Gilbert White as 'churn-owl' is now known as the nightjar, scientific name *Caprimulgus europaeus*. On other occasions Gilbert White refers to this bird as the fern owl or goatsucker, so these names are shown in brackets. If the species is referred to by an out-of-date scientific name only, that would be the index entry, and it would appear thus:

Merula torquata: 9/4/74 Ring ouzel *Turdus torquatus*

i.e. The bird Gilbert White identifies as *Merula torquata* is the ring ouzel, present-day scientific name *Turdus torquatus*.

An entry may appear with a note mark ¶ beside the date, which indicates that there is further information to be found in the *Notes* for that date.

Example
Sphinx forte ocellata: 29/6/76¶ Humming-bird hawkmoth *Macroglossum stellatarum*

Acer majus: 30/4/76¶ Sycamore *Acer pseudoplatanus*
Adoxa moschatellina: 18/3/75 Moschatel
Agrimonia eupatoria: 20/6/75 Agrimony
Alauda minima locusta voce: 29/4/74 Grasshopper warbler *Locustella naevia* (Grasshopper lark)
Alcove: 2/10/83 Small summerhouse or bower
Almond: 24/2/79 *Prunus amygdalus*
Alresford: 8/11/76 Town on R. Alre 7 m east of Winchester
Anemone nemorosa: 17/3/75 Wood anemone
Ant, horse: 22/3/75¶
Ant, little black: 23/7/75 ?Black garden ant *Lasius niger*
Ant, little yellow: 23/7/75 ?Yellow meadow ant *Lasius flavus*
Antirrhinum cymbalaria: 29/4/80 Ivy-leaved toadflax *Cymbalaria muralis*
Apis longicornis: 25/5/74 Wild bee *Eucera longicornis*
Arbutus: 25/10/75 Strawberry tree *Arbutus unedo*
Artichoke (globe): 1/6/79 *Cynara scolymus*
Arum dracunculus: 17/9/83 Dragon plant *Dracunculus vulgaris* (Dragons)
Arundo donax: 30/9/75¶ Giant reed
Ash: 15/10/74 *Fraxinus excelsior*
Asilus: 25/4/76 ?Robber fly *Asilus crabroniformis* (Wolf-fly)
Asparagus: 21/4/74 *Asparagus officinalis*
Aster Chinensis: 20/8/74 China aster *Callistephus chinensis*

Cornua Ammonis: 27/9/80 Ammonites – fossil cephalopods consisting of whorled chambered shells

Corvus cornix: 29/11/75 Hooded crow, Royston crow *Corvus corone cornix* (Grey crow)

Cran-berry: 27/7/81 Cranberry *Vaccinium oxycoccos*

Crataegus oxyacantha: 19/5/74 Hawthorn *Crataegus monogyna* (White-thorn)

Creeper: 27/3/75,¶ 1/5/79 Treecreeper *Certhia familiaris*

Cricket, field: 13/5/74, 2/5/81¶ *Gryllus campestris*

Cricket, house: 29/8/79, 22/4/80¶ *Acheta domesticus*

Cricket, mole: 29/4/74 *Gryllotalpa gryllotalpa*

Crocus, autumn: 21/8/78 *Crocus nudiflorus*

Crocus, yellow and purple: 3/3/74, 28/1/83¶ Spring crocus *Crocus purpureus*

Cross-bill: 5/8/75, 12/9/77¶ *Loxia curvirostra*

Crow: 13/5/74 Carrion crow *Corvus corone*

Crow, carrion: 3/10/76 *Corvus corone*

Crow, grey: 19/2/74 Hooded crow, Royston crow *Corvus corone cornix* (*Cornix cinerea frugilega*)

Cuckoo: 22/4/74, 30/6/83¶ *Cuculus canorus* (Cuckow)

Cuculus: 22/4/74 Cuckoo *Cuculus canorus* (Cuckow)

Cucumber: 10/4/74 *Cucumis sativus*

Cucumis sativus: 26/3/74 Cucumber

Curlew: 10/4/75 *Numenius arquata* (Long-billed curlew)

Currans: 24/6/78 Currants *Ribes* spp.

Currants: 21/6/75 *Ribes* spp. (Currans)

Curtis, Mr: 27/6/80¶

Cypress: 19/11/81 ?*Cupressus* spp.

Daffodil: 24/2/75 *Narcissus pseudo-narcissus* (*Narcissus palidus*)

Daisey: 24/2/75 Common daisy *Bellis perennis* (Double daisies)

Daisies, double: 14/9/83 *Bellis perennis*

Daisy, Michaelmas: 12/8/74 *Aster novi-belgii*

Dames violet: 1/6/76¶ *Hesperis matronalis*

Dandelion: 17/5/80 *Taraxacum officinale*

Daring: 27/10/76 To dazzle or fascinate (archaic)

Daws: 4/3/74 Jackdaw *Corvus monedula*

Dearling: 27/9/81¶ Variety of apple

Death's head moth: 11/10/77 Death's head hawkmoth *Acherontia atropos* (*Sphinx atropos*)

Deer: 7/11/83 Family *Cervidae*

Derham, Mr: 2/5/78 The Reverend William Derham, author of *Physico-theology* (1713) occasionally quoted by GW.

Dewey, Sarah: 7/8/83¶ Local woman who helped in the house when there were visitors

Digitalis purpurea: 14/6/74 Foxglove

Dog's toothed violet: 14/9/83 Dog's tooth violet *Erythronium dens-canis*

Dove, ring: 16/4/74 Wood pigeon *Columba palumbus*

Dove, Stock: 18/11/76 *Columba oenas*

Dove, turtle: 5/5/75 *Streptopelia turtur* (*Turtur*)

Draba verna: 30/3/78 Whitlow grass

Dragonflies: 30/4/81 Sub-order *Anisoptera*

Dragons: 17/9/83 Dragon plant *Dracunculus vulgaris* (*Arum dracunculus*)

Dun diver: 9/12/74¶ Goosander, female *Mergus merganser*

Dwarf elder: 19/7/76 *Sambucus ebulus*

Earthquake: 14/9/77

Earthworms: 21/9/76 *Lumbricus* spp.

Earwigs: 9/9/75 Family *Forficulidae*

East Tisted: 11/8/82 Nearby village 4 m south of Alton

Eft: 2/4/79 Newt *Triturus* spp.

Elder: 5/6/75 *Sambucus nigra*

Elder, dwarf: 19/7/76 *Sambucus ebulus*

Elder, water-: 20/6/78 ?Guelder rose *Viburnum opulus*
Elm: 24/2/79 English elm *Ulmus procera*
Elm, wych: 10/16/83 *Ulmus glabra*
Empis: 15/12/74 Dance flies *Empididae*
Endive: 29/8/74 *Cichorium endivia*
Ephemerae bisetae: 16/3/75 ?Mayflies, order *Ephemeroptera*
Etty, Charles: 11/3/83, 24/8/83¶ Son of Reverend Andrew Etty, Vicar of Selborne 1759–84
Fairy-rings: 24/7/79, 14/10/80¶
Falco peregrinus: 29/11/82 Peregrine falcon (Haggard falcon)
Falcon, peregrine: 29/11/82 *Falco peregrinus* (Haggard falcon)
Faringdon: 8/9/76 Villages (Upper and Lower) near Alton
Fell-wort: 6/8/79 Felwort or autumn gentian *Gentianella amarella*
Fern: 1/6/83 Probably male fern *Dryopteris filix-mas*
Fern-owl: 10/5/74, 15/7/75¶ Nightjar *Caprimulgus europaeus* (Churn owl, goatsucker)
Ferrugineous foxglove: 11/11/78 *Digitalis ferruginea*
Ficedulae affinis: 3/5/74 White throat *Sylvia communis*
Field-cricket: 13/5/74, 2/5/81¶ *Gryllus campestris*
Field-fare, great: 3/11/74, 7/11/76 Fieldfare *Turdus pilaris*
Field-pease: 14/7/82 Field peas *Pisum sativum* var. *arvense*
Filberts: 13/9/79 Hazel *Corylus avellana* (Hazle, Hasel)
Filipendula, double: 14/9/83¶ Meadowsweet *Filipendula ulmaria* var. *plena*
Findon: 2/8/75 Village in W. Sussex about 4 m N of Worthing
Firs, spruce: 8/10/74 *Picea* spp., probably *Picea abies*
Flag-iris: 27/5/80 *Iris germanica*
Flesh-fly: 24/4/76 *Sarcophaga carnaria* (*Musca vomitoria*)
Flycatcher: 20/5/74 Spotted flycatcher *Muscicapa striata* (*Stoparola*)
Forest fly: 9/6/76 *Hippobosca equina*
Fox: 26/12/77, 12/2/78 *Vulpes vulpes*
Foxglove: 8/6/75 *Digitalis purpurea*
Foxglove, ferrugineous: 11/11/78 *Digitalis ferruginea*
Foxglove, white: 14/9/83 *Digitalis purpurea* var. *alba*
Fraxinella: 4/6/75 Burning bush *Dictamnus alba* (White dittany)
Frog: 7/7/76 Common frog *Rana temporaria*
Fungi: 5/10/83
Furze: 4/12/75 Gorse *Ulex europaeus*
Fyfield: 7/3/75 Village west of Marlborough in Wiltshire, where GW's brother Henry (Harry) held
    the living from 1762 until his death in 1788
Geranium pratense: 12/7/76 Meadow cranesbill (Crow-foot geranium)
Globe-thistle: 17/5/80 *Echinops sphaerocephalus*
Glow worm: 4/6/75 *Lampyris noctiluca* (*Cicindela*)
Golden-rennet: 26/9/75¶Apple variety
Goldfish: 26/10/82 *Carassius auratus*
Goose, bernacle: 10/4/78 Probably Barnacle goose *Branta leucopsis*
Goose-berries: 21/6/75 *Grossularia uva-crispa*
Grasshopper: 18/4/79 *Locusta* spp. family *Acrididae*
Grass-hopper lark: 29/4/74 Grasshopper warbler *Locustella naevia* (*Alauda minima locustae voce;*
    Alauda trivialis)
Green-finch: 24/4/77 Greenfinch *Carduelis chloris*
Green hellebore: 21/2/80¶ *Helleborus viridis*
Green plover: 13/11/75, 18/3/80 Golden plover *Pluvialis apricaria* (*Charadrius pluvialis*)
Green woodpecker: 14/3/78 *Picus viridis*
Grey-crow: 29/11/75 Hooded crow, Royston crow *Corvus corone cornix* (*Corvus cornix*)
Grimm, Hieronymous: 8/7/76¶ A topographical artist (1733–94), specialising in rural and
    antiquarian subjects

Meonstoke: 15/8/74 Village on R. Meon 4 m E of Bishop's Waltham. John Mulso lived at the Rectory there from 1771
Mercury, planet: 3/2/77¶
Mergus serratus: 9/12/74 Goosander *Mergus merganser* (fem. = dun-diver or sparlin fowl)
Meris: 30/7/83¶ Wild cherry *Prunus avium* (Merry tree, merris)
Merula torquata: 9/4/74 Ring ouzel *Turdus torquatus*
Meteor: 18/8/83
Mezereon: 10/2/75 *Daphne mezereum*
Michaelmas daisy: 12/8/74 *Aster novi-belgii*
Missel thrush: 27/1/74 Mistle thrush *Turdus viscivorus* (Shrite, storm-cock, missle thrush)
Missel-toe: 16/12/80 Mistletoe *Viscum album*
Mole: 26/9/80 *Talpa europaea*
Mole cricket: 29/4/74 *Gryllotalpa gryllotalpa* (*Gryllus gryllo-talpa*)
Monotropa hypopithys: 4/7/76 Yellow birdsnest *Monotropa hypopitys*
Moor-buzzard: 19/9/74 Marsh harrier *Circus aeruginosus*
Moor hen: 10/6/74 *Gallinula chloropus*
Mountain ash: 21/7/81 Rowan *Sorbus aucuparia*
Mulberry: 4/6/74 Black mulberry *Morus nigra*
Mullein: 5/12/83 *Verbascum thapsus*
Mulso, John: 11/10/83 Contemporary of GW at Oriel College, Oxford, and a lifelong friend
Musca meridiana: 3/5/74 Species of housefly *Mesembrina meridiana*
Musca tenax: 7/6/75 Drone fly *Eristalis tenax* (Jakes fly)
Musca vomitoria: 21/4/74 Flesh fly *Sarcophaga carnaria*
Muscae: 23/10/75 Flies, family *Muscidae*
Muscae domesticae: 25/8/83 Common houseflies
Muscicapa grissola: 12/5/77 Spotted flycatcher *Muscicapa striata* (Flycatcher, *Stoparola*)
Mushroom: 9/9/74, 30/9/82¶ Field mushroom *Agaricus campestris*
Nasturtions: 12/7/83 Nasturtiums *Tropaeolum majus*
Nectarium: 11/5/82 Nectary, the part of the flower containing nectar
Nidification: 16/4/74 Nest building
Nightingale: 13/4/74 *Luscinia megarynchos*
Nonpariels: 16/10/82 Non-pareils, a variety of apple
Nose-fly: 30/6/77 ?Sheep nostril-fly *Oestrus ovis*
Nuthatch: 23/2/75 *Sitta europaea*
Oak: 5/3/74, 7/10/75¶ *Quercus* spp.
Oats: 10/9/74 *Avena sativa*
Oedicnemus: 6/4/74 Stone curlew *Burhinus oedicnemus*
Oestrus curvicauda: 19/8/74 ?Horse bot fly *Gasterophilus intestinalis*
Onion: 27/4/82 *Allium cepa*
Ophrys nidus avis: 24/5/74 Bird's nest orchid *Neottia nidus-avis*
Ophrys spiralis: 12/9/80 Autumn lady's tresses *Spiranthes spiralis* (Ladies-traces, *Ophris spiralis*)
Orchis, butterfly: 28/6/82 Butterfly orchid *Platanthera bifolia*
Orleans: 13/9/82 Variety of plum
Orobanche major: 27/6/74 Greater broomrape *Orobanche rapum-genistae*
Outlet: Field, garden or enclosure attached to a house
Owl, barn: 30/5/78 *Tyto alba* (White owl)
Owl, brown wood: 4/9/74 Tawny owl *Strix aluco*
Owl, white: 12/5/82 Barn owl *Tyto alba*
Pabulum: 30/4/76¶ Nourishment
Pansies, large-flowered: 14/9/83 Garden pansies *Viola × wittrockiana* vars.
Papilio Atalanta: 13/5/75¶ Red admiral butterfly *Vanessa atalanta*
Papilio Machaon: 2/8/80¶ Common swallowtail butterfly
Papilio rhamni: 22/3/75 Brimstone butterfly *Gonepteryx rhamni*
Parhelia: 28/4/75¶

BIBLIOGRAPHY

Bunyard, Edward	*A Handbook of Hardy Fruits* (2 vols., 1920)
Britten, J. & Holland, Robert A.	*A Dictionary of English Plant Names* (1886)
Chinery, Michael	*A Field Guide to the Insects of Britain and Northern Europe* (Collins, 1973)
	Collins Guide to the Insects of Britain and Western Europe (Collins, 1986)
Clapham, A. R., Tutin, T. G. & Warburg, E. F.	*Excursion Flora of the British Isles* (3rd ed., 1981)
	Flora of the British Isles (2nd edition, 1962)
Galpine, John Kingston	*The Georgian Garden – An Eighteenth-Century Nursery-man's Catalogue.* Introd. by John Harvey (Dovecote Press, 1983)
Harvey, John	*Early Nurserymen* (Phillimore, 1974)
	Early Gardening Catalogues (Phillimore, 1972)
Hitt, Thomas	*A Treatise of Fruit Trees* (1757)
Miller, Philip	*The Gardener's Dictionary* (1731 etc.)
Parkinson, John	*Paradisi in Sole Paradisus Terrestris* (1629)
Ray, John	*Catalogus Plantarum Anglicae* (1677)
	Historia Plantarum (1686–1704)
	Synopsis Methodica Stirpium Britannicarum (3rd ed. by J. J. Dillenius, 1724)*

Rye, Anthony   *Gilbert White and his Selborne*
                                (1970)
Smith, A. W. revised by   *A Gardener's Dictionary of*
    Stearn, William T.   *Plant Names* (1972)
South, Richard   *The Moths of the British Isles*
                                (Frederick Warne, 1961)
Stearn, William T.   *Botanical Latin* (2nd ed.,
                                1973)
Vilmorin-Andrieux   *The Vegetable Garden* (1905)
White, Rashleigh Holt   *Life and Letters of Gilbert White*
                                (1901)

The following editions of Gilbert White's works have been consulted or referred to:

Natural History and Antiquities of Selborne edited by R. Bowdler-Sharpe (1900–01), Sir William Jardine (1890), E. M. Nicholson (1929), Richard Mabey (1977).

Gilbert White's Journals edited by Walter Johnson (1931).

The Garden Kalendar included in the Bowdler-Sharpe edition of the *Natural History of Selborne* (see above).

---

*Facsimile edition with Introduction by William T. Stearn, published by the Ray Society 1973.